Of Making Many Books

seal 1a

seal 1b

seal 2b

seal 2

seal 2a

seal 2c

seal 3a

seal 3b

seal 3c

Of Making Many Books

AN ANNOTATED LIST OF THE BOOKS ISSUED
BY THE JEWISH PUBLICATION SOCIETY
OF AMERICA, 1890–1952

by

JOSHUA BLOCH

Chief, Jewish Division of The New York Public Library

PHILADELPHIA
THE JEWISH PUBLICATION SOCIETY OF AMERICA
5714–1953

Copyright, 1953, by

THE JEWISH PUBLICATION SOCIETY OF AMERICA

———————

Library of Congress Catalog Card Number: 53–13009

PRINTED IN THE UNITED STATES OF AMERICA

PRESS OF *Maurice Jacobs* INC.

224 N. 15TH ST., PHILADELPHIA 2, PENNA.

PREFACE

There is truth, as well as pungency and wit, in the observation by Ralph Waldo Emerson that: "The annals of bibliography afford many examples of the delirious extent to which book-fancying can go." We, of the Jewish Publication Society, entertain the hope that this volume will not be considered one more sample of bibliolatry. We intend it to be a useful and valuable description of the books of Jewish interest which have borne the Society's imprint.

We invited Dr. Joshua Bloch, Chief of the Jewish Division of the New York Public Library, an esteemed and veteran member of our Publication Committee, to prepare the manuscript for this work. We are grateful to him for having performed the arduous task so painstakingly.

The Society is a unique institution. A membership organization, aiming to promote good and useful Jewish literature and to bring it into Jewish homes, its method of distributing its publications was a pioneering forerunner of the modern "book clubs." The Society, however, continues to differ from all other book clubs in that it is essentially creative and non-commercial: creative, since it initiates its publications; non-commercial, since it does not seek primarily to make profit.

Throughout its history, the Society has represented no factional, partisan or organizational viewpoint. It has been the spokesman of *K'lal Yisrael* — Universal Israel — seeking to preserve and enrich the totality of our spiritual and cultural heritage.

The officers and trustees of the Society and the members of our Publication Committee have been drawn from all segments of the American Jewish community. They have freely volunteered their time and energy because of their conviction that the Society's contribution to the culture of America, and of the Jewish community particularly, merited whatever sacrifice was required of them. A list of the public-spirited men and women who have served the Society throughout its history is given in an appendix to this volume.

It is interesting to note that in its selection of manuscripts for publication the Society has operated continuously in accordance with the procedure established at its first meeting in 1888. A resolution was then adopted which provided that: "the consideration of questions concerning manuscripts submitted and the question of literary judgment shall be referred by the Chairman of the Publication Committee to sub-committees to be appointed by him, and the action of said sub-committees shall not be final, but shall be presented to the Publication Committee with a full statement of the sub-committee's reasons." The Publication Committee, in turn, reports its recommendations to the Board of Trustees for final decision.

Despite the obvious and inherent disadvantages of this democratic process, it has, on the whole, functioned satisfactorily. The entire Committee and Board have collectively accepted and assumed responsibility for the decisions reached by a majority of their members. Differences of opinion and occasional delay may be unavoidable, but there are the compensating benefits of cooperation and unity. The professional guidance of the distinguished Editors of the Society — Henrietta Szold, Benzion Halper, Isaac Husik, and now Solomon Grayzel — has proved invaluable.

One of the most difficult problems confronting the Society throughout its history has naturally been that of obtaining and retaining its annual members. By its very nature the Society cannot cater to the ultra-popular taste. We have, however, succeeded in building up a substantial body of discriminating, intellectually alert and Jewishly conscious readers who look to our Society for literary nourishment.

It must be clear that membership dues alone do not enable the Society to produce many of its ambitious projects. Had not Jacob H. Schiff, for example, come to the aid of the Society, it could not have undertaken and brought to completion the translation of the Bible which has been hailed as one of the outstanding achievements of American Jewry. The recent grant from the Estate of the late Jacob R. Schiff will make possible the publication of a series of books on the Jewish contributions to American civilization. Many other important projects have long been under consideration by the Society. Their realization will depend upon the measure of understanding of the American Jewish communities and upon the generosity of American Jews.

In a real sense, this volume may be regarded as an *interim* accounting rendered by the literary trustees of the Jewish community of America. Since Jewish culture is alive, growing and creative, and as eternal as the Jewish people, we believe that a *final* accounting of an organization like ours can never be submitted. We trust that the Society will be given the necessary support required to carry on its work in the years to come. We hope that this volume may be but the first, and the least impressive, of the bibliographies to be published by the Jewish Publication Society of America.

Louis E. Levinthal, *President*
The Jewish Publication Society of America

Philadelphia, October 21, 1953

CONTENTS

The Jewish Publication Society

THE JEWISH PUBLICATION SOCIETY
AN EVALUATION

The collection of books published by The Jewish Publication Society of America (= the Society) in the sixty-four years of its existence (1888–1952) furnishes ample material for the study of Jewish life and literature from the earliest time to the present day — a remarkable achievement which no other publishing house can claim. From its very inception the Society concerned itself with the spread of knowledge of Jewish history and of Jewish religious teachings and practices. It must be remembered that when the Society came into being there were hardly any books in English in which Jewish teachings, practices and experiences were presented with accuracy, authority and without any bias, by writers whose command of the English language was adequate for the purpose. The works of Grace Aguilar and Dean Henry Hart Milman were in existence; but these, while popular, were not altogether satisfactory.

The Society endeavored to fill this need in the life of American Jews by making Jewish knowledge available in various literary forms and in a manner at once well-written and authoritatively presented. In so doing, it availed itself of the competence and learning of experts in their respective fields. Eminent scholars and writers, Jewish and non-Jewish, drawn from every part of the world, were given the opportunity to present to the English-reading public the fruits of their scholarly and literary pursuits. To be sure, not all the authors offered their manuscripts in the English language. The list includes numerous works translated from French, German, Hebrew, Russian, Polish and Yiddish. Some of them are translations of works which had made their mark in

1

one or more of these languages; others are translations of manuscripts specially prepared for the Society but the original of which never saw the light. On the other hand, not a few of the works originally written in English for the Society were promptly translated into Hebrew, Yiddish, German, Spanish, French, Italian, Polish, Russian, etc. This is as it should be. Jewish literature, being a polyglot literature, it is not surprising that a goodly number of titles which the Society produced represented contributions to Jewish history and literature of such a nature as to merit a much wider reading public than the English language affords. Thus, the Society, although organized primarily for the purpose of making Jews and Judaism better known to the Jews in America, extended its service to Jews everywhere. Its influence has been far and wide and its fame universal.

No other organization or institution in American Jewry can claim a record of achievement equal to that of the Society in its endeavor to bring to bear the influence of Jewish ideas and ideals, as expounded in Jewish authoritative writings, upon the mind of the reading public. It is constantly engaged in presenting Jewish thought and life in a literature that reaches multitudes of Jews and non-Jews. By its achievements the Society can well point with pride to having given the largest impetus to the creation of an American Jewish literature. It has demonstrated to the world that American Jewry possesses an abundance of scholarly and literary talent of great worth.

There is good reason to assume that many a volume bearing the imprint of the Society would not have been written had it not been for the encouragement which the Society gave. After all, one of its prime objectives is to furnish to the Jewish population such literary productions in the English language as might otherwise not see the light of day. This is equally true of many a work translated into English from another language. Were it not for the Society's effort it might never have become accessible to readers in the English language.

The success of the Society is, in no small measure, responsible for the readiness of private publishers to issue books on Jewish subjects. Books which, for one reason or another, the Society was not in a position to publish have frequently found their way on the book lists of general publishers, largely because of the knowledge that the membership of the Society constitutes a reading public with a substantial interest in Jewish life and literature.

It has again and again been pointed out that the organization of the Society in Philadelphia on June 3, 1888, was not without precedent; two previous attempts had failed.* The success of the third experiment, despite moments of discouragement and crisis, is largely due to the fuller measure of co-operation in its work given by representatives of all groups comprising American Jewry.

In its early days the Society had difficulty in finding competent American authors for the writing of such books as it planned to publish. Like its two predecessors, the Society had to seek the co-operation of authors from foreign lands and it had to adopt for American use publications which served well the needs of English and German Jewries. The first book bearing the imprint of the Society is an edition of *Outlines of Jewish history* by Lady Magnus, revised by M. Friedländer (Philadelphia, 1890). To the American edition there was added a section on the history of the Jews in this country, a frontispiece (temple) and a map. The book was well received in American Jewish homes and was promptly adopted as a textbook in many a Jewish school. For almost half a century teachers and students in Jewish schools resorted to its pages

---

*On the earlier attempts to organize a Jewish publication society in this country see William B. Hackenburg in *The American Jewish Year Book* 5674, Philadelphia, 1913, pp. 164–166 and Solomon Grayzel, "The first American Jewish publication society" in *Jewish Book Annual*, New York, 1944, v. 3, pp. 42–44. Cf. also Ephraim Lederer, "The origin and growth of the Society" in *The American Jewish Year Book, Ibidem*, pp. 59–77.

in their study of the record of their people's experience through-out the ages. No wonder it went through many revisions and editions. A decade after World War I, the volume still being in demand, it was somewhat revised, brought up to date and even reset under the direction of Dr. Solomon Grayzel (Phila-delphia, 1929). This edition, too, was well received.

The widespread distribution of Magnus's *Outlines* served a remarkable purpose. In Jewish religious schools, where heretofore pupils had generally been taught no more of Jewish history than is covered in the Bible, Apocrypha and Josephus, the subject was now extended to embrace the entire post-biblical period. The *Outlines* could do no more than whet the appetite for a fuller knowledge of Israel's experience among the nations. There continued to be felt an urgent need for a more extensive treatment of Jewish history. American Jews discovered that the history of their people is at least as rich in experience and spiritually as stimulating as that of any other ancient people. Though it covers a period of several thousand years, it is a living and continuous history because it presents the uninterrupted record of an ancient, but an ever-living people. It is a richly rewarding history. A good knowledge of it is apt to instill pride in the hearts of those in whose veins flow the blood of martyrs and saints, of heroes and heroines, whose role in Jewish life contributed to the keeping alive of a people with a spirit and a sense of mission striving after the establishment on earth of the Kingdom of Heaven. Non-Jews, too, once they acquire a knowledge of Jewish history, realize that it is the history of an Eternal People. Such a history is worth knowing.

Again, the Society turned to England. When the nine-teenth century was on the threshold of its last decade, a group of young scholars, under the editorial supervision of Miss Bella Löwy, were engaged in rendering into English a text of the *History of the Jews* by Heinrich Graetz specially prepared for the purpose by its distinguished author. The rights to this work were controlled by Frederick D. Mocatta, an eminent London philanthropist, at whose expense the English translation had been made. Through the efforts of Dr. Charles Gross, the Society acquired the American rights. With improvements of its own, the Society reproduced the London edition of Graetz's *History of the Jews* in five volumes (1891–95). These represent a considerably condensed text of Graetz's original German *History* with its copious notes, appendices and full treatment in eleven (often bound into thirteen) volumes. While the notes and appendices were discarded in the English edition, each of its five volumes offers more material than any single volume of the original German work, the total constituting about two-thirds of the German text. The translation made in England was revised, largely by the hand of Henrietta Szold, to meet the requirements of the American reading public. A sixth volume was added (1898) consisting of a "Memoir" of Heinrich Graetz by Philipp Bloch; a Chronological Table of Jewish history; a comprehensive and helpful index to the whole work, compiled by Henrietta Szold under whose supervision the volumes had been issued, and four maps. Since this American edition of Graetz covered Jewish history to the year 1870 — long before the most "eventful years" in modern Jewish history — the Society commissioned Ismar Elbogen to write a running and readable account of *A century of Jewish life* (1944) and issued it "as a supplement to the masterwork of Graetz." It brought the work up to the outbreak of World War II.

Graetz's *History of the Jews* is still the leading work on the subject in the English language. By the comprehensiveness of its scope, by the exhaustiveness with which it treats the pilgrimage of Israel through the nations and ages, by its rare combination of sound scholarship and critical acumen and by the perfect fusion of solidity of learning with popularity of style, it still remains unsurpassed by any other work of its kind. Though not always objective, it is written in a spirit of enthusiasm and a tone of warmth that are contagious. It has become a classic in the literature of Jewish historiography. It serves a purpose unrivalled by any other work of its kind in the English language. It makes Jews and Judaism better known, better understood and more acceptable. On the other hand, it no longer presents the subject adequately. Written as it was in the middle of the last century, its author did not have at his command the wealth of information which subsequent research, exploration and study have yielded and through which our knowledge of many a period in the long record of Jewish experience has been virtually revolutionized. In the light of all this practically the entire history of the Jewish people requires a new presentation. This and like reasons account for the publication of such works as *A history of the Jewish people* by Max L. Margolis and Alexander Marx (1927) and *A history of the Jews from the Babylonian Exile to the Establishment of Israel* by Solomon Grayzel (1947) which offer succinct presentations of the subject based on trustworthy sources and with the aid of the latest results of research in archaeology and Jewish historiography. A like enterprise, on a much larger and more comprehensive scale, has been launched by the publication of the first two volumes of *A social and religious history of the Jews* by Salo W. Baron (1952). It is expected that upon completion the work will consist of seven volumes.

To keep alive and to stimulate a steady interest in the content and meaning of Jewish history the Society deemed it advisable to issue, from time to time, publications of lesser significance in which aspects of general Jewish history were dealt with from varying points of view. *A sketch of Jewish history* by Gustav Karpeles (1897) presents a bright, readable survey of the subject, and the same author's *Jews and Judaism in the nineteenth century* (1905) surveys the great movements and trends of Jewish history during that century. So fine a study as *Jewish history*, an essay in the philosophy of history by S. M. Dubnow (1903), enables the average reader to understand the meaning and the process of Jewish history.

The Society took up the subject of mediaeval Jewish life and furnished the means of acquiring an understanding of it and of the relations of the Jews to one another and to their non-Jewish neighbors. It published a splendid work, *Jewish life in the Middle Ages* by Israel Abrahams (1896), the first vivid and complete picture of the life of the mediaeval Jew to be offered the English reader. That life is portrayed in all its details with clarity and warmth. It depicts its sorrows and sufferings as well as its intellectual heroism and social degradation in a world hostile to both Jews and Judaism. It also published *Old European Jewries* by David Philipson (1894), a book which so eminent an authority as Gustav Karpeles described as "a very valuable historical and ethnographical contribution;" and *The Jewish community*, its history and structure to the American Revolution, by Salo W. Baron (1942). Considerable light is cast upon many a trend in the history of the Jewish people in the fine study of *The Messiah idea in Jewish history* by Julius H. Greenstone (1906), in which the great hope that has sustained Israel throughout its long history, and often compensated it for inevitable sorrows, is fully discussed. The diversity and richness of the Jewish share in the world's progress are brilliantly portrayed in *Jewish contributions to civilization*, an estimate by Joseph Jacobs (1919). It is a work in which superb scholarship, vast knowledge and painstaking research made possible the presentation of a dignified and restrained account of a subject not yet sufficiently appreciated. These are books which have enabled Jews and non-Jews to know and to understand the role played by the Jewish people throughout their history and in all the lands of their dispersion. A large scale attempt to attain similar ends is made by various hands in a four (or two) volume work on *The Jews*, their history, culture and religion, edited by Louis Finkelstein (1949).

Significant periods and movements in Jewish history have been given particular attention by specialists whom the Society encouraged to write works through which those periods and movements become better known. *The Jews among the Greeks and Romans* by Max Radin (1915) is a fascinating treatment of Jewish life and thought in the classical world, a subject that is not sufficiently well known to the average student of Jewish history. Nor is it well understood without a knowledge of the trends and personalities which touched Jewish life in that period and after. Intended for the popular reader, such works as *Hellenism* (1919), *Philo-Judaeus* (1910) and *Josephus* (1914) by Norman Bentwich furnish, in an admirable manner, a large measure of the knowledge essential for the understanding of the Hellenistic period in Jewish history and of some of the men who played a significant role in it.

The much maligned Pharisees have been the subject of a rich literature in the making of which Jewish and non-Jewish scholars have shared. Their activity and the influence of their teachings have been described by many more or less competent hands. It remained for the Society to produce *The Pharisees*, a striking study of the sociological background of their faith, by Dr. Louis Finkelstein (1938).

In the many years of their dispersion the Jews have found more or less permanent homes in various lands. In some countries they fared better than in others, but in all of them they sought an opportunity to participate in the economic, social, political and cultural life of their neighbors. In *The Jews in Spain*, Dr. Abraham A. Neuman (1942) tells in a fascinating manner of the inner life of the Iberian Jewish communities prior to their expulsion, and Dr. Cecil Roth offers *A history of the Marranos* (1932, 2nd edition 1947). Many of the Jews who were forced to flee from Spain and Portugal found a haven of refuge in Italy, a country which harbors one of the oldest Jewish settlements in Europe. How they fared there is skillfully narrated in *The history of the Jews of Italy* by Cecil

Roth (1946), the first book on the subject in any language. The same author's account of the Jewish community of *Venice* (1930) is a fine companion volume to that of *Rome* by Hermann Vogelstein (1940) and both of them contribute to the enrichment of our knowledge of Italian Jewish life.

Like Italy, Germany, too, had an old Jewish settlement. In *The Jews of Germany*, Marvin Lowenthal (1936) tells a story of sixteen centuries of Jewish experience in that country. To his story must be added individual accounts of several old German Jewish communities: *Frankfort* by Aron Freimann and F. Kracauer (1929), *Regensburg and Augsburg* by Raphael Straus (1939), *Cologne* by Adolf Kober (1940) and *Vienna* by Max Grunwald (1936). An extraordinary contribution to the history of the period of absolutism is *The Court Jew* by Selma Stern (1950). In it many aspects of Jewish experiences in a variety of outstanding communities in Germany are described. The fate of the Jews in Germany under the Nazis and in countries under their domination has not yet been described in its fullest gruesome details. A bit of it is offered in *Blessed is the match*; the story of Jewish resistance, by Marie Syrkin (1947). It presents a remarkable description of the martyrdom and heroism of the Jews in Europe, gleaned through personal contact with survivors in Europe and Palestine.

It would be altogether false to assume that in its efforts to widen the horizon of the American reader the Society concerned itself entirely with presenting Jewish life and lore of the past. Superficially speaking, one may gain such an impression seeing that, of the major titles listed, those which deal directly with "up-to-date" subjects are rather few. The fact is, however, that most of the major works, though devoted to Jewish thought and experience in all ages, represent fine contributions which carry the reader to spheres of Jewish life which, while rooted in the past, often even in antiquity, reveal some interesting, though sometimes exotic, manifestations of contemporary Jewish experience.

One of the major concerns of the Society is the advancement of knowledge of Jewish life in this country. Several works which it issued in recent years deal with men and events which have contributed to the making of American Jewish history. *Jewish pioneers and patriots* (1942) and *Pilgrims in a new land* (1948) by Lee M. Friedman are exactly what these titles imply; they deal with Jews who made notable contributions to the economic and political development of the country, while in *American overture* Abram Vossen Goodman (1947) discusses Jewish rights in colonial times. By assaying the attitude of each colony towards its Jews and other minorities on the early American scene he traces the steps taken in state after state, from those of New England to Georgia, in the struggle for religious liberty and equality for men of all faiths. Some of the same ground is covered in *Early American Jewry* by Jacob Rader Marcus (1951). The early development of the inner life of the largest Jewish community in the world is described in *The rise of the Jewish community of New York 1654–1860* by Hyman B. Grinstein (1945). It concerns itself with the growth of New York's Jewish communal institutions — religious, cultural, social, philanthropic — and their efforts to maintain a homogeneous Jewish life. A like treatment is accorded *The Jews of Charleston*, a history of an American Jewish community by Charles Reznikoff, with the collaboration of Uriah Z. Engelman (1950). Mordecai Manuel Noah, a distinguished leader in New York Jewry, is the subject of a fascinating biographical study, *Major Noah: American Jewish pioneer*, by Isaac Goldberg (1936), while *The life of Judah Touro* (1775–1854) by Leon Huhner (1946) presents the remarkable career of an American Jewish merchant who became distinguished as a philanthropist. Interesting are the *Letters of Rebecca Gratz* edited with an introduction and notes by Rabbi David Philipson (1929). Presenting "a vivid picture of the lovely personality who stands forth as one of the glories of American-Jewish womanhood," they also cast much light

10

on the social life of an early American Jewish family. A solid contribution to American Jewish historiography is *American Jewry and the Civil War* by Bertram Wallace Korn (1951).

A remarkable publication bearing the imprint of the Society is the *American Jewish Year Book* of which fifty-three volumes have been issued since the appearance of the first volume in 1899. It has been published without interruption, more or less regularly, in the early autumn of every year. Each volume contains the calendar of the year and other useful features designed to furnish accurate and essential Jewish information. In virtually all of the volumes one meets with special articles generally dealing with matters of timely and often even of urgent interest; they, as a rule, convey information needed for a correct understanding of current problems. The volumes constitute a veritable mine of information for the contemporary history of our people in all lands.

At the beginning of this century and prior to World War I, Russia and Poland were the home of the largest Jewish community on the European continent. Its political, economic, social and cultural life was in many ways so different from that of their co-religionists in other lands as to arouse a constant interest in them and in their welfare. To make that community better known the Society published the first three-volume work on the *History of the Jews in Russia and Poland*, from the earliest times until the present day, by S. M. Dubnow (1916–1920). Several other publications issued by the Society present special aspects of cultural manifestations in the Jewry of Russia and Poland. *The Haskalah movement in Russia* by Jacob S. Raisin (1913) and *Leon Gordon*, an appreciation, by Abraham B. Rhine (1910) reveal some of the secular trends which found their way into Russian Jewry of the nineteenth century. Some of those trends account for *The renascence of Hebrew literature* (1743–1895) so interestingly described by Nahum Slouschz (1909). *Vilna* was an old center of Jewish life in Eastern Europe. Its history is well presented by Israel Cohen (1943). It offers a glimpse into Jewish life of a community that became known as the Jerusalem of Lithuania.

When Russian Jewry was the victim of Czarist persecution the Society endeavored to make the plight of that community known to the world in the hope that public opinion may be so aroused as to bring about an amelioration of the intolerable situation. It republished in this country *The persecution of the Jews in Russia*, with a map of Russia showing the pale of Jewish settlement, issued by the Russo-Jewish Committee of London (1891). Full of facts, this publication furnished adequate information to the public in regard to the basis of the complaints then being made by the Jews against Russia. It issued a special edition of *Within the pale*, the true story of antisemitic persecution in Russia, by Michael Davitt (1903), the warm-hearted Irish leader who, knowing the sufferings of his own people, was able to appreciate and describe in glowing language the unspeakable persecutions of the Jews in Czarist Russia. When American public opinion was outraged by the Kishineff pogrom of 1903 and gave voice to the indignation of Americans of all creeds against the horrors of Czarist persecution, the Society published a volume giving expression to *The voice of America on Kishineff*, edited by Cyrus Adler (1904). Almost a quarter of a century after the famous ritual murder trial of Mendel Beilis in Kiev, it made available in the English language *The decay of Czarism*; the Beilis trial, a contribution to the history of the political reaction during the last years of Russian Czarism, based on unpublished materials in the Russian archives, by Alexander B. Tager, translated from the Russian original (1935). These publications serve a dual purpose: they are documents testifying to injustices perpetrated against the Jews directly or indirectly by a great power, and they are instruments of defense against false but oft repeated charges aimed at the Jews everywhere. The story of the migration of millions of Jews from European

12

lands to the far corners of the world since 1800 is offered in *To dwell in safety* by Mark Wischnitzer (1948). It forms an interesting chapter in the history of the Jews in modern times.

Jewish literature as a whole is not very rich in works of travel. Not many are the Jewish travelers who have handed down a literary account of their experiences and encounters. The few who did so have, in a measure, enabled the historian and the student of social life to remove many a doubt in our knowledge of Jewish life in various countries. The books of travel which the Society has issued serve just such a purpose. The late Dr. Elkan N. Adler, the author of *London*, one of the volumes in the Jewish Communities Series (1930), in addition to having been a fine scholar, a diligent collector of Hebrew books, was also a seasoned traveler who frequently visited his co-religionists in so-called out-of-the-way places. In issuing his *Jews in many lands* (1905) the Society offered accounts of his trips to Jewish communities in Egypt, Palestine, Turkey, Aleppo, Tetuan, Persia, Zakaspie, Argentine and Lithuania. The volume is rich in information on the curious and exotic aspects of life in those Jewish communities. This is equally true of *Travels in North Africa* by Nahum Slouschz (1927). The latter is the result of ten years of travel amongst the Jews of Africa and of much study and research into their history and ethnography.

The interest of Jews in ancient and modern Palestine is an obvious one. The Land of Israel was the cradle of their birth as a people and the object of their hope for the restoration of their national home in the country that has been made sacred to them by ties of blood and soil. Such travel books as *In the steps of Moses* by Louis Golding (1943) and *The feet of the messenger* by Yehoash (Solomon Bloomgarden) — the latter translated from the Yiddish by Isaac Goldberg (1923) — serve as a link between the Palestine of the biblical period and that of our own. So does the charmingly written volume on *The River Jordan* by Nelson Glueck (1946), which is an illustrated account of earth's most storied river. The yearning of the Jews for the return of their people to the Land of Israel as expressed through organized efforts is well described in *Zionism* by Richard Gottheil (1914) and additional information on the subject is incorporated in Alexander Bein's splendid biography of *Theodore Herzl* (1940). The fascinating story of the efforts of Zionists and others to reclaim for the Jews the Land of Israel is presented, with warmth and understanding, in *Harvest in the desert* by Maurice Samuel (1944). In *Selected essays* by Ahad Ha'am (1912) spiritual Zionism is expounded by its foremost champion who also deals with striking aspects in Jewish life. Some aspects of later developments in Zionism leading to the establishment of the State of Israel are well described in *Trial and error*, the autobiography of Chaim Weizmann (1949). It offers, in addition, the richly personal story of the embattled and colorful life of the first president of the new State of Israel.

Jewish history is a record of Jewish life, but Jewish life cannot be adequately understood without a knowledge of its lore. This in turn is largely embodied in the various forms of Jewish literary expression. To make Jews and Judaism in their totality better known it is necessary to take full cognizance of the literature the Jews produced. While the literature has not been altogether neglected by the Jewish historian the Society deemed it advisable to issue, from time to time, works written exclusively for the purpose of elucidating all or any of the facets of the literary expression of the Jewish people. Such a collection of essays as make up *Jewish literature* by Gustav Karpeles (1895) has the charm of an attractive style, combined with subjects of great and varied interest. This holds true of virtually all collections of essays published by the Society. *Chapters on Jewish literature* by Israel Abrahams (1899) enable the reader to gain a glimpse into the highways of the subject. Designed as a primer, it offers a sketch in outline. Some of the by-ways of Jewish lore and literature are trodden

14

by the same author in his *The book of delight* and other papers (1912) and his *By-paths in Hebraic bookland* (1920). They deal with delightful aspects of Hebrew literature often neglected in larger treatments of it. In the three extraordinary collections of *Studies in Judaism* by Solomon Schechter (1896, 1908 and 1924) a large variety of subjects gleaned from Jewish life, lore and thought are discussed with dignity and charm. The essays they contain convey much of the profound reverence for Jewish tradition which Schechter so effectively advocated. They are rich in phrases and passages which have become winged words often advantageously employed by both scholar and layman. In her modest collection of *Hearth and home essays* Esther J. Ruskay (1902) discusses with a measure of simplicity some familiar Jewish practices of the synagogue and home. Pleading for the conservation of Jewish tradition in the homes and lives of the Jews of America, the essays convey the warmth and devotion to Jewish values of a truly religious woman, testifying to the strength of her faith and the depth of her convictions. In *As a mighty stream* (1949) Dr. Julian Morgenstern endeavors to trace the growth of Jewish beliefs and practices through history showing that, as a historic religion, Judaism is the outgrowth of an evolutionary process in which the Reform movement is a late but by no means the final stage.

The earliest specimens of Jewish literature are preserved in the text of the Hebrew Scriptures. From its very inception the Society felt that without an adequate knowledge of the Bible by America's Jewish population all its efforts in advancing Jewish literature would not be effective. At an early date it undertook the preparation of a new English version of the Hebrew Scriptures by a group of competent American Jewish scholars. In itself the translation of the Bible seemed to present a herculean task. The Society had to overcome various difficulties in connection with its Bible plans; above all, it had to meet the challenge of the magnificent English of the existing versions. Nevertheless, the task had to be undertaken, for, as Israel Zangwill correctly stated, "the English of the Bible may be magnificent, but it is not always truth. The Hebraic concept is too often distorted by ignorance or prejudice." Fortunately the Society was able to cope with the difficulties. Plans for the execution of the task were made and each book of the Holy Scriptures was assigned to a carefully selected translator. These plans and assignments were subsequently abandoned and a board of editors, with Max L. Margolis as editor-in-chief, was appointed. Their labors culminated in the publication, in 1917, of *The Holy Scriptures according to the Masoretic Text*; a new translation with the aid of previous versions and with constant consultation of Jewish authorities. This publication gradually replaced all other English versions previously used in the synagogues, Jewish schools and homes.

The urgent need of such a version had been felt for some years. At the beginning of the century (1903) the Society, in order to meet popular need, had issued the text of *The Book of Psalms* [translated by Kaufmann Kohler]. It was well received as "a product of the highest scholarship." The same judgment was rendered on *Micah*, by Max L. Margolis (1908), likewise a new translation but provided with a brief yet splendid commentary. It formed the first of a proposed series of Commentaries on the Books of Holy Scriptures undertaken by the Society. The second volume in the series is the text of *Deuteronomy* in the Society's translation, with a commentary by Dr. Joseph Reider (1937) and the third *Numbers*, with a commentary by Julius H. Greenstone (1939), who is also responsible for the commentary on *Proverbs* (1950). Others are to follow. Intended primarily for the teacher, they are also helpful to the general Jewish reader who desires a knowledge of Jewish Scriptures at once reliable and Jewish. Written from the Jewish point of view, they draw "more largely than do the general commentaries on the traditional interpretations found in the classical Jewish literature of mediaeval and modern times." They are instinct not only with Jewish tradition but also with Jewish sentiment.

In its persistent endeavor to popularize the Bible among the Jews the Society was not satisfied with merely issuing its new English version of the Scriptures and with publishing commentaries on several biblical books. It did more than that. It subjected its new English version to abridgment and adaptation so that it might find its way to the classroom of the Jewish religious schools and to those who read or study the Holy Scriptures at home. It published *The Holy Scriptures*; an abridgment [compiled, edited and prepared by Miss Emily Solis-Cohen] (1931). Other works of a similar nature and designed to serve a like purpose but on a larger scale are *Pathways through the Bible* by Mortimer J. Cohen, with illustrations by Arthur Szyk (1946), and *The Book of Books*; an Introduction, by Solomon Goldman (1948), who is also responsible for its companion volume, *In the beginning* (1949). They are works in which their respective authors endeavor, each in his own way, to make the contents of the Jewish Bible attractive to a wide and intelligent lay reading public. Such succinctly written accounts of *The story of Bible translations* (1917) and *The Hebrew Scriptures in the making*, by Max L. Margolis (1922), tell of the origin and spread of the Holy Scriptures. *The life of the people in biblical times*, by Max Radin (1929), serves admirably as background knowledge of the history and social conditions of the time and place which gave rise to the writing of the books of the Bible. In *Rembrandt, the Jews and the Bible*, by Franz Landsberger (1946), there are fresh discussions of those aspects of the artist's life and work which have a direct bearing upon his interest in the Jews and in their Scriptures. These are all excellent handbooks competently written by reputable scholars which serve most admirably as aids to the study and understanding of the text of the Sacred Scriptures and of the life, times and circumstances under which they were produced.

17

The most significant and certainly the largest portion of post-biblical Jewish literature consists of the body of writings generally spoken of as rabbinical literature. This includes the Talmud and the Midrash, the Halakah and the Agadah. It is a literature which the Society did not neglect. It endeavored to familiarize English-speaking readers with its content and character by republishing in succession two great essays on *The Talmud* by Emanuel Deutsch (1895) and by Arsène Darmesteter (1897); the latter was translated from the French by Henrietta Szold. Relatively few persons know what the Talmud signifies. Each of these two essays is *multum in parvo* on the subject. The "sea of the Talmud," that stupendous library of rabbinic learning and lore, is described in them with a fullness and a charm not surpassed in many larger and more pretentious works. To facilitate the study of the text the Society issued a very useful *Introduction to the Talmud and Midrash* by Hermann L. Strack; an authorized translation on the basis of the author's revised copy of the fifth German edition [by Max L. Margolis] (1931). It also published the critically edited texts and English translations of such rabbinic works as *The treatise Ta'anit* of the Babylonian Talmud with notes by Henry Malter (1928) and the *Mekilta de-Rabbi Ishmael* with introduction and notes by Jacob Z. Lauterbach (1933–35). Fine specimens of post-biblical Hebrew writings, brought together, edited and translated into elegant English by Ben-zion Halper, were published in two volumes under the title *Post-biblical Hebrew literature* (1921). A truly monumental contribution is the seven-volume work, *The legends of the Jews*, by Louis Ginzberg (1909–1938). It is the largest and most complete collection of Agadic lore culled from the entire body of classical rabbinic and kindred writings. Ancient legends and myths distinctly Jewish revolving around events and personalities familiar from Scriptural writing, they unfold a great portion of the imaginative genius of Israel. The seventh volume, which presents an exhaustive index competently

18

compiled by Dr. Boaz Cohen, facilitates the ready use of this treasure-trove of Jewish legendary lore. A work of a similar character, of greater age and smaller size, is the *Ma'aseh book*, a collection of Jewish tales and legends translated from a mediaeval Judaeo-German text by Moses Gaster (1934). The affection in which Palestine has been held in Jewish lore is brought out quite clearly in *Legends of Palestine* by Zev Vilnay (1932). Much legendary lore in prose and poetry, drawn from rabbinical sources, found its way also into *Readings and recitations for Jewish homes and schools* (1895), *Legends and tales* in prose and verse (1905) compiled by Isabel E. Cohen, and *Selections for homes and schools* by Marion L. Misch (1911). Legendary lore also forms the primary source of the collection of delightful *Stories and Fantasies* from the Jewish past by Emil Bernhard Cohn (1951). In their pages is reflected the spirit of Israel as it finds expression in the literature of the past and as it lives in the creative literary works of the present.

Jewish philosophy and Jewish ethics are deeply rooted in the teachings of the sages which are recorded in the pages of the Talmud and Midrash. To be sure, here and there Jewish philosophers and Jewish ethical writers allowed themselves to become directly or indirectly influenced by non-Jewish systems of thinking, but basically they depended largely on the Scriptures and their interpretation in rabbinical lore. This is well discussed in the remarkably comprehensive presentation of *A history of mediaeval Jewish philosophy* by Isaac Husik (1916) and exemplified in the *Sefer ha-'Ikkarim, Book of Principles* by Joseph Albo, edited with an English translation and notes by Isaac Husik (1929–1930). In *The ethics of Judaism* by Moritz Lazarus (1900–1901) there was offered a modern presentation of the subject which the Rev. Dr. Samuel Schulman so aptly described as "the most eloquent and convincing apologetic of Judaism in the nineteenth century." The two-volume collection of *Hebrew ethical wills*; selected, edited and translated into English by Israel Abrahams (1926), serve as documents which prove the scrupulous observance of Jewish ethical precepts by Jews in all ages and in various lands. By issuing the *Mesillat Yesharim; the path of the upright* by Moses Hayyim Luzzatto, with an English translation and notes by Mordecai M. Kaplan (1936), the Society made available a classic in popular Jewish ethical writings. Some of the problems with which the mediaeval Jewish philosophers and ethical writers endeavored to cope are also dealt with in the charmingly written *Man is not alone*, a philosophy of religion by Abraham Joshua Heschel (1951), in the pages of which are reflected many of the teachings and much of the lore of the masters of Hasidism. In *Judaism and modern man* Will Herberg (1951) shows the impact of modern theological thinking, Jewish and non-Jewish, upon the theology of Judaism. Folklore and theology, both Jewish and non-Jewish, contributed their share to the fine study of *Fallen angels* by Bernard J. Bamberger (1952).

In the long run all the publications of the Society helped much in the spread of knowledge of the Jewish people, their beliefs and practices, and thus contributed to the deepening of Jewish conviction. As a corollary there arose the need of special works on religious practices in the home and in the synagogue and on the manner of observances of Jewish fast and festive days. Such a book as *Jewish services in synagogue and home*, by Lewis N. Dembitz (1898), though issued over fifty years ago, is still regarded as a useful work of reference to which one turns with a measure of confidence. It presents a complete survey of Jewish worship as developed for all seasons and occasions in the liturgy of the Synagogue and in the practice in the home. Indeed, it is a work which kept up the knowledge and remembrance of the devotional life of the Jews as it was in the past and of the liturgical literature as it evolved throughout the ages and in various countries. Jewish liturgy has drawn abundantly upon the writings of the leading mediaeval Hebrew poets. In such publications as *Selected religious poems of Solomon Ibn Gabirol*, edited by Israel Davidson and translated into English verse by Israel Zangwill (1923); *Selected poems of Jehudah Halevi*, edited by Heinrich Brody and translated into English by Nina Salaman (1924); and *Selected poems of Moses Ibn Ezra*, edited by Heinrich Brody and translated into English by Solomon Solis-Cohen (1934) one meets with many a specimen of the hymnody of the Synagogue.

The festivals and the manner of their observance in Jewish life as expressed in the literature and lore of the Jews are dealt with in a series of publications each one of which is devoted to a given Holy Day or festival. A volume of *Sabbath hours*, short but charming talks by Liebman Adler (1893), is a worthy forerunner of the collection on the *Sabbath*; the Day of delight, by Abraham E. Millgram (1944), in which the day is dealt with as an institution in the pattern of Jewish life. It is a compilation which includes essays, stories, poems, anecdotes and songs suitable for the understanding and observance of the Sabbath Day. As such it is an appropriate companion volume to *Hanukkah*, the feast of lights, compiled and edited by Emily Solis-Cohen, Jr. (1937), which provides an abundance of material suitable for the observance of the festival by young and old. A worthy and interesting companion volume is *The Purim anthology* by Philip Goodman (1949). Interesting, too, is *Purim* or the feast of Esther, an historical study by N. S. Doniach (1933). A masterly interpretation of the significance of the Holy Days (Rosh Ha-Shanah and Yom Kippur) in the spiritual life of the Jewish people is furnished by the Rev. Dr. Samuel Schulman (1920) as the first number of *Little studies in Judaism*. *Worlds that passed* by Abraham Simha Sachs (1928) contains stories of the customs and institutions of Jewish life and the manner in which fast and festive days were observed in Lithuania before World War I. It depicts much of the life now extinct in what was a quaintly characteristic East European ghetto. The festivals also inspired Irma Kraft

21

to write *The power of Purim* and other one act plays designed for Jewish religious schools (1915).

The lives of eminent figures are always of interest to wide circles of readers. Jewish literature is not very rich in such works. Hero worship is not a Jewish trait. In Jewry the role of the group rather than that of the individual is stressed in the appraising of events, experiences, movements and achievements. Yet there are some personalities who, in one way or another, have left a durable impress by the respective roles they played in the lives of men. Some such figures have become synonymous with movements and achievements in Jewish life with which they were associated. To make them and their work better known the Society, every now and then, issues autobiographical and biographical works. At an early date in its career it issued *Some Jewish women*, by Henry Zirndorf (1892), a series of sketches on women whose names have been perpetuated in post-biblical Jewish history and who represent beautiful types of Jewish womanhood of the past. Many a side-light which these sketches cast upon rabbinic life and thought attract a goodly number of readers. In *Students, scholars and saints*, by Louis Ginzberg (1928), and in *Essays in Jewish biography* by Alexander Marx (1947) we have biographical and literary appraisals of men who have played notable roles in the promotion of Jewish life and learning.

In Jewish biographical literature *Saadia Gaon*; his life and works, by Henry Malter (1921), certainly occupies a ranking place. The result of painstaking research it is executed with the meticulous care which characterized the work of its learned author. Learned yet popular is *Rashi*, by Maurice Liber (1906). It deals with the life and work of the most beloved and certainly most popular Jewish commentator on the Bible and the Talmud. So, too, is *Maimonides*, by David Yellin and Israel Abrahams (1903), which presents the life and achievements of the great spirit by whose thought the

22

Jewish intellect was nourished for over seven centuries. The *House of Nasi*, by Cecil Roth, presents a rounded account of the amazing careers of the "Duke of Naxos" (1948) and his aunt "Doña Gracia" (1947). From the prolific pen of the same author came *A life of Menasseh Ben Israel*, rabbi, printer and diplomat (1934), who played so remarkable a role in securing permission for his co-religionists to resettle in England. Biographies of men nearer to our own time are those of *Adolphe Crémieux*, by S. Posener (1940); *Moses Montefiore*, by Paul Goodman (1925); *Solomon Schechter*, by Norman Bentwich (1938), and a collection of studies of a group of *Germany's stepchildren*, by Solomon Liptzin (1944). Actually the last-named volume consists of character sketches through which the Jewish contribution to German culture is appraised.

The extraordinary collection of *Memoirs of my people* through a thousand years, selected and edited by Leo W. Schwarz (1943), presents significant autobiographical texts which cast much light not only on their authors but on the times and places in which they flourished. Of a like character is *I have considered the days* by Cyrus Adler (1941). It was published posthumously. An appropriate supplement to it is the well-written biographical sketch of *Cyrus Adler* by Abraham A. Neuman (1942). In these biographical and autobiographical writings, and in the many studies of eminent figures in Jewry scattered in various collections of essays in the field of history and biography by distinguished authors which the Society published, the constant endeavor is maintained to keep open the treasure-house of Israel's past and to hold up for posterity the great personalities who lived the life of the spirit and whose intellectual role in Jewry is immortal.

In employing fiction as an effective instrument in the dissemination of knowledge of Jewish ideas and experiences, the Society tried, with no small measure of success, to place on its list of authors some of the outstanding writers who have won for themselves wide recognition as authors of fiction

23

in the fullest sense of that term. *Children of the ghetto*, being pictures of a peculiar people, by Israel Zangwill (1892) is one of the Society's early publications which has had a wide distribution in English and in several other languages. "Nowhere else have been given us more realistic pictures of the shabbiness, the unwholesomeness, the close-packed human misery, the squalor, the vulgarity, the sharp struggle in the mean competition of life, in the East End of London . . . [But] there is a world of poetry, of dreams, of imagination, of high calling, of intellectual subtlety even, in which sordid London, non-Jewish, has no part nor lot."— Charles Dudley Warner, *Harper's Magazine*. This is equally true of the same author's *Dreamers of the ghetto* (1898), a work in which, with no small amount of erudition, he managed to pack together into the scenes dealing with Uriel Acosta, Sabbatai Zevi, Spinoza, the Ba'al Shem, Maimon, Heine, Lassalle and Beaconsfield, just those incidents and sayings of their careers which bring out most clearly their Jewish aspects. It is likewise true of *"They that walk in darkness," Ghetto tragedies* (1899). *Children of the Ghetto, Ghetto tragedies* and *Ghetto comedies* were republished in his *Selected works* (1938). They all present remarkable stories illumined by flashes of fancy, satire, irony and humor. In the portrayal of ghetto types and episodes they are incisive, sharp, unrelievedly realistic, often even unsparingly black. In this connection one calls to mind Zangwill's own testimony that, without the Society's stimulation, he might never have written his *Children of the ghetto*. "I do not speak merely of pecuniary stimulation. What was needed to draw this book from my subconsciousness was the wise and understanding policy of your institution in giving the artist a free hand. It is the tragedy of the artist to supply what the public does not yet demand." The life and lore of the denizens of the Polish ghetto are well reflected in the Hebrew and Yiddish writings of Isaac Loeb Perez, portions of which the Society has made available to the English readers. An interpretative introduction

24

to Perez and his world is offered in the *Prince of the ghetto* (1948) by Maurice Samuel.

Personalities and events play their respective, often, indeed, decisive roles in history. To exploit them in fiction is but another way of making them known to those who are interested in experiences of days long gone by. The Society did not hesitate to take advantage of fiction as an instrument for the effective spread of knowledge of periods and personalities in Jewish history. It realized that this type of literature has a constant appeal to many readers, especially to young ones. Accordingly most of the fiction in the list of the Society's publications consists of titles which have been written and published with an eye to such readers. Many of them have fired the imagination of Jewish youngsters with stories of heroism by which their minds are carried back to great moments in various periods of Jewish history. In no small measure such books often supplement instruction given in Jewish religious schools. Interesting is the fact that in this sphere of literary endeavor considerable attention was given to personalities and episodes familiar from the Scriptural record. In *Jacob's dream*, a drama in poetry by Richard Beer-Hofmann (1946), the Society made available to adults an English version of a work which, originally written in German, has become a classic in modern European literature. The beautifully printed and illustrated collection of *Stories of King David* by Lillian S. Freehof (1952) retells in a most delightful manner some of the striking legends of King David gleaned from rabbinic lore. A charmingly written story of the little Prince Jehoash, son of Ahaziah, whom the High Priest Jehoiadah had rescued from the clutches of Athaliah, is *Lost Prince Almon*, by Louis Pendleton (1898). This and his *In Assyrian tents* (1904), as their titles indicate, deal with biblical themes. So do also *The sign above the door*, by William W. Canfield (1912), and *The game of Doeg*, by Eleanor E. Harris (1914). A story about the Jews in mediaeval England is offered in *The lion-*

hearted, by Charles Reznikoff (1944). It is a magnificently told story, remarkable for the beauty of its style and the ingenuity of its construction. Jewish life in the Spain of the Middle Ages is warmly described in *The vale of cedars*, by Grace Aguilar (1902), and in *The ship of hope*, by Ruben Rothgiesser (1939). Other periods of Jewish life are depicted in *Beating sea and changeless bar*, by Jacob Lazarre (1905). A story of the days of Maimonides that abounds in stirring incidents is furnished in *Under the eagle's wing*, by Sara Miller (1899). Several books offer sketches of European Jewish life; *Voegele's marriage* and other tales, by Louis Schnabel (1892); *Stories of Jewish home life*, by S. H. Mosenthal (1907); *Simon Eichelkatz the patriarch*, by Ulrich Frank (1907). Stories and legends of the life of the Jews in Russia are told in *In the pale*, by Henry Iliowizi, a master of both humor and pathos (1897); *Rabbi and priest*, by Milton Goldsmith (1891), is a strong and well-written story in which an attempt is made to depict faithfully the customs and practices of the Russian people and government in connection with the Jewish population of that country during the last decades of the nineteenth century. Well written, too, is the collection of stories *Strangers at the gate*, by Samuel Gordon (1902) which, likewise, deals with phases of Jewish life in the Russia of those days.

Like Zangwill's *Children of the ghetto*, Samuel Gordon's *Sons of the covenant* (1900) presents a tale of London Jewry. Martha Wolfenstein, in her *Idyls of the gass* (1901) and *A renegade and other tales* (1905), offers charming sketches in which there is depicted the simplicity and dignity of ghetto life in the Austrian communities of pre-World War days. They are full of poetry, sentiment, geniality, a happy mingling of the old and the new, of sublime tragedy relieved by humor.

Delightfully written stories for children are offered in *David the giant killer* and other tales of Grandma Lopez, by Emily Solis-Cohen (1908). They give in beautiful biblical language the story of some heroes of Bible times, incidentally offering a picture of life in a true Jewish home. Stories of our time for old and young are told in *Under the Sabbath lamp* (1919) and *School days in home town* (1928), both by Abram S. Isaacs. Written in the guise of fiction, they discuss problems of Jewish religious and spiritual interest. Quite popular are the several collections of stories by Elma Ehrlich Levinger. Her *Playmates in Egypt* and other stories (1920); *Wonder tales* (1929) and *Pilgrims to Palestine* and other stories (1940) have gone through more than one edition.

Stories derived from Jewish life on the American scene are told in *Kasriel the watchman* and other stories, by Rufus Learsi [pseudonym of Israel Goldberg] (1925). It consists of a number of tales which have a fascinating appeal to the Jewish child in America. It served as a fitting forerunner to *The fire eater* (1941) and *Boot camp* (1948) by Henry J. Berkowitz, and *The nightingale's song*, by Dorothy Alofsin (1945). The latter is a novel for young adults in which the story is told of how a Jewish family of farmers wins the regard of their community, while their daughter, who struggles to become an author, renews her pride in her people's heritage and in America. *Room for a son* by Robert D. Abrahams (1951) is a heart-warming tale of the adjustments of a young Jewish refugee adopted by a Jewish family in a small American community. *Joel*, a novel of young America by Nora Benjamin Kubie (1952), likewise deals with a young Jewish refugee of an earlier day, who, to escape persecution in his native land, came to America in 1775 and ultimately found himself proud and happy to be "both an American and a Jew, with loyalty to the democratic ideals which played so large a part in both traditions."

Quite popular are the books of a biographical character which have been written for young readers. They are among the frequently reprinted publications of the Society. *Think and thank*, a tale by Samuel W. Cooper (1890), was the first book of fiction issued by the Society. It presents the life of Moses

Montefiore, one of the greatest philanthropists and lovers of his people in the nineteenth century. It still holds its own as a popular book, having been reprinted again and again. Such books tend to quicken the ambition, the love of knowledge and the admiration for the great sons and daughters of Israel in modern times. Such popular books by Abram S. Isaacs as *Step by step*, a story of the early days of Moses Mendelssohn, the first great Jew in our modern era (1910), and *The young champion*, one year in Grace Aguilar's girlhood (1913), belong to that category. *Mr. Benjamin's sword*, by Robert D. Abrahams (1948), is sure to meet with the same success. It deals with the life of Judah P. Benjamin, who, during the Civil War, played so remarkable a role in the Confederacy.

In its desire to bring to the American Jewish reader a measure of the spirit which dominates the literature and life of Eastern European Jews, the Society made available translations of works originally written in modern Hebrew or Yiddish. They are examples of very fine writing in those languages. *Stories and pictures*, by Isaac Loeb Perez (1906), and *Yiddish tales*, translated by Helena Frank (1912), were among the specimens of such contributions to Jewish literature. They were followed by *Kiddush ha-shem*, an epic of 1648 by Sholom Ash (1926), and *Sabbatai Zevi*, a tragedy in three acts and six scenes with a prologue and an epilogue by the same author (1930). Of the writings of Joseph Opatoshu, a contemporary of Ash, the Society offered *In Polish woods* (1938) and *The last revolt*, the story of Rabbi Akiba (1952). Of modern Hebrew fiction the Society published translations of *In those days*, an old man's reminiscences about the Cantonists of Russia, by Judah Steinberg (1915), and *Aftergrowth* and other stories by Hayyim Nahman Bialik (1939). Other works of striking fiction include *Tomorrow's bread*, a novel in which Beatrice Bisno (1938) tells the story of a Jewish labor leader in the needle trade and the problems with which he had to cope. It was chosen for the Edwin Wolf Award "for the best novel of Jewish interest." In *Renegade*, a novel by Ludwig Lewisohn (1942), the Society added to its list a work by an author whose fame in American literature is well established. Likewise, in issuing *For the sake of heaven*, by Martin Buber (1945), it introduced to its reading public a historical novel by a leading expounder of Hasidic lore. It is a work in which the oneness of Israel is typified in a story of those holy leaders in Polish Jewry of the Napoleonic period one of whom tried by theurgic means to turn the Napoleonic wars into those which are supposed to lead to the coming of the Messiah. *The spirit returneth*, by Selma Stern (1946), is another historical novel by the publication of which the Society introduced to the English reader a work by a leading historian of modern Jewry, in which some striking episodes in mediaeval Jewish history are clarified. It deals with the massacres of the Jews during the Black Death scourge in fourteenth century Germany, which in no small degree are comparable to those of Germany in recent years. The plight of the Jews in the Third Reich forms the subject of *Cold pogrom* by Max L. Berges (1939). It is a novel "of indignation, of exasperation, and of truth." *Unambo*, a novel of the war in Israel by Max Brod (1952) is a fine piece of historical fiction dealing with recent experience in Israel. The trilogy consisting of *The son of the lost son* (1946), *In my father's pastures* (1947) and *The testament of the lost son* (1950) by Soma Morgenstern, adds lustre to a very creditable record in the realm of Jewish fiction which the Society can proudly claim as its own. Thus one meets with the names of some of the leading Jewish writers of fiction, American and foreign, who are represented in the Society's publications by works originally written for its press or by translations from works which have made their mark when published elsewhere in a foreign language. Reading in a lighter vein is provided in *Let laughter ring*, a compilation of Jewish humorous stories by Rabbi S. Felix Mendelsohn (1941).

If there is a meagerness in the Society's output of poetry

it is in proportion no smaller than that which marks the output of poetry in general. Yet the Society can point with pride to the fact that it was first to issue volumes of English translations of the leading mediaeval Hebrew poets as well as of a collection of *Songs of exile* by Hebrew poets translated by Nina Davis (1901). In addition to several anthologies, consisting largely of prose selections but including considerable portions of verse as well, the Society also published such collections of poetry as *Songs of a wanderer*, by Philip M. Raskin (1917); *Brand plucked from the fire*, by Jessie Sampter (1937), and *Poems*, by A. M. Klein, a distinguished Canadian Jewish poet (1944), which in style and content are as Jewish as those poems which comprise the Scriptural collection of Psalms. In its fictional output the Society endeavored to introduce into Jewish literature works which, in one way or another, attempt to portray Jewish life as it was and as it is in all its finest manifestations. It issued works in which one meets with characters and events familiar in Jewish history in an atmosphere and environment in which they play their role sometimes in a manner quite realistic; often the Jewish reader is transplanted into a place and period quite remote and different from his own but in which he finds himself not altogether a stranger. He brushes elbows, as it were, with men and women who were known to him merely by name. It is the Jewish spirit in its various manifestations and in different times. Like many another work which the Society has issued, its distinguished list of fiction is such as to contribute abundantly to the fostering of the Jewish spirit, to the strengthening of the Jewish consciousness and to the giving of adequate expression in literature to Jewish life, Jewish character and the Jewish spirit.

The portrayal of the Jew by non-Jewish writers, as revealed in the literatures of the various nations, is a subject not yet fully explored. Literary samples of such treatment have been made available by the Society in *Among the nations*, three tales and a play about Jews . . . edited with an introduc-

30

tion by Ludwig Lewisohn (1948), and *Candles in the night*, Jewish tales by Gentile authors, compiled by Joseph L. Baron (1940). The same compiler provided a companion volume, *Stars and sand*, Jewish notes by non-Jewish notables (1943). It presents selections from more than seven hundred of the world's foremost non-Jewish statesmen, religious leaders, philosophers and artists. The Society also published a splendid study of *The Jew in the literature of England* to the end of the 19th century, by Montagu Frank Modder (1939), showing "that invariably the poet, the novelist, and the dramatist reflect the attitude of contemporary society in their presentation of the Jewish character, and that the portrayal changes with the economic and social changes of each decade."

Books attractive to the child, and especially such as are written and designed to meet the particular needs of the Jewish child, are among the most popular ones issued by the Society. *A Jewish child's book*, by Katherine Myrtilla Cohen (1913), is meant for the very young Jewish reader. On the other hand, the older child is offered a series of books beautifully printed and illustrated with good taste. They include *The breakfast of the birds* and other stories from the Hebrew by Judah Steinberg, by Emily Solis-Cohen (1917). Delightful is *The Aleph-Bet story book* in which Deborah Pessin (1946) created a magic world and peopled it with fascinating creatures — personified letters of the Hebrew alphabet — who introduce themselves to Adam and to adventuring in the days of the early Hebrews. She has breathed life into the Hebrew alphabet and made the letters meaningful and full of color. *What the moon brought* (1942) and *Little new angel* (1947), both by Mrs. Sadie R. Weilerstein, are the kind of books which charm and delight and from which considerable knowledge of Jewish life is acquired by the juvenile reader.

This rapid survey does not claim to be an adequate appraisal of a literary output of more than six decades. It is a bird's-eye review of the character and content of most of the titles comprising the bibliography of works bearing the imprint of The Jewish Publication Society of America. It does not include publications bearing imprints of other publishers in the production of which the Society often had a generous share. It is not generally known that, conscious of the role which learning plays in Jewish life, the Society often granted subventions to scholars engaged in the pursuit of original research whose works, though, as a rule, not always calculated to interest the average reader as represented by the rank and file of the Society's membership, satisfy the needs of the more learned and tend to advance knowledge which the popular writer is later able to exploit advantageously.

At its very outset the Society conceived of its duty as that of publishing and of distributing books not for material profit but solely in order to spread knowledge relating to the Jewish people, their life and lore. In the performance of this duty it remained steadfast and thereby created an atmosphere friendly to the Jewish book. Its primary concern being with the literary expression of every aspect of Jewish life and lore, it endeavored to reproduce, as far as this can be done more or less in popular form, the elements that entered into the make-up of Jewish belief and practice as they find expression in the synagogue, school and home. It did not neglect the role of the Jews and of Judaism in the life of their non-Jewish neighbors. In its search for competent writers it turned to some of the foremost of Jewish scholars and convinced not a few of them that to popularize Jews and Judaism is not unworthy even of the greatest of them. To awaken slumbering possibilities the Society every now and then resorted to the device of offering Prize Competitions. It met with a measure of success. By encouraging young gifted writers it was able to launch the literary careers of a number of men who have attained fame in the world of letters and learning. In brief, it has been catholic in its hospitality to authors. The writers represented

32

in its literary output have come from all sections of Jewry and even from non-Jewish ranks. They include men and women of national and international fame as masters in their respective fields of literary or scholarly endeavor, indeed, in all branches of literary expression.

Literature and learning have in every age been among the supreme unifying forces of the scattered Jewish communities. In spreading a knowledge of Jewish life and literature and in making that knowledge available in attractive literary form the Society is constantly endeavoring to satisfy a great need: it provides a strong bulwark against disintegrating forces in Jewish life in English-speaking Jewry which finds itself in the midst of an attractive culture and which comprises Jewish settlements in several lands. The work of the Society has exerted a most wholesome influence in these settlements. Indeed, it has contributed much to the raising of the intellectual level of English-speaking Jewry everywhere. The literature it has produced often plays a conciliatory role between the thought of the Jewish world and its non-Jewish environment. Moreover, it tends to increase the self-respect of the Jews and thus to maintain the dignity of the Jewish people. In these and in other ways the Society endeavors to provide a channel for the communication of a full understanding of the specifically Jewish message in any form of literature and by any writer, Jewish or non-Jewish. It is a worthy task, the consummation of which is as devoutly to be wished by the world as it is by the Jews.

It is quite obvious that in its endeavor to serve Jewry at large the Society could admit into its program neither the sensational "best-seller" on which some commercial publishers thrive nor the "timely" book which concerns itself with matters of passing interest or curiosity. It certainly had to exclude from its program the apologia, no matter in what literary form, though many of its publications serve, in various ways, as instruments for the defense of the Jewish people,

33

"TEMPLE ISRAEL"

their teachings and practices. Publications designed to serve propaganda and other special needs of particular parties or factions in Jewry have, as a rule, likewise been kept out of the Society's scope. No wonder the Society has been able to draw upon the support of all groups comprising American Jewry. Among those who have contributed to the making of its books are men and women of all shades of Jewish opinion. The names of some of the foremost Jewish writers are among the authors of books it has published. They, too, are drawn from the ranks of various groups of thought in modern Judaism. In this and in other ways, the Society has been a great force for unity in American Jewry. Considering the fact that the Society is constantly promoting that type of Jewish culture which literature alone can enshrine and propagate, the cumulative effect of its work has been "to magnify and glorify the Torah," in the finest and widest sense of the phrase, and to strengthen the loyalties of Jews to the faith of their fathers and to the land of which they are devoted citizens.

The Bibliography

The notes accompanying the entries are, with but few exceptions, actual quotations which have been culled from a variety of sources, but mostly from the publications themselves and from the reports, communications, and the like, issued by the officers of the Society. They thus serve as "documents" which present, as it were, official attestation to the purpose, content and character of the works recorded as given by their respective authors, compilers, editors and publisher. They do not necessarily represent opinions or judgments of the compiler of this bibliography. His own appraisal of the literary worth of the Society's publications is given in the introductory study presenting a bird's-eye survey of the literary output of the Jewish Publication Society of America. Obviously he alone assumes responsibility for opinions expressed therein.

The number of editions and of copies printed of any work are given in instances where the information was obtainable from a trustworthy source. Such information was readily procurable in connection with "reprints" of recent years only.

The indexes of authors and titles are arranged alphabetically while the one listing Serial Publications follows the chronological order.

1890

Outlines of Jewish History

Outlines | of | JEWISH HISTORY | From B. C. 586 to C. E. 1890 |
With Three Maps | By | Lady Magnus | Revised by M.
Friedländer, Ph.D. | [*seal 1a*] | Philadelphia | The Jewish
Publication Society of America | 1890 |

COLLATION: 12°. xxi, 388 p. (p. [i] Half-title; p. [iii] Title;
p. [iv] Copyright, Press and Bindery of Isaac Friedenwald, Baltimore;
p. [v] Preface to the Society's edition; p. [ii, vi] blank; p. [vii]–viii,
Preface; p. [ix]–xxi, Contents; p. [1]–367, Text; p. [368–375]
Chronological Table; p. [376]–378, Dates of chief events; p. [379]–
388, Index; 1 unnumbered page of publisher's advertisement.) plate
(front.), maps.

Issued in red cloth; front cover: title, seal 1 (in gilt), and
publisher in black; back: title, rule and author in gilt.

The "Chronological Tables" are derived from Théodore
Reinach, *Histoire des Israélites* (Paris, 1884). Chapters XL–XLII
were written under the editorship of Henrietta Szold and "Lady
Magnus is in no wise responsible" for them. — Cf. Preface to the
Society's edition.

"800 copies were bound in different colored cloth from the
remainder and sold as the School Edition." — *JPSA*, 2nd biennial
report [1892] p. 19.

Second revised edition: undated, title-page reset, with seal 2a
without advertisement, plate or maps.

Third revised American edition: see 1929.

Think and Thank

THINK AND THANK | A Tale | By | Samuel W . Cooper. |
[*seal 1a*] | Philadelphia: | The Jewish Publication Society of
America. | 1890. |

COLLATION: 12°. iv, 120 p. (p. [i] Title; p. [ii] Copyright, Press of Edward Stern & Co., Philadelphia; p. [iii]–iv, Table of Contents; p. 1–120, Text; 2 unnumbered pages of publisher's advertisements.) plates (including front.).

Issued in red cloth; front cover: title, seal 1, publisher; back: title, rule, author all in gilt.

Sir Moses Montefiore is the hero of this juvenile story.

1900 edition: as above, with 5 unnumbered pages of publisher's advertisements.

1929 edition: as above, with seal 2a, without plates or advertisements.

1940: "1,100 copies reprinted."— *AJYB*, 5702, p. 777.

5707–1946 edition: as above, with seal 3b, without plates or advertisements. Verso of title-page: "All rights reserved .. Reprinted 1946."

First Biennial Report

FIRST BIENNIAL REPORT | of the | Jewish Publication Society | — of— | America. | 1888–90. | [*rule*] | Office, | No. 714 Market Street, | Philadelphia. |

COLLATION: 16°. 73 p. (p. [1] Title; p. [2] Press of Edward Stern & Co., Philadelphia; p. [3]–73, Text; 1 unnumbered page of publisher's advertisement.)

1891

History of the Jews

HISTORY OF THE JEWS. | By | Professor H. Graetz. | * | Vol. I. | From the Earliest Period to the Death of Simon | The Maccabee (135 B. C. E.). | [*seal 1a*] | Philadelphia: | The Jewish Publication Society of America. | 1891. |

COLLATION: 8°. xvi, 553 p. (1 l., Half-title, verso blank; p. [i] Title; p. [ii] Copyright, Press of the Friedenwald Co.; p. [iii]

Preface to the Society's edition; p. [v]–vii, Preface; p. [iv; viii] blank; p. [ix]–xvi, Contents; p. [1]–531, Text; p. [532] blank; p. [533]–553, Index.)

Issued in light red cloth; front cover: title, seal 1 (in gilt), and publisher in black; back: title, rule, author, volume, and publisher in gilt.

Published originally in 5 v.: v. 1, 1891; v. 2, 1893; v. 3, 1894; v. 4, 1894; v. 5, 1895. Vol. 6, Index Volume, published in 1898.

"This translation, in five volumes, is not a mere excerpt of my 'Geschichte der Juden' (like my 'Volksthümliche Geschichte der Juden'), but a condensed reproduction of the entire eleven volumes. But the foot-notes have been omitted, so as to render the present work less voluminous for the general reader. Historical students are usually acquainted with the German language, and can read the notes in the original. In this English edition the 'History of the Present Day' is brought down to 1870, whilst the original only goes as far as the memorable events of 1848." — H. Graetz, Preface, p. vi.

". . . While the first volume, as far as the period of the Hasmonaeans, has been translated by me, the other volumes have for the greater part 'been done into English by various hands,' and have afterwards been revised and edited by me." — Bella Löwy, Preface, p. vii.

Reprint, undated, title-page reset: HISTORY OF THE | JEWS | By | Professor H. Graetz | Vol[s]. I[–VI] . . . [seal 2a] | Philadelphia | The Jewish Publication Society of America | . Title and seal in red. Reprinted many times, with title and seal in black.

5707–1946 edition: title-page reset, with seal 3b. See also 1898, *Index Volume*.

No information is available as to the total number of copies originally printed nor as to the number of reprints that have been made. However, frequent references are made to sets reprinted and to the fact that it continues to be a "best seller". Cf. *AJYB*, 5708, p. 813; 1950, p. 569.

Rabbi and Priest

RABBI AND PRIEST. | A Story | By | Milton Goldsmith. | [*seal
1b*] | Philadelphia: | Jewish Publication Society of America. |
1891. |

COLLATION: 12°. 314 p. (p. [1] Title; p. [2] Press of Edward
Stern & Co., Philadelphia.; p. [3] Preface; p. [4] blank; p. 5–314,
Text; 6 unnumbered pages of publisher's advertisements.)

Issued in red cloth; front cover: title, seal 1 (in gilt), and
publisher in black; back: title, rule and author in gilt.

"Towards the end of 1882, there arrived . . . in Philadelphia,
several hundred Russian refugees, driven from their native land by
the inhuman treatment of the Muscovite Government. Among them
were . . . Joseph Kierson . . . and his wife." — Preface, p. [3].

"The Society has also issued a popular edition for the Union
News Company of Mr. Goldsmith's 'Rabbi and Priest' in paper
covers." — *JPSA*, 2nd biennial report [1892] p. 19.

1936 edition: title-page reset, with seal 3b, without advertisements. Verso of title-page: "Copyright, 1891 . . . reprinted 1936."

The Persecution of the Jews
in Russia

. . . | THE PERSECUTION OF THE JEWS | IN RUSSIA, | With a map
of Russia, showing the Pale of | Jewish Settlement. | [*seal 1a*] |
Issued by the | Russo-Jewish Committee of London. | [*rule*] |
(Reprinted.) | [*rule*] | Philadelphia: | Jewish Publication Society
of America. | 1891. |

At head of title: Special Series. No. 1.

COLLATION: 12°. 87 p. (p. [1] Title; p. [2] Press of S. W.
Goodman, Philadelphia; p. [3]–47, Text; p. [48] blank; p. [49]–87,

Appendix. An abridged summary of laws, special and restrictive, relating to the Jews in Russia, brought down to the year 1890; 5 unnumbered pages of publisher's advertisements.) front. (colored map)

Issued in gray paper covers: title as above.

Reprinted from the London, 1890 edition.

Edited by Joseph Jacobs.

Verso of paper-cover: "The Special Series, of which this is the initial number, is supplementary to the books issued by the Jewish Publication Society of America, and will be supplied to all members of the Society without extra cost. It will be published from time to time and will be devoted to papers, original and selected, on topics of timely interest. The later issues will be uniform in style and shape with this, so that they can be preserved and bound in volumes." — The Publication Committee.

1892

Voegele's Marriage

. . . | VOEGELE'S MARRIAGE | And | Other Tales | By | Louis Schnabel. | [seal ıa] | Philadelphia: | The Jewish Publication Society of America. | 1892. |

At head of title: Special Series. No. 2.

COLLATION: 12°. 83 p. (p. [1] Title; p. [2] Bill Stein & Son Printers, Philadelphia; p. [3] Letter to Joseph Weisse; p. [5] Contents; p. [4, 6] blank; p. 7–83, Text; 8 unnumbered pages of publisher's advertisements; 3 blank leaves.)

Issued in red paper covers; title as above, within border.

Sketches of European Jewish life.

Children of the Ghetto

CHILDREN OF THE GHETTO. | Being | Pictures of a Peculiar People. | By | I. Zangwill, | Author of "The Bachelors' Club;" "The Big Bow Mystery;" etc. | Joint Author of "The Premier and the Painter." | [*rule*] | Vol[s]. I. [and II.] | [*rule*] | [*seal 1a*] |Philadelphia: | The Jewish Publication Society. | 1892. |

COLLATION: 12°. 2 v. v. 1: 451 p. (p. [1] Title; p. [2] Copyright, Press of Sherman & Co.; p. [3] Contents; p. [4] blank; p. 5–451, Text.); v. 2: 328 p. (p. [1–4] same as v. 1; p. 5–324, Text; p. 325–328, Glossary; 8 unnumbered pages of publisher's advertisements.)

Issued in red cloth; front cover: title, seal 1 (in gilt) and publisher in black; back: title, rule, author and volume in gilt.

"Portrays two phases of London Jewish life, the sordid poor of White Chapel, and the coarsely prosperous of the West End. Shows profound knowledge of Jewish characters and characteristics. Full of pathos and humor. The best of Ghetto novels. When he depicts Ghetto life it is as a sympathetic observer; Jewish life of the West End, on the other hand, he records as a critic." — *AJYB*, 5667, p. 142.

See also his: *Selected works*, 1938.

Translations into Hebrew:

ילדי הגיטו. ספר ראשון: בני הגיטו. תרגום ש. ל. גרדון. פיעטרקוב: הוצאת „תושיה." תרס"א.

ילדי הגיטו. ספורים. מעבד ע"י מ. טשודנר. ורשה: הוצאת „אחיספר." [1928?]

Some Jewish Women

SOME JEWISH WOMEN | By | Henry Zirndorf. | [*rule*] | Translated from the German. | [*seal 1b*] | Philadelphia: | The Jewish Publication Society of America. | 1892. |

COLLATION: 12°. viii, 280 p. (p. [i] Title; p. [ii] Copyright, Press of Edward Stern & Co.; p. [iii] Dedication*; p. [iv] blank;

p. v–viii, Preface; p. [1] Contents; p. [2] blank; p. [3]–270, Text; p. 271–280, Index; 1 unnumbered page, Works of Henry Zirndorf; 10 unnumbered pages of publisher's advertisements.)

Issued in red and white cloth; top edges gilted; front and back covers in red and white with a gilt tooled vertical line on the white; front cover: seal 1 in gilt on the red; back: title, rule, author, rules, and publisher in gilt on white.

*"To the memory | of my daughter, | Emilie Esther Zirndorf, | who departed this life in | Detroit, April 23, 1882, | these sketches of notable womanhood | are inscribed in undying | tenderness | ."

An English translation [by Sylvan Drey] of the author's sketches originally published in German in *Die Deborah*. — See Preface, p. vii.

CONTENTS: From the Apocrypha: Judith. — The mother of the seven martyrs. — The Graeco-Roman Period: Queen Salome Alexandra. — Mariamne, the Hasmonean. — Helena, queen and proselyte. — Berenice. — The Talmudic Age: Martha, daughter of Boëthus. — Ima Shalom. — Rachel, Rabbi Akiba's wife. — Beruria. — Rabbi Meïr's pupil. — Rabbi Ishmael's mother. — Rabbi Judah's maid-servant. — The married couple of Sidon. — A group of Xanthippes. — Jalta. — Abaji's foster-mother. — The two Chomas. — Weasel and Well as witnesses.

Second Biennial Report

Second Biennial Report | of the | Jewish Publication Society | of | America. | 1890–92. | [*seal 1b*] | Office, | No. 714 Market Street, | Philadelphia. |

COLLATION: 16°. 72 p. (p. [1] Title; p. [2] Press of Edward Stern & Co. Philadelphia; p. [3]–72, Text.)

1893

Sabbath Hours

SABBATH HOURS | Thoughts | By | Liebman Adler | [*seal 1a*] | Philadelphia: | The Jewish Publication Society of America | 1893 |

COLLATION: 12°. xiii, 338 p. (p. [i] Title; p. [ii] Copyright, Press of Edward Stern & Co.; p. [iii] Dedication*; p. [iv] blank; p. v–vi, Preface; p. vii–x, Biographical sketch; p. xi–xiii, Table of Contents; p. 1–338, Text; 11 unnumbered pages of publisher's advertisements.) front. (port.)

Issued in dark blue cloth; front cover: title, author and publisher in gilt, seal 1a, ornamental border and designs in silver; back: title, author, and publisher in gilt, with ornamental designs in silver.

*"To the | faithful keepers | of the | perpetual light | of | Jewish feeling and practice, The Jewish Women, | this work is dedicated. | "

"The following fifty-four sermons, one for each Sabbath of the year, with two additional for leap years, were culled from two volumes of German sermons on texts from the Pentateuch, published by the late Rabbi Liebman Adler, of Chicago." — Preface of the editor, p. v.

Translated from the German by Wilhemina Jastrow (Wallerstein).

History of the Jews

HISTORY OF THE JEWS. | By | Professor H. Graetz. | ★ ★ | Vol. II. | From the Reign of Hyrcanus (135 B. C. E.) to the Com | pletion of the Babylonian Talmud (500 C. E.) | [seal 1a] | Philadelphia: | The Jewish Publication Society of America. | 1893. |

COLLATION: 8°. xi, 656 p. (1 l., Half-title, verso blank; p, [i] Title; p. [ii] Copyright, Press of the Friedenwald Co.; p. [iii]–xi, Contents; p. 1–635, Text; p. [636] blank; p. 637–656, Index.)

See 1891 for original binding and reprints. Contents on title-page of reprints reset: From the Reign of Hyrcanus (135 B. C. E.) to the | Completion of the Babylonian Talmud (500 C. E.) |

1894

History of the Jews

HISTORY OF THE JEWS. | By | Professor H. Graetz. | ★ ★ ★ |
Vol. III. | From the Revolt against the Zendik (511 C. E.)
to | the Capture of St. Jean d'Acre by the | Mahometans
(1291 C. E.). | [*seal 1a*] | Philadelphia: | Jewish Publication
Society of America. | 1894. |

COLLATION: 8°. viii, 675 p. (1 l., Half-title, verso blank; p.
[i] Title; p. [ii] Copyright, Press and bindery of the Friedenwald Co.;
p. [iii]–viii, Contents; p. [1]–650, Text; p. [651]–675, Index.)

See 1891 for original binding and reprints.

Papers of the Jewish Women's Congress

PAPERS | of the | JEWISH WOMEN'S CONGRESS. | [*rule*] | Held
at Chicago, September 4, 5, 6 and 7, | 1893. | [*seal 1b*] | Phila-
delphia: | The Jewish Publication Society of America. | 1894. |

COLLATION: 8°. 1 l., 268 p. (1 l., Title, verso Copyright; p.
[1–2] Contents; p. 3–268, Text; 12 unnumbered pages of publisher's
advertisements.)

Issued in green cloth; front cover: title, seal 1a, publisher; back:
title, rule, publisher all in gilt.

CONTENTS: Introduction by the chairman. Hannah G. Solomon.
— Programme of the Congress. — Prayer. Ray Frank. — Address.
Ellen M. Henrotin. — Address by the chairman. Hannah G.
Solomon. — White day of peace. Miriam del Banco. — Jewish
women of Biblical and of mediaeval times. Louise Mannheimer. —
Jewish women of modern days. Helen Kahn Weil. — Woman in
the synagogue. Ray Frank. — Influence of the discovery of America

on the Jews. Pauline H. Rosenberg. — Women wage-workers: with reference to directing immigrants. Julia Richman. — The influence of the Jewish religion on the home. Mary M. Cohen. — Israel to the world in greeting. Cora Wilburn. — Charity as taught by the Mosaic Law. Eva L. Stern. — Woman's place in charitable work. Carrie Shevelson Benjamin. — Address of the Chairman. Hannah G. Solomon. — Presentation of Hymn Book. E. Frank. — Mission work among the unenlightened Jews. Minnie D. Louis. — How can nations be influenced to protest or interfere in cases of persecution? Laura Davis Jacobson. — Organization. Sadie American. — Report of the business meeting.

Old European Jewries

OLD EUROPEAN JEWRIES | By | David Philipson, D.D. | Author of "The Jew in English Fiction," etc. | "By the Ghetto's plague, | By the garb's disgrace" | Browning | [*seal 1a*] | Philadelphia | The Jewish Publication Society of America | 1894 |

COLLATION: 12°. 3 p. l., 281 p. (l. 1, Half-title, verso blank; l. 2, Title, verso Copyright, Meyers Printing and Publishing House, Harrisburg, Pa.; l. 3, Dedication*, verso blank; p. 1–2, Preface; p. [3] Contents; p. 5–251, Text; p. [4, 252] blank; p. [253]–281, Notes and Index; 11 unnumbered pages of publisher's advertisements).

Issued in red cloth; front cover: title, seal 1a, publisher; back: title, rule, author, publisher all in gilt.

*"To my wife, | who, with sympathetic interest, visited | with me many of the places | herein mentioned, | this book is lovingly inscribed. | "

CONTENTS: I. Early settlements of Jews in Europe. II. The institution of the Ghetto. III. The Ghetto in church legislation. IV. The Judengasse of Frankfort-on-the-Main. V. The Judenstadt

46

of Prague. VI. The Ghetto of Rome. VII. The Russian Ghetto. VIII. Effects and results. IX. The Ghetto in literature.

Reprint, undated, title-page reset, with seal 2a, without advertisements.

5703–1943 edition: title-page reset, with seal 3b, without advertisements. Verso of title-page: "Reprinted 1943."

Hebrew translation:

הגיטות האירפיות העתיקות מאת דוד פילפזון. תרגם מאנגלית על ידי דוד ילין בירושלם ... הוצאת „תושיה." ורשה, תרס"ג. Warsaw, 1902.

History of the Jews

HISTORY OF THE JEWS. | By | Professor H. Graetz. | ★ ★ ★ | ★ | Vol. IV. | From the Rise of the Kabbala (1270 C. E.) to the | Permanent Settlement of the Marranos | in Holland (1618 C. E.) | [seal 1a] | Philadelphia: | Jewish Publication Society of America. | 1894 |

COLLATION: 8°. xi, 743 p. (1 l., Half-title, verso blank; p. [i] Title; p. [ii] Copyright, Press of Edward Stern & Co., Inc.; p. [iii]–xi, Contents; p. [1]–708, Text; p. [709]–743, Index.)

See 1891 for original binding and reprints.

Third Biennial Report

THIRD BIENNIAL REPORT | of the | Jewish Publication Society | of | America. | 1892–94. | [seal 1a] | Office: | No. 1015 Arch Street, | Philadelphia, Pa. |

COLLATION: 16°. 68 p. (p. [1] Title; p. [2] Press of Edward Stern & Co., Inc., Philadelphia; p. [3]–68, Text.)

1895

Jewish Literature

JEWISH LITERATURE | And | Other Essays | By | Gustav Karpeles | [*seal 1a*] | Philadelphia | The Jewish Publication Society of America | 1895 |

COLLATION: 12°. 404 p. (p. [1] Half-title; p. [3] Title; p. [4] Copyright, Press of The Friedenwald Co. Baltimore; p. [5]–6, Preface; p. [7] Contents; p. [2, 8] blank; p. 9–379, Text; p. [380] blank; p. 381–404, Index; 12 unnumbered pages of publisher's advertisements.)

Issued in red cloth; front cover: title, author, seal 1a, publisher; back: title, author, publisher all in gilt.

Translated from the German by Harriet Liebér Cohen and Henrietta Szold.

CONTENTS: A glance at Jewish literature. — The Talmud. — The Jew in the history of civilization. — Women in Jewish literature. — Moses Maimonides. — Jewish troubadours and minnesingers. — Humor and love in Jewish poetry. — The Jewish stage. — The Jew's quest in Africa. — A Jewish king in Poland. — Jewish society in the time of Mendelssohn. — Leopold Zunz. — Heinrich Heine and Judaism. — The music of the synagogue.

"These addresses were born of devoted love to Judaism. The consciousness that Israel is charged with a great historical mission, not yet accomplished, ushered them into existence. Truth and sincerity stood sponsor to every word." — Preface, p. [5].

1911 edition: as above, with seal 2a, without advertisements.

The Talmud

. . . | THE TALMUD | By | Emanuel Deutsch | [*seal 1b*] | Philadelphia | The Jewish Publication Society of America | 1895 |

At head of title: Special Series. No. 3.

COLLATION: 12°. 107 p. (p. [1] Title; p. [2] Reprinted from "Literary Remains of the Late Emanuel Deutsch," London, 1874. Press of Edward Stern & Co., Inc., Philadelphia; p. [3]–107, Text; 12 unnumbered pages of publisher's advertisements.)

Issued in red paper covers; title as above.

1896 edition: as above.

191–? edition.

History of the Jews

HISTORY OF THE JEWS. | By | Professor H. Graetz. | * * * | * * | Vol. V. | From the Chmielnicki Persecution of the Jews in | Poland (1648 C. E.) to the Present Time (1870 C. E.). | [seal 1a] | Philadelphia: | Jewish Publication Society of America. | 1895. |

COLLATION: 8°. ix, 766 p. (1 l, Half-title, verso blank; p. [i] Title; p. [ii] Copyright, Press and bindery of The Friedenwald Co.; p. [iii]–ix, Contents; p. [1]–731, Text; p. [732] blank; p. 733–766, Index.)

See 1891 for original binding and reprints.

Readings and Recitations for Jewish Homes and Schools

Readings and Recitations | for | Jewish Homes and Schools | Compiled by | Isabel E. Cohen | [seal 1a] | Philadelphia | The Jewish Publication Society of America | 1895 |

COLLATION: 12°. 294 p. (p. [1] Title; p. [2] Copyright, Press of Ed. Stern & Co.; p. [3] Preface; p. [4] blank; p. [5]–6, Acknowledgment; p. [7]–11, Contents; p. [12] [Quotation from] John Bunyan; p. [13]–288, Text; p. [289] [Quotation from] 2 Maccabees xv, 37–39; p. [290] blank; p. [291]–292, Index of authors; p. [293]–294, Index of subjects; 1 l. blank; 13 unnumbered pages of publisher's advertisements.)

Issued in red cloth; all edges gilted; front cover: title, author, seal 1a, publisher; back: title, author, publisher all in gilt.

"The object in making the present collection is to provide matter suitable for reading and recitation in Sabbath-schools and Sunday-schools, at entertainments of Jewish societies, and in the home circle. Incidentally there has been an endeavor to illustrate some phases of Hebrew history and character, and to show the influence for good that the Bible of the Jews has had upon the history and literature of the English-speaking peoples." — Preface.

1896

Studies in Judaism

STUDIES IN JUDAISM | by | S. Schechter, M.A. | Reader in Talmudic in the | University of Cambridge | [*seal 1a*] | Philadelphia | The Jewish Publication Society of America | 1896 |

COLLATION: 8°. xxv, 366 p. (p. [i] Half-title; p. [iii] Title; p. [iv] Copyright, 1896, by Macmillan and Co., Norwood Press, Norwood, Mass.; p. [v] Dedication*; p. [vii–viii] Preface; p. ix, Contents; p. [ii, vi, x] blank; p. xi–xxv, Introduction; p. 1–340, Text; p. 341–359, Notes; p. [360] blank; p. 361–366, Index; 13 unnumbered pages of publisher's advertisements.)

*"To | the ever-cherished memory | of | the late Dr. P. F. Frankl, Rabbi in Berlin | these studies are reverently | dedicated | ."

Issued in red cloth; front cover: title, author, seal 1a, publisher; back: title, rule, author, publisher all in gilt.

"These studies appeared originally in their first form in the *Jewish Quarterly Review* and the *Jewish Chronicle*." — Preface, p. vii.

CONTENTS: The Chassidim. — Nachman Krochmal and the "Perplexities of the Time". — Rabbi Elijah Wilna, Gaon. — Nachmanides. — A Jewish Boswell. — The dogmas of Judaism. — The history of Jewish tradition. — The doctrine of divine retribution in rabbinical literature. — The law and recent criticism. — The Hebrew collection of the British Museum. — Titles of Jewish books. — The child in Jewish literature. — Woman in temple and synagogue. — The earliest Jewish community in Europe.

"Issued by arrangement with Messers. Macmillan & Co., of New York, who are its American publishers." — *JPSA*, 4th biennial report [1896], p. 16.

Reprinted July 1905. See Joshua Bloch, *Journal of Jewish Bibliography*, 1939, v. 1, p. 58.

1911 edition. "First series" added to title-page of this and all subsequent editions.

1938 reprint. — *AJYB*, 5700, p. 675.

5706–1945 edition: title-page reset, with seal 3b, without advertisements. Verso of title-page: "Reprinted 1945."

Fourth Biennial Report

FOURTH BIENNIAL REPORT | of the | Jewish Publication Society | of | America. | 1894–96. | [*seal 1a*] | Office: | No. 1015 Arch Street, | Philadelphia, Pa. |

COLLATION: 16°. 79 p. (p. [1] Title; p. [2] Press of Edward Stern & Co., Inc., Philadelphia; p. [3]–79, Text; 1 unnumbered page of publisher's advertisement.)

Jewish Life
in the Middle Ages

JEWISH LIFE | In The Middle Ages | By | Israel Abrahams, M.A. | [*seal 1a*] | Philadelphia | The Jewish Publication Society of America | 1896 |

COLLATION: 8°. xxvi, 452 p. (p. [i] Half-title; p. [iii] Title; p. [iv] Copyright, 1896, by the Macmillan Co., Norwood Press . . . Norwood, Mass.; p. [v] Dedication: "To my wife;" p. vii–viii, Preface; p. ix–xv, Contents; p. [ii, vi, xvi] blank; p. xvii–xxvi,

Introduction; p. 1–429, Text; p. [430] blank; p. 431–436, Index of Hebrew authorities; p. 437–452, General Index; 14 unnumbered pages of publisher's advertisements.)

Issued in green cloth; front cover: title, rule, author, ornamental decoration, seal 1a, publisher; back: title, rule, author, decoration, publisher all in yellow.

Hebrew translation:

חיי היהודים בימי הבינים [תמצית הספר . . .] מאת דוד ילין.
In השלח, Berlin, 1898. v. 4, pp. 24–36, 124–133, 230–238, 318–327, 413–421, 518–528.

1903 edition: as above, with 6 unnumbered pages of advertisements. Verso of half-title: "An edition of this book can also be obtained from The Jewish Publication Society of America, 1015 Arch Street, Philadelphia, Penn." Verso of title-page: ". . . Set up and electrotyped August, 1896. Reprinted February, 1897."

1911 edition: "Reprinted . . . June 1911."

1897

Report of the Ninth Year

Report | of the | Ninth Year | of the Jewish Publication Society | of | America | 1896–97 | [*seal 1a*] | Office: | No. 1015 Arch Street | Philadelphia, Pa. |

COLLATION: 16°. 92 p. (p. [1] Title; p. [2] Press of Edward Stern & Co., Inc., Philadelphia; p. [3]–92, Text.)

In the Pale

In The Pale | Stories and legends of the Russian Jews | By | Henry Iliowizi | [*seal 1b*] | Philadelphia: | The Jewish Publication Society of America | 1897 |

COLLATION: 12°. 367 p. (p. [1] Half-title; p. [3] Title; p. [4] Copyright, Press of Edward Stern & Co., Inc., Philadelphia; p. [5] Dedication*; p. 7–8, A word to the reader; p. 9, Contents; p. [2, 6, 10] blank; p. 11–367, Text; 15 unnumbered pages of publisher's advertisements.)

Issued in light green cloth; front cover: title, author, seal 1a, publisher; back: title, author, decoration, publisher all in gilt.

*"To my wife | these pages are most affectionately | inscribed |."

CONTENTS: Ezra and Huldah. — The Baal-Shem and his Golem. — Friends in life and in death. — Czar Nicholas the First and Sir Moses Montefiore. — The Czar in Rothschild's castle. — The legend of the ten lost tribes. — The legend of the B'nai Mosheh.

1900 edition: 5 p. l., vii, 408 p. front. (plate.). Without seal. Imprint reads: Philadelphia | Henry T. Coates & Co. | 1900 |. Verso of title-page: ". . . Copyright, 1900 by Henry T. Coates & Co.," with a new "Word to the reader" by the author, p. i–vii; and "An apple of Eden", p. 368–408.

Proceedings of the First Convention of the National Council of Jewish Women

PROCEEDINGS | of the | FIRST CONVENTION | of the | National Council of Jewish Women | Held at New York, Nov. 15, 16, 17, 18 and 19 | 1896 | [*seal 1a*] | Philadelphia | The Jewish Publication Society of America | 1897 |

COLLATION: 8°. 2 p. l., 426 p. (l. 1, Half-title, verso blank; l. 2, Title, verso Copyright, Press of The Friedenwald Co. Baltimore; p. [1]–2, Contents; p. [3]–426, Text; 16 unnumbered pages of publisher's advertisements.)

Issued in green cloth; front cover: title, seal 1a, publisher; back: date, rule, title, publisher all in gilt.

The Talmud

...| THE TALMUD | By | Arsène Darmesteter | Translated From The French | By | Henrietta Szold | [*seal 1a*] | Philadelphia | The Jewish Publication Society of America | 1897 |

At head of title: Special Series. No. 4.

COLLATION: 12°. 97 p. (p. [1] Half-title; p. [2] blank; p. [3] Title; p. [4] Copyright, Press of Edward Stern & Co., Inc., Philadelphia; p. [5]-6, Prefatory Note [by the translator]; p. 7-97, Text; p. [98] blank; 17 unnumbered pages of publisher's advertisements.)

Issued in red paper covers; title as above.

191-? edition.

A Sketch of Jewish History

... | A | SKETCH OF JEWISH HISTORY | By | Gustav Karpeles | Translated from the German | [*seal 1a*] | Philadelphia | The Jewish Publication Society of America | 1897 |

At head of title: Special Series No. 5.

COLLATION: 12°. 109 p. (p. [1] Half-title; p. [3] Title; p. [4] Copyright, Press of Edward Stern & Co., Inc.; p. [5] Prefatory Note; p. [2, 6] blank; p. 7-109, Text; 18 unnumbered pages of publisher's advertisements.)

Issued in red paper covers; title as above.

Lectures delivered during the winter of 1895-96 before the lodges of the Independent Order of B'ne B'rith at Berlin. The translation is done [by Henrietta Szold] from stenographic notes printed as manuscript and not published. — Cf. Prefatory note.

1898

Report of the Tenth Year

REPORT | of the Tenth Year | of the | Jewish Publication Society | of | America | 1897–98 | With Decennial Address Delivered by | Mayer Sulzberger | [*seal 1a*] | Office: No. 1015 Arch Street | Philadelphia, Pa. |

COLLATION: 16°. 133 p. (p. [1] Title; p. [2] Press of Edward Stern & Co., Inc., Philadelphia; p. [3]–133, Text; 4 unnumbered pages of publisher's advertisements.)

Issued in red paper covers; title as above.

Dreamers of the Ghetto

DREAMERS OF | THE GHETTO | by I. Zangwill | [*seal 1a*] | Philadelphia | The Jewish Publication Society of America | 1898 |

COLLATION: 12°. viii, 537 p. (p. [i] Title; p. [ii] Copyright . . . by I. Zangwill . . . Harper & Brothers . . . The Jewish Publication Society of America. All rights reserved; p. iii–[iv] Preface; p. [v] Contents; p. [vi] blank; p. [vii] Half-title; p. [viii] Sonnet: "Moses and Jesus;" p. 1–[537] Text; 4 p. of publisher's advertisements.)

Issued in maroon cloth; top edges gilted; front cover: title, author, seal 1a, publisher, border; back: title, author, decoration, publisher all in gilt.

"Imaginary conversations and memories of Jewish celebrities, especially such as have rebelled against orthodox Judaism. Not very successful as a portrayal of the past, yet shows a remarkable insight into the Jewish characteristics of such men as Spinoza, Heine, and Disraeli." — *AJYB*, 5667, p. 142.

Reprints: 1943: "2,000 copies."— *AJYB*, 5705, p. 606; 1945: "1,000 copies."— *AJYB*, 5707, p. 649; 1946: "1,000 copies."— *AJYB*, 5708, p. 813.

5708–1908 edition: title-page reset, with seal 3b. Verso of title-page: ". . . Copyright, 1938, All rights reserved." "3,000 copies reprinted."— *AJYB*, 1950, p. 568.

Translations into Hebrew, Polish and Yiddish:

יוסף בעל החלומות; see also p. 62, his *They that walk in darkness*, 1899.

חולמי הגיטו. תרגם מאנגלית ראובן גרוסמן. תל-אביב, „מצפה." תרצ"ב.

Reissued in 2 v. with vocalized text:

חולמי הגטו. תל-אביב, י. שרברק [תש"ו] תוכן: בן הגיטו. יוסף בעל
החלומות. אוריאל אקוסטא.

חולמי גאלה. תל-אביב, י. שרברק [תש"ו] תוכן: המשיח התורכי. הבעש"ט.
אוריאל אקוסטא. תרגום ש. מארגאלין.

(In המאסף, ed. L. Rabinowitz. St. Petersburg, 1902. [part 3], p. 129–165.)

לוטש הזכוכיות. ספור. תרגם פ[סח] ג[ינזבורג]. תל-אביב, דפוס „הארץ,"
1927. (ספריה קטנה, ב'.)

Marzyciele ghetta. Przekład z angielskiego M. Kreczowskiej. Brody, F. West, 1905.

די טרוימער פון דער נהעטא. איברזעצט פון א. פרומקין. לאנדאָן,
ראדיקאל פוב. קא. 1907–10.

Contents:

בוך 1. — א קינד פון דער נהעטא. יוסף דער טרוימער. בוך .2 —
מיימון דער נאר און נתן דער חכם. בוך 3. — אוריאל אקאסטא. בוך .4 —
דער טערקישער משיח.

טרוימערס פונ'ם געטא. איברזעצט פון ענגליש פון מארק שוויד.
ניו יארק, פארלאג מ. יאנקאוויטש, 1929.

History of the Jews

HISTORY OF THE JEWS. | By | Professor H. Graetz. | Index Volume, | With a Memoir of the Author by | Dr. Philipp Bloch, | A Chronological Table of Jewish History, and | Four Maps. | [*seal 1a*] | Philadelphia: | The Jewish Publication Society of America. | 1898. |

COLLATION: 8°. xiii, 644 p. (p. [i] Half-title; p. [iii] Title; p. [iv] Copyright, All rights reserved, Press of The Friedenwald Company; p. [v]–xi, Preface, p. [ii, xii] blank; p. [xiii] Contents; 1 l. and p. [1]–644, Text.) 4 folded maps in pocket.

See 1891 for original binding and reprints.

In later editions called: Volume VI.

"Graetz . . . the celebrated historian cannot be held directly responsible for anything this volume contains." — Preface, p. [v].

"[The four maps] . . . have been inserted in a pocket and not bound with the book . . . The two maps of Palestine and that of the Semitic World are reproduced, with modifications, from Professor George Adam Smith's forthcoming Bible Atlas. The one of the Jewish-Mahometan World was made for the Society by Mr. J. G. Bartholomew of the Edinburgh Geographical Institute, the cartographer who drew the other three maps. The maps of the Jewish-Mahometan World and the Semitic World are general reference maps; the two of Palestine represent the political divisions of the land, the one at the time of the Judges, the other at the time of Herod the Great." — Preface, p. xi.

In later editions these maps and the last paragraph in the preface were omitted. Beginning with editions issued in 1946 there appears on the title-page of this volume the statement: "Thirteen maps in color." These are taken from Margolis and Marx, "A History of the Jewish people," 1927, and replace the maps used for the earlier editions.

Memoir of the author by Dr. Philipp Bloch, translated from the German by Henrietta Szold; index prepared by Henrietta Szold.

Jewish Services in Synagogue and Home

JEWISH SERVICES | IN SYNAGOGUE AND HOME | By Lewis N. Dembitz | [*seal ıa*] | Philadelphia: | The Jewish Publication Society of America | 1898 |

COLLATION: 12°. 487 p. (p. [1] Half-title; p. [2] blank; p. [3] Title; p. [4] Copyright, Press of Edward Stern & Co., Inc.; p. 5–6, Preface; p. 7–8, Table of Contents; p. [9]–367, Text; p. [368] blank; p. [369]–438, Notes; p. [439]–487, Indexes; 1 l. blank; 4 unnumbered pages of publisher's advertisements.) front. (plate)

57

Issued in maroon cloth; front cover: title, author, seal 1a, publisher, border; back: title, author, decoration, publisher all in gilt.

This work treats "of everything that is spoken or read in the Synagogue or in the Jewish Home by way of religious duty, and incidentally of what is done to suit the action to the word." It treats "only of the services according to the old rituals, unaffected by those reforms, beginning at Hamburg in 1819, based on the rejection of a part of the beliefs on which the old order of services was founded." — p. 11.

Lost Prince Almon

LOST PRINCE ALMON | By | Louis Pendleton | Author of "King Tom and the Runaways," "In the | Okefenokee," etc. | [*seal 1a*] | Philadelphia | The Jewish Publication Society of America | 1898 |

COLLATION: 12°. 3 p. l., 218 p. (l. 1, Half-title; l. 2, Title, verso Copyright, All rights reserved, Lord Baltimore Press; l. 3, [Contents]; verso of l. 1 and 3, blank; p. 1–218, Text; 5 unnumbered pages of publisher's advertisements.) plates (including front.).

Issued in dark blue cloth; front cover: on top and bottom; title and author in gilt; in center; seal 1a within decorations and double rule box; all within a double rule box and all in silver; back: title, author and publisher in gilt.

1938 edition: as above, with seal 3b, without plates or advertisements. Verso of title-page: "Second Impression, 1929; Third Impression, 1938."

Hebrew translations:

אלמון האובד. ספור הסטורי מימי מלוכת עתליה ויואש מלך יהודה. (עם תמונות וציורים). מאת ל. פנדלטון. תרגום י. מיוחס. הוצאת „תושיה." ורשה, תרס"ז. Warsaw, 1907.

אלמון האובד. ספור הסטורי מימי מלוכת עתליהו ויואש מלך יהודה. מאת ל. פנדלטון. תרגם יוסף בר"נ מיחס איש ירושלם. ציר נחום גוטמן. בהוצאת מרכז הסתדרות המורים. [מהדורה ב' תרח"ץ. דפוס „ארץ־ישראל"]

58

Second edition [Jerusalem, 1938] was published by the Merkaz Histadruth ha-Morim on the seventieth birthday of the translator who dedicated it to the memory of his nephew Avinoam Yellin who died on October 23, 1937.

1899

Report of the Eleventh Year

Report | of the | Eleventh Year | of the | Jewish Publication Society | of | America | 1898–99 | [*seal* 1*a*] | Office | No. 1015 Arch Street | Philadelphia, Pa. |

COLLATION: 16°. 106 p. (p. [1] Title; p. [2] Press of Edward Stern & Co., Inc., Philadelphia; p. [3]–106, Text; 5 unnumbered pages of publisher's advertisements.)

The American Jewish Year Book
5660

The American Jewish | Year Book | 5660 | September 5, 1899 to September 23, 1900 | Edited by | Cyrus Adler | [*seal* 1*a*] | Philadelphia | The Jewish Publication Society of America | 1899 |

COLLATION: 12°. xi, 299 p. (p. ii–vi, Advertisements; p. [vii] Title; p. [viii] Copyright, The Lord Baltimore Press; p. [ix]–x, Preface; p. [xi] Contents; p. 1–290, Text; p. 291–299, Advertisements.)

Issued in dark gray cloth; front and back covers: seal 1, blind stamped; back: rules, title and rules (on black), dates, publisher all in gilt.

"The spread of Jews all over our vast country seemed to make it desirable that a Directory should form the principal feature of the Year Book." — Preface, p. [ix].

SPECIAL ARTICLE: A list of Jewish periodicals published in the United States. Compiled by A. S. Freidus, of the New York Public Library, pp. 271–282.

Chapters on Jewish Literature

CHAPTERS | on | JEWISH LITERATURE | By | Israel Abrahams, M.A. | Author of "Jewish Life in the Middle Ages" | [*seal 1a*] Philadelpha | The Jewish Publication Society of America | 1899 |

COLLATION: 12°. 275 p. (p. [1] Half-title; p. [2] blank; p. [3] Title; p. [4] Copyright, The Lord Baltimore Press; p. [5]–13, Preface; p. [14] blank; p. [15]–18, Contents; p. [19]–260, Text; p. [261]–275, Index; 5 unnumbered pages of publisher's advertisements.)

Issued in tan cloth; front cover: seal 1, in black; back: rules, title, rules in gilt (on black), and publisher in black.

"These twenty-five short chapters on Jewish Literature open with the fall of Jerusalem in the year 70 of the current era, and end with the death of Moses Mendelssohn in 1786." — Preface p. [v].

Bibliography at end of each chapter.

CONTENTS: The "Vineyard" at Jamnia. — Flavius Josephus and the Jewish Sibyl. — The Talmud. — The Midrash and its poetry. — The letters of the Gaonim. — The Karaitic literature. — The new-Hebrew Piyut. — Saadiah of Fayum. — Dawn of the Spanish era. — The Spanish-Jewish poets. — Rashi and Alfassi. — Moses Maimonides. — The diffusion of science. — The diffusion of folk-tales. — Moses Nachmanides. — The Zohar and later mysticism. — Italian Jewish poetry. — Ethical literature. — Travellers' tales. — Historians and chroniclers. — Isaac Abarbanel. — The Shulchan Aruch. — Amsterdam in the seventeenth century. — Moses Mendelssohn.

Reprint, undated, title-page reset with seal 2a, without advertisements.

"They that Walk in Darkness"

"They that Walk in | Darkness" | Ghetto Tragedies | By | I. Zangwill | Author of "Children of the Ghetto" | "The King of Schnorrers," etc. | With a photogravure frontispiece after | a picture by Louis Loeb | [*seal 1a*] | Philadelphia | The Jewish Publication Society of America | 1899 |

COLLATION: 12°. viii, 486 p. (p. [i] Half-title; p. [iii] Title; p. [iv] Copyright, 1899, By I. Zangwill. Norwood Press ... Norwood, Mass.; p. v, Preface; p. [ii, vi] blank; p. vii–viii, Contents; 1 l. and p. 1–486, Text; 4 unnumbered pages of publisher's advertisements.) front.

Issued in maroon cloth; top edges gilted; front cover: title, author, seal 1a, publisher, border; back: title, author, decoration, publisher all in gilt.

CONTENTS: "They that walk in darkness." — Transitional. — Noah's ark. — The land of promise. — To die in Jerusalem. — Bethulah. — The keeper of conscience. — Satan Mekatrig. — Diary of a Meshumad. — Incurable. — The Sabbath-breaker.

"The 'Ghetto Tragedies' collected in a little volume in 1893 have been so submerged in the present collection that I have relegated the original name to the sub-title. ... 'Ghetto Tragedies' was inscribed [to Mrs. N. S. Joseph who] ... in the prime of life ... went down into the valley of the shadow ... [To her memory the book] must now, alas! be dedicated." — Author's preface, p. v.

"Several Ghetto tragedies illumined by flashes of fancy, satire, irony, and humor. Leaves the reader with a sense of compassion and admiration for the Jew." — *AJYB*, 5667, p. 142.

See also his: *Selected works*, 1938.

Translations into Hebrew of *Ghetto Tragedies*:

מחזות הגיטו. ((תמונות וציורים). תרגום ש. ל. גרדון. (עם תמונת המחבר ותולדת חייו ערוכה בידי ר. ברייניו). ווארשא: הוצאת „תושיה". Warsaw, Piotrkow, 1898–99. תרנ"ח–תר"ס.

תוכן: ספר א: א) שטן מקטרג. ב) לאין מרפא. ג) מחללת השבת.
ספר ב: א) יוסף בעל החלומות. ב) ספר-זכרונות.
יוסף בעל החלומות is from his *Dreamers of the Ghetto*, 1898.

Under the Eagle's Wing

UNDER THE EAGLE'S WING | By | Sara Miller | [*seal 1a*] | Philadelphia | The Jewish Publication Society of America | 1899 |

COLLATION: 12°. 1 p. l., 229 p. (1 l. Half-title, verso blank; p. [1] Title; p. [2] Copyright, The Lord Baltimore Press; p. [3] Prefatory note; p. [5] Contents; p. [4, 6, blank]; p. [7]–229, Text; 6 unnumbered pages of publisher's advertisements.) front. (port.), plates.

Issued in tan cloth; front cover: title, illustration, author, rules; back: title, author, publisher and designs all in blue.

A story of the days of Maimonides.

Hebrew translation:

תחת כנפי הנשר. ספור מתקופת הרמב״ם ז״ל מאת שרה מילר. תרגם יוסף בר״נ מיחס. תל-אביב, „דביר.״ תרצ״ח.

1900

The Ethics of Judaism

The Ethics of Judaism | By | M. Lazarus, Ph.D. | Translated from the German | by | Henrietta Szold | In four parts | Part I | [*seal 1a*] | Philadelphia | The Jewish Publication Society of America | 1900 |

Only part 1 and part 2 (1901) published.

COLLATION: 12°. xv, 309 p. (p. [i] Half-title; p. [iii] Title; p. [iv] Copyright, The Lord Baltimore Press; p. [v] Dedication*; p. [vii] [Note]; p. [ix]–xi, Preface [signed Lazarus]; p. [xiii] Part I |

Foundation of Jewish Ethics; p. [ii, vi, viii, xii, xiv] blank; p. [xv] Contents of Part I; p. [1]–244, Text; p. [245]–309, Appendix; 6 unnumbered pages of publisher's advertisements.)

Issued in brown cloth; front cover: seal 1; back: title, volume, author, publisher all in gilt.

*"Dedicated | to the memory of my noble friend | Wilhelm von Gutmann | ."

The American Jewish Year Book
5661

The American Jewish | Year Book | 5661 | September 24, 1900, to September 13, 1901 | Edited by | Cyrus Adler | [*seal ia*] | Philadelphia | The Jewish Publication Society of America | 1900 |

COLLATION: 12°. xii, 763 p. (p. ii–iv, Advertisements; p. [v] Title; p. [vi] Copyright, The Lord Baltimore Press; p. [vii]–ix, Preface; p. [x] blank; p. [xi]–xii, Contents; p. 1–644, Text; p. [645]– 754, Report of the 12th year of the Jewish Publication Society of America 1899–1900; p. 755–763, Advertisements.)

Bound uniformly with 5660 (1899–1900).

"Jews in America are profoundly interested in the welfare of their brethren in all parts of the world, and it was deemed advisable to publish in condensed form a statement of the ecclesiastical, scholastic and national organizations of Jews abroad, and in view of the interest which centred in France, to devote especial attention to that country and to the great international organization which has its seat in Paris, the *Alliance Israélite Universelle.*" — Preface, p. viii–ix.

SPECIAL ARTICLES: The Alliance Israélite Universelle, By Jacques Bigart, pp. 45–65. — Biographical sketches of Jews who have served in the Congress of the United States, pp. 517–524. — Preliminary list of Jewish soldiers and sailors who served in the Spanish-American War, pp. 525–622.

Sons of the Covenant

Sons | of the | Covenant | A Tale of | London Jewry | By | Samuel Gordon | Author of "Lesser Destinies," | Etc., Etc. | [*seal 1a*] | Philadelphia | The Jewish Publication Society of America | 1900 |

[Note: Title and sub-title in parallel lines.]

COLLATION: 12°. 500 p. (1 l., Half-title, verso blank; p. [1] Title; p. [2] Copyright, Lord Baltimore Press; p. [3] Illustrations drawn by Mark Zangwill; p. [4] blank; p. [5]–500, Text; 1 l. blank; 5 unnumbered pages of publisher's advertisements.) 8 plates (including front.).

Issued in olive green cloth; front cover: title and author in gilt, seal 1, blind stamped; back: title, author and publisher in gilt.

"An optimistic study of the development of the lives of two London Jewish youths. The book does not shirk realities, seeing these, however, through kindly glasses. The note of 'tendenz' is the uplifting of the Ghetto dwellers to a higher plane." — *AJYB*, 5667, p. 135.

1901

Songs of Exile by Hebrew Poets

זמרות בלילה | Songs of Exile | By Hebrew Poets | Translated by | Nina Davis | [*floret*] | Philadelphia | The Jewish Publication Society of America | 1901 |

[Note: The foregoing appears within an orange rule box. Initial letters S and E of title also in orange.]

COLLATION: 16°. 146 p. (p. [1] Half-title; p. [2] [Hebrew text and English translation of] Psalm cxxx,6; p. [3] Title; p. [4] Copyright, All rights reserved, Press of Edward Stern & Co., Inc. Philadelphia; p. [5] Dedication: "To my father;" p. [6] blank; p. [7]–8, Contents; p. [9]–146, Text.)

Issued in light green cloth; top edges gilted; front cover: title, author; back: title, author, publisher all in gilt; back cover: seal 1a, blind stamped.

Colophon: נָתַן זְמִרוֹת בַּלַּיְלָה.

The Ethics of Judaism

The Ethics of Judaism | By | M. Lazarus, Ph.D. | Translated from the German | by | Henrietta Szold | In four parts | Part II | [seal 1a] | Philadelphia | The Jewish Publication Society of America | 1901 |

Only part 1 (1900) and part 2 published.

Bound uniformly with part 1.

Collation: 12°. 4 p. l., 301 p. (l. 1, Half-title; l. 2, Title, verso Copyright, The Lord Baltimore Press; l. 3, Part II | Sanctification of Life the Aim | of Morality; l. 4, Contents of Part II; verso of l. 1, 3–4, blank; p. [1]–253, Text; p. [254] blank; p. [255]–301, Appendix; 7 unnumbered pages of publisher's advertisements.)

The American Jewish Year Book
5662

The American Jewish | Year Book | 5662 | September 14, 1901, to October 1, 1902 | Edited by | Cyrus Adler | [seal 1a] | Philadelphia | The Jewish Publication Society of America | 1901 |

Collation: 12°. xi, 321 p. (p. ii–vi, Advertisements; p. [vii] Title; p. [viii] Copyright, The Lord Baltimore Press; p. [ix]–x,

Preface; p. [xi] Contents; p. 1–190, Text; p. [191]–308, Report of the 13th year of the Jewish Publication Society of America 1900–1901; p. 309–321, Advertisements.)

Bound uniformly with 5660 (1899–1900).

"The third issue of the American Jewish Year Book . . . differs from that of previous years in devoting no space whatever to directories, and in laying special stress upon the history of the Jews in Roumania, whose unrelenting persecution by the Government has produced a condition of affairs which will inevitably bring about a considerable migration to the United States . . ." — Preface, p. [ix].

SPECIAL ARTICLES: The Jews of Roumania, from the earliest times to the present day, by Dr. E. Schwarzfeld, pp. 25–62. — The situation of the Jews in Roumania since the Treaty of Berlin (1878) by Dr. E. Schwarzfeld, pp. 63–87. — The Roumanian Jews in America, by D. M. Hermalin, pp. 88–103.

Idyls of the Gass

IDYLS OF THE GASS | By | Martha Wolfenstein | [*seal 1a*] | Philadelphia | The Jewish Publication Society of America | 1901 |

COLLATION: 12°. 295 p. (p. [1] Half-title; p. [2] blank; p. [3] Title; p. [4] Copyright, All rights reserved, The Lord Baltimore Press; p. [5] Dedication*; p. [7] Contents; p. [6, 8] blank; p. [9]–295, Text; 8 unnumbered pages of publisher's advertisements.)

Issued in light green cloth; front cover: title, author, rule and design all within a single rule box; back: design, title, floret, author, design and publisher all in gilt, except designs in dark green.

*"To the original | Shimmelè, | the precious source | of all I have accomplished | or may accomplish | in this life | ."

1929 edition: as above, with seal 2a, without advertisements.

1938 edition: as above, with seal 3b, without advertisements.
Verso of title-page: "Reprinted 1938."

1902

Hearth and Home Essays

... | HEARTH AND HOME ESSAYS | By | Esther J. Ruskay |
[*seal 1a*] | Philadelphia | The Jewish Publication Society of
America | 1902 |

At head of title: Special Series No. 6.

COLLATION: 12°. 96 p. (p. [1] Half-title; p. [3] Title; p. [4]
Copyright, 1901; p. [5] Contents; p. [2, 6] blank; p. 7–96, Text;
8 unnumbered pages of publisher's advertisements.)

Issued in red papers covers; title as above; paper label on back:
title and author.

CONTENTS: Sabbath eve. — Sabbath and character. — The once-
upon-a-time gude wife in Israel. — New Year in a Jewish home. —
New Year's day. — Women infidels. — Atonement Day thoughts.—
Sukkoth. — Simchath Torah. — Unassimilative Jews. — A one-time
background for Chanukkah. — Our mothers. — Merry Purim. —
Purim. — Intermarriage. — Preparations for Passover. — Passover
customs and traditions. — An ideal new grandmother. — A seder
party. — Pictures of Jewish home life. — Sobriety in Jewish life.

Strangers at the Gate

STRANGERS AT THE GATE | Tales of Russian Jewry | By | Samuel
Gordon | Author of "Sons of the Covenant," "Lesser Des-
tinies," etc. | [*seal 1a*] | Philadelphia 1902 | The Jewish Pub-
lication Society of America |

COLLATION: 12°. 458 p. (p. [1] Half-title; p. [3] Title; p. [4] Copyright, The Lord Baltimore Press; p. [5] Contents; p. [2, 6] blank; p. [7]–458, Text; 1 l. blank; 10 unnumbered pages of publisher's advertisements.)

Issued in olive green cloth; front cover: title and author in gilt, seal 1, blind stamped; back: title, author and publisher in gilt.

CONTENTS: Daughters of Shem. — Mummer and moralist. — The fourth dimension. — The sunken kingdom. — Towards the sunrise. — On the road to Zion. — An alien immigrant. — Hindelah's clothes-prop. — The grandchildren. — To the glory of God. — The road-makers. — The broken pane. — The leader. — Rabbi Elchanan's quest. — "Whose judgment is justice." — The Mordecai of the serfs. — The ambush of conscience. — Cossack and chorister.

Papers of the Jewish Chautauqua Society

... | PAPERS | Presented | at the | Fifth Annual Session | of the | Summer Assembly | of the | Jewish Chautauqua Society | held at | Atlantic City, N. J., July 7 to July 28, 1901 | [seal 1a] | The Jewish Publication Society of America | Philadelphia | 1902|

At head of title: Special Series No. 7.

COLLATION: 12°. 118 p. (p. [1] Half-title; p. [3] Title; p. [5] Contents; p. [2, 4, 6] blank; p. 7–118, Text; 10 unnumbered pages of publisher's advertisements.)

Issued in red paper covers; title as above; paper label on back: Fifth Jewish Chautauqua Assembly.

Among the PAPERS presented are the following: Settlement and club work, Charles S. Bernheimer. — The equipment of the worker, Lee K. Frankel. — Introductory address to the course on American Jewish history, Cyrus Adler. — Interpretation of the Book of Job,

Max Margolis. — Three discourses on Jewish ethics, K. Kohler. — School of practice, Corinne B. Arnold. — Chautauqua sermon, Joseph Stolz.

The American Jewish Year Book
5663

The American Jewish | Year Book | 5663 | October 2, 1902, to September 21, 1903 | Edited by | Cyrus Adler | [*seal 1a*] | Philadelphia | The Jewish Publication Society of America | 1902 |

COLLATION: 12°. xi, 321 p. (p. ii–vi, Advertisements; p. [vii] Title; p. [viii] Copyright, The Lord Baltimore Press; p. [ix]–x, Preface; p. [xi] Contents; p. 1–201, Text; p. [202] blank; p. [203]– 306, Report of the 14th year of the Jewish Publication Society of America 1901–1902; p. 307–321, Advertisements.)

Bound uniformly with 5660 (1899–1900). On front cover: titles of special articles in white.

"The fourth issue of the American Jewish Year Book is largely devoted to information concerning National Jewish Organizations, lists of important events, dedications of synagogues and other public buildings, and certain special articles.

"The Year Book for 5662 dealt mainly with the condition of the Jews in Roumania. In the present volume there is printed a dispatch recently sent by the Secretary of State, the Honorable John Hay, to the Government of Roumania, through the United States Minister to Athens, copies of the document being forwarded also to the Foreign Offices of the Powers who were signatories to the Treaty of Berlin, which established Roumania as an independent State." — Preface, p. [ix].

SPECIAL ARTICLES: Biographical sketch of Commodore Uriah P. Levy, by Simon Wolf, pp. 42–45. — The Jewish population of Maryland, by Geo. E. Barnett, pp. 46–62. — A sketch of the history of the Jews in the United States, pp. 63–77. — Biographical sketches of Jews in the 57th Congress, pp. 172–174.

The Vale of Cedars

[*Design*] THE [*design*] | VALE OF CEDARS | & Other Tales |
By | Grace Aguilar | with an introduction | [*floret*] By [*floret*] |
Walter Jerrold | [*design*] | Illustrated by | T. H. Robinson |
[*design*] | MDCCCCII | London: J. M. Dent & Co. | Phila-
delphia: The Jewish Publication | Society of America |

[Note: The foregoing appears within a tri-colored ornamental
border. Title-page set in red, green and brown type.]

COLLATION: 8°. viii, 428 p. (including plates). (1 l., Half-title,
verso blank; p. [i] Title; p. [ii] blank; p. iii–vi, Introductory note;
p. vii, Contents; p. viii, List of Illustrations; p. [1]–428, Text.)
colored front. Illustrated lining papers, with name and dates of
author.

Issued in tan cloth; top edges gilted, leaves uncut; front cover:
illustration in green and brown; title in green; back: illustration in
green and brown; title, author, illustrator and publisher (JPSA) in
green; back cover: double rule box in brown, in lower right hand
corner, initials of author in green.

At bottom of p. 428: "Colston & Coy. Limited, Printers,
Edinburgh."

CONTENTS: The vale of cedars; or, the martyr. — The Perez
family. — Amete and Yafeh. — The fugitive. — The edict. — The
escape. — Helon. — The spirit's entreaty. — The spirit of night. —
The triumph of love.

"Written before 1835, published in 1850, and twice translated
into German and twice into Hebrew." — *Jewish Encyclopedia*, v. 1,
p. 274.

Translations into Hebrew and Yiddish:

ספור מלחמת האמונה והאהבה... ונעתק לשפת עבר מאת ישעיה
געלבהויז. מאינץ, יחיאל בריל, תרל"ה.

עמק הארזים. ספור מראשית דרכי האינקוויזיציה בספרד בעקבות ...
עם נוספות מאת א. ש. פרידברג. ורשה, תרל"ו.

— הוצאה שניה בתקונים הרבה. ווארשא, תרנ"ג.

דיא אונגליקליכע מרים אדער דיא בלוטישע געשיכטע פון דער
אינקוויזיציע. איין ... היסטאארישער ראמאן פון ... איספאניע. איבערזעטצט
פרייא פאן יונה טרובניק. ווילנא, תרמ"ח.

1903

Jewish History

JEWISH HISTORY | An Essay in the Philosophy of | History |
By | S. M. Dubnow | [*seal ıa*] | The Jewish Publication Society
of America | Philadelphia | 1903 |

COLLATION: 12°. xv, 184 p. (p. [i] Title; p. [ii] Copyright, Lord
Baltimore Press; p. [iii]–ix, Preface to the German translation by
J. F.; p. ix, Preface to the English translation by H. S.; p. [x] blank;
p. [xi]–xv, Table of Contents; p. [1]–184, Text; 1 l. blank; 10 unnumbered pages of publisher's advertisements.)

Issued in maroon cloth; front cover: title; back: title, rule and
author within single rule box, publisher all in gilt.

The English translation by H. S. [Henrietta Szold] is based
upon the authorized German translation by J. F. [Israel Fried-
laender] (Berlin, 1898) which was made from the original Russian
(Odessa, 1896–1897). "It is published under the joint auspices of
the Jewish Publication Society of America and the Jewish Historical
Society of England." — Preface p. ix.

"Compact in form, clear in expression, summing up Jewish
history in general, it gives a splendidly comprehensive conception of
the part played by the Jews. It is an excellent illustration of the
essay form of literature . . . a work that is simple in style, but backed

by knowledge and scholarship . . ." — Edwin Wolf in *AJYB*, 5665, p. 227.

1927 edition: title-page reset, without seal or advertisements.

Maimonides

MAIMONIDES | By | David Yellin | and | Israel Abrahams | [*seal 1a*] | The Jewish Publication Society of America | Philadelphia | 1903 |

COLLATION: 12°. xii, 239 p. (p. [i] Half-title; p. [ii] blank; p. [iii] Title; p. [iv] Copyright, Lord Baltimore Press; p. [v]–vi, Preface; p. [vii]–viii, Contents; p. [ix]–xii, Illustrations; p. [1]–218, Text; p. [219]–233, Notes; p. [234] Genealogical Table; p. [235]–239, Index; 11 unnumbered pages of publisher's advertisements.) plates, port. (front.)

Issued in green cloth; front cover: title within double rule box; back: title, design, authors, publisher all in gilt.

"This volume, published under the joint auspices of the Jewish Publication Society of America and the Jewish Historical Society of England, forms the first of a series of books dealing with 'Jewish Worthies.' The aim of this series is to present biographies of famous Jews, with special regard to the general history of the periods at which they lived." — Preface, p. [v].

Based on Yellin's רבנו משה בן מיימון Warsaw, 1898 ("Tushia series").

1935 British edition: Imprint reads: ". . . Published by the | Jewish Historical Society of England | London 1935 | ." xv, 178 p. Dedicated "to | Dr. M. Friedlander | principal of Jews' College. London, and editor | of Maimonides' 'Guide of the Perplexed' | this volume is inscribed | in affection and esteem | ."

1936 edition: title-page reset with seal 3b, without plates or advertisements. Verso of title-page: "Reprinted, 1936."

5706–1946 edition: same as 1936. Verso of title-page: "Reprinted 1944, Reprinted 1946."

The American Jewish Year Book 5664

The American Jewish | Year Book | 5664 | September 22, 1903, to September 9, 1904 | Edited by | Cyrus Adler | [*seal ıa*] | Philadelphia | The Jewish Publication Society of America | 1903 |

COLLATION: 12°. xi, 329 p. (p. ii–iv, Advertisements; p. [v] Title; p. [vi] Copyright, The Lord Baltimore Press; p. [vii]–ix, Preface; p. [x] blank; p. [xi] Contents; p. [1]–220, Text; p. [221]–316, Report of the 15th year of the Jewish Publication Society of America 1902–1903; p. 317–329, Advertisements.)

Bound uniformly with 5660 (1899–1900). On front cover: title of special article in white.

"The new feature in the American Jewish Year Book for 5664 is the series of Biographical Sketches of Rabbis and Cantors in the United States, which was compiled because of the interest necessarily attaching to the education and literary activity of the spiritual guides of American Jewry. The 363 sketches here presented form the first installment of an American Jewish Who's Who." — Preface, p. [vii].

Within the Pale

WITHIN | THE | PALE | The True Story of Anti-Semitic | Persecution in Russia | [*rule*] | By | Michael Davitt | Author of "Leaves from a Prison Diary," | "Life and Progress in Australasia," | "The Boer Fight for | Freedom," Etc. | Special Edition | Philadelphia | The Jewish Publication | Society of America | New York | A. S. Barnes & Co. | 1903 |

[Note: The foregoing appears within a black single rule box.]

COLLATION: 12°. xiv, 300 p. (p. [i] Half-title; p. [iii] Title; p. [iv] Copyright, 1903, by A. S. Barnes & Co., Published October; p. v–xi, Preface; p. [ii, xii] blank; p. xiii–xiv, Contents; p. [1]–300, Text; 4 unnumbered pages of advertisements.)

Issued in black cloth; front cover: title, design and author in red; seal 1a, blind stamped; back: title, design, author and publisher in red.

"Published in a special edition of the Society in accordance with an arrangement with the publishers [A. S. Barnes & Co., New York] of the regular edition." — *AJYB*, 5665, p. 393.

"Michael Davitt, being a trained non-Jewish writer, his strong impartial story of Kishineff has been effective in helping to form an unprejudiced opinion of the Russian atrocities." — *AJYB*, 5665, p. 385.

The Book of Psalms

תהלים | THE | BOOK OF PSALMS | [*floret*] | 5664–1903 | The Jewish Publication Society | of America, Philadelphia |

[Note: Each page, including text and title-pages, within a black single rule box, and running captions are underlined.]

COLLATION: 32°. 311 p. (p. [1] (Note)*; p. [2] Added title**; p. [3] Title; p. [4] Copyright, The Lord Baltimore Press; p. [5]–305, Text; p. [306] blank; p. 307–311, Appendix.)

Issued in dark green cloth; front cover: title; back: six rule boxes with title in English and Hebrew all in gilt.

*"The Holy Scriptures | תורה נביאים וכתובים | ."

תורה נביאים וכתובים | The Twenty-four Books | of the | HOLY SCRIPTURES | Translated from the Massoretic Text for the | Jewish Publication Society of America | [*floret*] | 5664–1903 | The Jewish Publication Society | of America, Philadelphia |

Translated by the Rev. Dr. Kaufmann Kohler.

"It is a product of the highest scholarship, both as to literalness of translation and as to style." — *AJYB*, 5665, p. 385.

"The first instalment of the new English translation of the Bible. It has been received with such *éclat* as to give encouragement to the great work which the Society has planned in translating the Bible into English according to the latest Jewish scholarship." — *AJYB*, 5665, p. 393.

Review: "Critical notes on the new English version of the Book of Psalms published by the Jewish Publication Society" by J. D. Eisenstein, New York, 1906.

1904

The Voice of America on Kishineff

The Voice of America | on Kishineff | Edited by | Cyrus Adler | [*seal 1a*] | Philadelphia: | The Jewish Publication Society of America | 1904 |

COLLATION: 12°. xxvi, 491 p. (p. [i] Half-title; p. [iii] Title; p. [iv] Copyright; p. [v] Contents; p. [ii, vi] blank; p. [vii]–xxvi, Introduction; p. [1]–481, Text; p. [482] blank; p. [483]–491, Indexes.)

Issued in black cloth; front cover: title, seal 1a, blind stamped; back: title, design, author, publisher all in red.

For "Additions and Corrections". — See *AJYB*, 5665, p. 378–380.

"A resumé of the discourses, the resolutions, and the editorials, by Jews and non-Jews throughout the country, expressive of the feelings and the opinions of Americans on the barbarian acts of Russians against their townsmen, this volume will stand in the history of civilization as a record of the sympathetic humanitarian attitude of Americans toward the Jews." — *AJYB*, 5665, p. 386.

In Assyrian Tents

In Assyrian Tents | The Story of the Strange Adventures | of Uriel | By | Louis Pendleton | Author of "Lost Prince Almon" | [*seal 1a*] | Philadelphia | The Jewish Publication Society of America | 1904 |

COLLATION: 12°. 248 p. (p. [1] Half-title; p. [3] Title; p. [4] Copyright; p. [5] Contents; p. [2, 6] blank; p. [7]–248, Text; 1 l., blank; xii p. of publisher's advertisements.) 3 plates (including front.).

Issued in dark blue cloth; front cover: title, illustration, author; back: title, author, publisher all in white.

1929 edition: as above, with seal 2a, without plates or advertisements.

1940–5700 edition: same as 1929, with seal 3b. Verso of title-page: "Reprinted 1940."

1948–5708 edition: same as 1940. Verso of title-page: "Reprinted 1948."

Hebrew translation:

באהלי אשור. ספור המלחמה עם האשורים. עברית א. ל. יעקבוביץ. תל־אביב, הוצאת „יורעאל" [1936?].

The American Jewish Year Book 5665

The American Jewish | Year Book | 5665 | September 10, 1904, to September 29, 1905 | Edited by | Cyrus Adler | and | Henrietta Szold | [*seal 1a*] | Philadelphia | The Jewish Publication Society of America | 1904 |

COLLATION: 12°. xiii, 517 p. (p. ii–iv, Advertisements; p. [v] Title; p. [vi] Copyright; p. [vii]–ix, Preface; p. [xi] Contents; p. [x, xii] blank; p. [xiii] Notable articles in previous issues; p. [1]–380,

Text; p. [381]–502, Report of the 16th year of the Jewish Publication Society of America 1903–1904; p. 503–517, Advertisements.)

Bound uniformly with 5660 (1899–1900). On front cover: titles of special articles in white.

"The present, which is the sixth, issue of the American Jewish Year Book is prevailingly biographical in character. . . . A list of over a thousand names was compiled, which . . . will introduce new acquaintances even to those most intimately conversant with Jewish affairs and conditions in the United States. . . . The other important feature of the present issue is the compilation made from the 'Foreign Relations' documents on the passport question mooted between Russia and the United States." — Preface, p. [vii]–viii.

SPECIAL ARTICLES: Rev. Gershom Mendez Seixas, "The Patriot Jewish Minister of the American Revolution", by N. Taylor Phillips, pp. 40–51. — Biographical sketches of Jews prominent in the professions, etc., in the United States, pp. 52–213.

1905

Legends and Tales

Legends and Tales | in | Prose and Verse | Compiled by | Isabel E. Cohen | [*floret*] | Philadelphia | The Jewish Publication Society of America | 1905 |

[Note: The foregoing appears within an orange rule box. Initial letters L and T of title also in orange.]

COLLATION: 16°. 260 p. (p. [1] Half-title; p. [3] Title; p. [4] Copyright; p. [5] Acknowledgment; p. [7]–9, Contents; p. [2, 6, 10] blank; p. [11]–260, Text.)

Issued in light green cloth; front cover: title, author; back: title, author, publisher all in gilt; back cover: seal 1a, blind stamped.

"A book serving a useful purpose for entertaining the young, and any comparison between it and works of real scientific merit is unfair. It is quite unpretentious and has its proper and useful place among the books in the average household." — *AJYB*, 5666, p. *14.

Jews in Many Lands

Jews in Many Lands | By | Elkan Nathan Adler | [*seal 1a*] | Philadelphia | The Jewish Publication Society of America | 1905 |

COLLATION: 12°. 259 p. (p. [1] Half-title; p. [3] Title; p. [4] Copyright; p. [5] Dedication*; p. [7]–8, Contents; p. [9] Illustrations; p. [2, 6, 10] blank; p. [11]–14, Preface; p. [15]–243, Text; p. [244] blank; p. [245]–259, Index.) plates and illus. (including front.)

Issued in dark gray cloth; back: rules, title, rule, author and rules in gilt on red label, publisher in gilt.

*" | את אחי אנכי מבקש | To my kind and hospitable | co-religionists | in many lands | ."

CONTENTS: Egypt in 1888. — From Jaffa to Jerusalem. — Jerusalem. — The environs of Jersusalem. — Hebron, the Dead Sea, and the Jordan. — Agricultural colonies in Palestine. — Palestine revisited in 1895. — Salonica. — Smyrna. — Aleppo. — The schools at Tetuan. — Persian Jews. — Zakaspie. — A visit to Moisesville. — A visit to the Kowno Rav.

"A bright and entertaining book, introducing the reader not to the results of mere historical research concerning people long dead and buried, but to living Jews in out of the way corners of the world into which they have wandered and where they preserve their traditions and faith amid the surroundings, differing in every respect from those of Occidental communities with which we are more or less familiar. The author of this book is the first modern Jewish traveller of sufficient ability, literary skill, and love of his subject to compile a book of travels comparable in interest with those of the old travellers and chroniclers of the Middle Ages." — *AJYB*, 5666, p. *14.

78

Beating Sea and Changeless Bar

BEATING SEA AND | CHANGELESS BAR | By | Jacob Lazarre [pseud.] [*seal ıa*] | Philadelphia: The Jewish Publication Society of America | 1905 |

COLLATION: 12°. 133 p. (2 blank l.; p. [1] Half-title; p. [3] Title; p. [4] Copyright, Published May, 1905; p. [5] Dedication*; p. [7] [15 lines of verse from] Henley; p. [9] Contents; [p. 2, 6, 8, 10] blank; p. [11]–133, Text; 3 blank l.)

Issued in olive green cloth; front cover: title and border in white; back: rules in white; title, design, author and publisher in gilt.

*"To | my people, | the bar that has, | for centuries on centuries, | withstood the beating sea | ."

CONTENTS: Wave and spar. — Once in some memorable before. — On some fortunate yet thrice blasted shore. — So hesitate and turn and cling, — yet go.

"A charming little volume, full of poetry, rich in literary grace, and presenting a great life problem of the Jew." — *AJYB*, 5666, p. *14.

"Four poetic love tales intended to show that no power can force a true Jewess to surrender her religion. Profoundly pathetic."— *AJYB*, 5667, p. 138.

The American Jewish Year Book 5666

The American Jewish | Year Book | 5666 | September 30, 1905, to September 19, 1906 | Edited by | Cyrus Adler | and | Henrietta Szold | [*seal ıa*] | Philadelphia | The Jewish Publication Society of America | 1905 |

COLLATION: 12°. xi, 271, *95 p. (p. ii–iv, Advertisements; p. [v] Title; p. [vi] Copyright; p. [vii]–ix, Preface; p. [x] Special articles in previous issues; p. [xi] Contents; p. [1]–271, Text; p. [*1]–*86, Report of the 17th year of the Jewish Publication Society of America 1904–1905; p. *87–*95, Advertisements.)

Bound uniformly with 5660 (1899–1900). On front cover: title of special article in white.

"The last instalment of the Biographical Sketches appears this year. The three series, incomplete though they have been, have demonstrated the presence in America of an amount of Jewish personality and achievement hitherto unsuspected, and they point out the desirability of further work and publication in American Jewish biography." — Preface, p. viii.

SPECIAL ARTICLES: Penina Moïse, woman and writer, by Lee C. Harby, pp. 17–31. — Biographical sketches of Jewish communal workers in the United States, pp. 32–118. — A syllabus of Jewish history, pp. 163–170.

Jews and Judaism in the
Nineteenth Century

. . . | JEWS AND JUDAISM | In The | Nineteenth Century | By | Gustav Karpeles | Translated From The German | [seal 1a] Philadelphia | The Jewish Publication Society of America | 1905 |

At head of title: Special Series No. 8.

COLLATION: 12°. 83 p. (p. [1] Half-title; p. [3] Title; p. [4] Copyright; p. [5] Prefatory Note; p. [2, 6] blank; p. [7]–83, Text; 4 unnumbered pages of publisher's advertisements.)

Issued in red paper covers; title as above; paper label on back: title and author.

Translated by Henrietta Szold and Adele Szold (Seltzer).

"A bright, readable survey of the great movements of Jewish history during the last century, and is especially excellent in its treatment of the anti-Semitic movement and the modern Renaissance." — *AJYB*, 5667, p. *13.

Reprint undated, with seal 2a, without advertisements.

A Renegade and Other Tales

A RENEGADE | And Other Tales | By | Martha Wolfenstein | Author of "Idyls of the Gass" | [*seal 1a*] | Philadelphia | The Jewish Publication Society of America | 1905 |

COLLATION: 12°. 322 p. (p. [1] Half-title; p. [3] Title; p. [4] Copyright, all rights reserved; p. [5] Acknowledgment; p. [7] Contents; p. [2, 6, 8] blank; p. [9]–322, Text; 1 l. blank; 4 unnumbered pages of publisher's advertisements.)

Issued in light green cloth; front cover: title, author, rule and design all within a single rule box; back: design, title, floret, author, design and publisher all in gilt, except designs in dark green.

Partly reprinted from various periodicals.

CONTENTS: A renegade. — Dovid and Resel. — Loebelè Shlemiel. — A sinner in Israel. — Nittel-Nacht. — A judgment of Solomon. — A Goy in the good place. — Genendel the pious. — A monk from the Ghetto. — Grandmother speaks: Chayah. — Grandmother speaks: Our friend. — Babette. — The beast.

"A collection of tender and sympathetic stories and character sketches." — *AJYB*, 5667, p. *13.

"Collection of short stories of excellent merit, descriptive of Ghetto and American Jewish life." — *AJYB*, 5667, p. 142.

Reprint, undated, with seal 2a, without advertisements.

1940–5700 edition: as above, with seal 3b, without advertisements. Verso of title-page: "Reprinted 1940."

1906

Rashi

RASHI | By Maurice Liber | Translated from the French | By | Adele Szold | [*seal 1a*] | The Jewish Publication Society of America | 1906 |

COLLATION: 12°. 3 p. l., 3–278 p. (l. 1, Half-title, verso [Quotation from] Rashi, on Psalm xlix.11.; l. 2, Title, verso Copyright; l. 3, Dedication*, verso blank; p. [3]–6, Preface; p. [7]–11, Contents; p. [12] blank; p. [13]–14, Introduction; p. [15]–224, Text; p. [225–227] Appendix I — The Family of Rashi; p. [229]–239, Appendix II — Bibliography; p. [241]–259, Notes; p. [228, 240, 260] blank; p. [261]–278, Index; 4 unnumbered pages of publisher's advertisements.) plates, front. (map)

Issued in green cloth; front cover: title within double rule box; back: title, design, author, publisher all in gilt.

*"To the memory of | Zadoc Kahn | Grand-Rabbin of France | ."

"A learned, yet popularly written account of one of the great Jewish worthies, the second in the series of that name, and highly creditable to the author and the translator." — *AJYB*, 5667, p. *13.

1926 edition.

1938 reprint. — *AJYB*, 5700, p. 675.

5708–1948 edition: title-page reset, with seal 3b, without advertisements. Verso of title-page: "Reprinted 1945, 1948."

The American Jewish Year Book 5667

The American Jewish | Year Book | 5667 | September 20, 1906, to September 8, 1907 | Edited by | Henrietta Szold | [*seal 2a*] | Philadelphia | The Jewish Publication Society of America | 1906 |

COLLATION: 12°. x, 275, *31 p. (p. [ii–iv] Advertisements; p. [v] Title; p. [vi] Copyright; p. [vii]–ix, Preface; p. [x] Special articles in previous issues; p. [1] Contents; p. [2]–275, Text; p. [*1]–*23, Report of the 18th year of the Jewish Publication Society of America 1905–1906; p. *24–*31, Advertisements.)

Bound uniformly with 5660 (1899–1900) with seal 2. On front cover: title of special article in white.

"The central feature of this year's book is the table of massacres of Jews in Russia during the period whose entrance and exit are guarded by Kishineff and Bialystok as bloodstained sentinels. The figures frightfully arrayed are so heartrending that one is impelled to apologize for perpetuating them. It would be a wanton harassment of the feelings, were it not a document tending to stimulate Israel to self-help and the gentiles to self-introspection." — Preface, p. viii.

SPECIAL ARTICLES: Myer S. Isaacs, a memoir, by Abram S. Isaacs, pp. 19–33. — From Kishineff to Bialystok, a table of pogroms from 1903 to 1906, pp. 34–89.

Stories and Pictures

STORIES AND PICTURES | By | Isaac Loeb Perez | Translated from the Yiddish by | Helena Frank | [*seal 2*] | Philadelphia | The Jewish Publication Society of America | 1906 |

[Note: Title, place of printing and date in red.]

COLLATION: 12°. 455 p. (p. [1] Half-title; p. [3] Title; p. [4] Copyright; p. [5]–7, Preface by Helena Frank; p. [2, 8] blank; p. [9]–10, Contents; p. [11]–450, Text; p. [451]–455, Glossary.)

Issued in red cloth; front cover: ornamental design and title within green double rule box, author and seal 2a; back: ornamental design, title and author within green double rule box, publisher all in gilt.

CONTENTS: I. If not higher. II. Domestic happiness. III. In the post-chaise. IV. The new tune. V. Married. VI. The seventh candle of blessing. VII. The widow. VIII. The messenger.

IX. What is the soul? X. In time of pestilence. XI. Bontzye Shweig. XII. The dead town. XIII. The days of the Messiah. XIV. Kabbalists. XV. Travel-pictures. XVI. The outcast. XVII. A chat. XVIII. The pike. XIX. The fast. XX. The woman Mistress Hannah. XXI. In the pond. XXII. The Chanukah light. XXIII. The poor little boy. XXIV. Underground. XXV. Between two mountains. XXVI. The image.

"Collection of sketches of Russian Jewish life, written with simplicity and force. Remarkable for their psychological insight; full of symbolism." — *AJYB*, 5667, p. 139.

"The translation of Perez constitutes one of the finest achievements of the Society. It has introduced to the English-speaking world the greatest of Yiddish writers, a genius who would constitute an ornament to any literature. The translation is admirable in preserving to a remarkable degree the atmosphere of the original, with all of its unique phrasing and idiomatic expression, and while retaining all of the wit, humor, and picturesqueness, the purity of the English medium is in no wise sacrificed." — *AJYB*, 5668, p. *15.

1936 edition: title-page reset, with seal 3b. Verso of title-page: "Reprinted, 1936."

5707–1947 edition: same as 1936. Verso of title-page: "Reprinted 1936, 1943, 1947."

The Messiah Idea in Jewish History

The Messiah Idea in | Jewish History | By | Julius H. Greenstone, Ph.D. | [*seal 2a*] | Philadelphia | The Jewish Publication Society of America | 1906 |

COLLATION: 12°. 347 p. (p. [1] Half-title; p. [3] Title; p. [4] Copyright; p. [5] Dedication*; p. [7]–11, Preface; p. [13]–19, Contents; p. [2, 6, 12, 20] blank; p. [21]–279, Text; p. [281]–302, Appendix; p. [303]–335, Notes; p. [280, 336] blank; p. [337]–347, Indexes.)

*"To the memory | of | my mother | ."

Issued in brown cloth; front cover: seal 2a, blind stamped; back: title, author and publisher in gilt.

"It is the object of the present volume to trace the development of this ideal from its early origins to the present day, to elucidate the influences it exerted upon the lives and habits of the Jews, and to explain the causes by which it, in turn, was influenced, giving in outline the historical conditions of every period. It does not pretend to be an exhaustive study of the subject, but a mere outline of the marvellous development of this hope in the Jewish heart." — Preface, p. 9.

"Investigating and giving a clear exposition of a highly characteristic Jewish idea, it illuminates great movements in Jewish and general history." — *AJYB*, 5668, p. *16.)

5708–1948 edition: title-page reset, with seal 3b. Verso of title-page: "Reprinted 1943, 1948."

1907

Simon Eichelkatz the Patriarch

Simon Eichelkatz [*in red*] | [*rule*] | The Patriarch | [*rule*] | Two Stories of Jewish Life | By Ulrich Frank [pseud. of Ulla Wolff] | [*3 florets*] | Translated [*5 florets*] | From the German [*4 florets*] | [*seal 2a*] | Philadelphia: The Jewish Publication | Society of America [*4 florets*] | 1907 |

[Note: The foregoing appears within a black single rule box. Publisher in red.]

COLLATION: 12°. 431 p. (4 blank l.; p. [1] Half-title; p. [3] Title; p. [4] Copyright; p. [5] Contents; p. [2, 6] blank; p. [7]–426, Text; p. [427]–431, Glossary; 4 blank l.)

Issued in gray cloth; front cover: illustration in green; title and author in red; back: decorations in green; title, author and publisher in red; back cover: seal 2a in green.

Translated by Adele Szold (Seltzer).

"Affords an insight into contemporaneous Jewish life in Germany which is instructive." — *AJYB*, 5668, p. *15.

The American Jewish Year Book 5668

The American Jewish | Year Book | 5668 | September 9, 1907, to September 25, 1908 | Edited by | Henrietta Szold | [*seal 2a*] | Philadelphia | The Jewish Publication Society of America | 1907 |

COLLATION: 12°. xii, 557, *89 p. (p. ii–iv, Advertisements; p. [v] Title; p. [vi] Copyright; p. [vii]–xi, Preface; p. [xii] Special articles in previous issues; 1 l., Contents; p. [1]–557, Text; p. [*1]–*83, Report of the 19th year of the Jewish Publication Society of America 1906–1907; p. *84–*89, Advertisements.)

Bound uniformly with 5660 (1899–1900) without seal.

"The two Directories of [national and local] Jewish Organizations in the United States . . . make up the bulk of the present issue of the American Jewish Year Book." — Preface, p. [vii].

Stories of Jewish Home Life

Stories of | Jewish Home | Life [*6 florets*] | By S. H. Mosenthal [*4 florets*] | Translated from the German | [*double rule* | [*seal 2a*] | [*double rule*] | Philadelphia | The Jewish Publication Society of America | 1907 |

[Note: The foregoing appears within an orange double rule box. Initial letter S of title and rules in orange.]

COLLATION: 12°. 387 p. (p. [1] Half-title; p. [3] Title; p. [4] Copyright; p. [5] Contents; p. [2, 6] blank; p. [7]–381, Text; p. [382] blank; p. [383]–387, Glossary.)

Issued in red cloth; white paper label pasted on back with title in red and Shield of David in green within a yellow circle, both within a green ornamental border; the foregoing appears within a yellow ornamental border.

CONTENTS: Aunt Guttraud. — Schlemihlchen. — Rav's mine. — Jephthah's daughter. — Raschelchen.

Translated by Adele Szold (Seltzer).

"These stories are annals of the beautiful simplicity of Jewish home life, as it existed in Germany half a century ago. The elemental virtues are admirably depicted, an atmosphere of wholesome sentiment has been created, and the characters are convincing and genuine. Even the blasé reader will find his best emotions stimulated by a perusal of these stories." — *AJYB*, 5669, p. 275.

1908

Studies in Judaism
Second Series

STUDIES IN JUDAISM | Second Series | By | S. Schechter, M.A., Litt.D. | [*seal 2a*] | Philadelphia | The Jewish Publication Society of America | 1908 |

COLLATION: 8°. xiii, 362 p. (p. [i] Half-title; p. [iii] Title; p. [iv] Copyright; p. [v] Dedication*; p. [vii]–xi, Preface; p. [ii, vi, xii] blank; p. [xiii] Contents; p. [1]–285, Text; p. [286] blank; p. [287]–306, Appendixes; p. [307]–328, Notes; p. [329]–362, Index.)

Issued in light green cloth; front cover: title, author; back: rules, title, author, publisher, rules all in gilt.

*"To my wife | in devotion and gratitude | ."

CONTENTS: A hoard of Hebrew manuscripts I, II. — The study of the Bible. — A glimpse of the social life of the Jews in the age of Jesus the son of Sirach. — On the study of the Talmud. — The

87

memoirs of a Jewess of the seventeenth century. — Saints and saint-liness. — Four epistles to the Jews of England. — Safed in the sixteenth century — a city of legists and mystics.

"A triumph for the Society is the publication of Dr. Schechter's 'Studies in Judaism, Second Series.' It is a remarkably fine production from every standpoint. As a specimen of typography and of book-making, it has never been equaled by the Society. It is a fitting receptacle for the gems which it contains. Whether one considers the contents as the work of an historian, of an essayist, of a student of mankind, of a thinker, or of a litterateur, they stand forth in bold relief, and are, at the same time, impressive and fascinating. They are profound and scintillating. They have the picturesqueness of outdoor life, and the scholasticism of the student's closet. They have the polish of literary artisanship and the ruggedness of vigorous thought." — *AJYB*, 5669, p. 274.

1938 edition: title-page reset, with seal 3b. Verso of title-page: "Reprinted, 1938."

1945: "1,500 copies reprinted."— *AJYB*, 5707, p. 649.

David the Giant Killer

David The Giant Killer | And Other Tales | of Grandma Lopez | By | Emily Solis-Cohen, Jr. | With illustrations by Alfred Feinberg | [*seal 2a*] | Philadelphia | The Jewish Publication Society of America | 1908 |

[Note: The foregoing appears within an ornamental box surrounded by a single rule box, all in red. Title and imprint within single rule boxes and initial letters of title, author and publisher all in red.]

COLLATION: sq. 12°. 250 p. (p. [1] Half-title; p. [3] Title; p. [4] Copyright; p. [5] Dedication: "To my grandmothers;" p. 7–9, Preface; p. 11–12, Contents; p. 13, List of illustrations; [p. 2, 6, 10, 14] blank; p. [15]–247, Text; p. [248] blank; p. 249–250, Glossary.) 5 illus. (including front.)

Issued in tan cloth; front cover: title, author, decoration; back: title, author, publisher all in black.

CONTENTS: David the giant killer. — In Shushan the capital. — The sacrifice at Modin. — The hidden smithy. — The fall of Michmash. — At the fork of the roads. — Carmel. — Amid the alien corn. — How Daniel became judge. — The golden image. — Conclusion.

"Some of the tales here collected have appeared in print over the author's pen-name of "Emma Leigh." — Preface, p. 9.

"It contains a number of stories dealing with Biblical episodes, and it is written primarily to appeal to young readers, though it may be perused with profit by the older members of the family. The volume is very attractively made up, and contains several illustrations." — *AJYB*, 5669, p. 264.

"The subjects are well selected, the stories are charmingly told, and cannot fail to attract young and old. The framework which contains these stories of the Bible introduces us to an amiable family, to pleasant memories, and to the rare beauty of the ancient ceremonies prevailing in enlightened Jewish households." — *AJYB*, 5669, p. 275.

1938 reprint. — *AJYB*, 5700, p. 675.

5706–1945 edition: title-page reset, with seal 3b. Verso of title-page: "Fourth Printing, 1945."

5707–1946 edition: same as 1945. Verso of title-page: "Fourth Printing 1945; Reprinted 1946."

The American Jewish Year Book 5669

The American Jewish | Year Book | 5669 | September 26, 1908, to September 15, 1909 | Edited by | Herbert Friedenwald | for the | American Jewish Committee | [*seal 2a*] | Philadelphia | The Jewish Publication Society of America | 1908 |

COLLATION: 12°. xii, 349 p. (p. ii–iv, Advertisements; p. [v] Title; p. [vi] Copyright; p. [vii]–ix, Preface; p. [x] Special articles in previous issues; p. [xi] Contents; p. [xii] and [1]–236, Text; p. 237–258, Report of the American Jewish Committee, November,

1906, to June 1, 1908; p. [259]–344, Report of the 20th year of the Jewish Publication Society of America 1907–1908; p. [345]–349, Catalogue of the Jewish Publication Society of America.)

Bound uniformly with 5660 (1899–1900), without seal. On front cover: title of special article in white.

"The present, which is the tenth issue of the American Jewish Year Book, appears under a slightly different arrangement than has heretofore obtained with regard to this annual. Though the publisher is still The Jewish Publication Society of America, the compilation of the work has been taken over by the American Jewish Committee . . . In view of this arrangement, it has been thought proper to include in this volume a report of the activities of the American Jewish Committee as well as the usual one of The Jewish Publication Society of America.

"The summary of Sunday legislation and court decisions, for which we are indebted to Albert M. Friedenberg, Esq., presents in succinct form material on a subject which has engaged the attention of a large number of Jewish citizens and of other Americans who either belong to creeds not observing Sunday as a Sabbath, or who are concerned with the general problem of religious liberty." — Preface, p. viii–ix.

The Sunday Laws of the United States

The Sunday Laws of the United States | and Leading Judicial Decisions | Having Special Reference | to the Jews | by | Albert M. Friedenberg | of the New York Bar | [*seal 2a*] | Philadelphia | The Jewish Publication Society of America | 1908 |

COLLATION: 12°. 42 p. (p. [1] Half-title; p. [3] Title; p. [2, 4] blank; p. [5]–42, Text.)

Issued in gray paper covers; title as above, within single rule box.

Originally printed in *AJYB*, 5669, pp. 152–189.

Micah

... MICAH | By | Max L. Margolis, Ph.D. | [*seal 2a*] | Philadelphia | The Jewish Publication Society of America | 5669–1908 |

At head of title: The Holy Scriptures | with commentary | *rule* |.

COLLATION: 12°. 3 p. l., 104 p. (l. 1, blank, verso Advertisement to the Series*; l. 2, Half-title, verso blank; l. 3, Title, verso Copyright; p. [1]–16, Introduction; p. [17]–80, Text; p. [81]–94, Additional Notes; p. [95]–99, Index to References to the Scriptures ...; p. [100]–104, Index.)

Issued in black cloth; front cover: series title, rule, title, author; back: rule, series title, rule, title, rule, J. P. S., rule; back cover: seal 2a, all in gilt.

*"The present volume is the first of a proposed series of Commentaries on the Books of Holy Scriptures which the Jewish Publication Society of America has undertaken to prepare. This series is intended primarily for the teacher, the inquiring pupil, and the general reader, who need help to obtain an understanding of the Scriptures, at once reliable and Jewish ..."

"Forms the initial volume of a proposed series of Bible commentaries. Dr. Margolis, being thoroughly conversant with the results of the latest scholarship, and with the Jewish traditional point of view, has thrown light upon passages which escape the notice of non-Jewish scholars." — *AJYB*, 5670, p. 260.

5703–1943 edition: as above, with seal 3b. Verso of title-page: "Reprinted, 1943."

1909
The Legends of the Jews

THE LEGENDS OF | THE JEWS | By | Louis Ginzberg | Translated from the German Manuscript by | Henrietta Szold | I | Bible Times and Characters | From the Creation to Jacob |

[*seal 2a*] | Philadelphia | The Jewish Publication Society of America | 1909 |

COLLATION: 8°. xviii, 424 p. (p. [i] Half-title; p. [iii] Title; p. [iv] Copyright; p. [v] Dedication*; p. [vii]–xv, Preface; p. [ii, vi, xvi] blank; p. [xvii]–xviii, Contents; p. [1]–424, Text.)

Issued in dark blue cloth; back: rule, title, rule, author, volume, title, publisher, rules all in gilt.

*"To | My Brother Asher | ."

"I have made the first attempt to gather from the original sources all Jewish legends, in so far as they refer to Biblical personages and events, and reproduce them with the greatest attainable completeness and accuracy. I use the expression Jewish, rather than Rabbinic, because the sources from which I have levied contributions are not limited to the Rabbinic literature." — Author's preface, p. xi.

v. 2 issued in 1910; v. 3, 1911; v. 4, 1913; v. 5, 1925; v. 6, 1928; v. 7, 1938.

"Written by one of the leading Talmudical scholars in the world, the work represents the first attempt to gather from original sources all the Jewish legends referring to Biblical personages and events, reproducing them completely and accurately. The work has been specially prepared for us, and though written in German, has never appeared in that or any other language." — *AJYB*, 5670, p. 260.

1913 edition: as above. Verso of title-page: "Seventh Impression Twenty-first Thousand."

1942: "1,000 copies reprinted."— *AJYB*, 5704, p. 687.

5707–1948 edition: as above, with seal 3b. Verso of title-page: "Ninth Impression Twenty-five Thousand."

The American Jewish Year Book
5670

The American Jewish | Year Book | 5670 | September 16 | 1909, to October 3, 9110 | Edited by | Herbert Friedenwald | for the | American Jewish Committee | [*seal 2a*] | Philadelphia | The Jewish Publication Society of America | 1909 |

COLLATION: 12°. x, 355 p. (p. ii–iv, Advertisements; p. [v]
Title; p. [vi] Copyright; p. [vii]–ix, Preface; p. [x] Special articles
in previous issues; 1 l., Contents; p. [1]–236, Text; p. 237–254, 2nd
annual report of the American Jewish Committee; p. [255]–351,
Report of the 21st year of the Jewish Publication Society of America
1908–1909; p. 352–355, Advertisements.)

Bound uniformly with 5660 (1899–1900) without seal.

"As the experience of previous years has resulted in bringing
together, in handy form, the matter most needed for communal work
and of the greatest general interest to all people concerned in Jewish
affairs in America, no important innovations have been made. The
order of the matter has been somewhat rearranged in the hope that
it might prove more useful, and the list of Leading Events has
been considerably extended and classified by countries." — Preface,
p. viii.

SPECIAL ARTICLES: The Passport question in Congress, pp. 21–
43. — The Jewish community of New York City, p. 44–54.

The Renascence of Hebrew Literature

THE RENASCENCE | of | HEBREW LITERATURE | (1743–1885) |
By | Nahum Slouschz | Translated from the French | [*seal 2a*] |
Philadelphia | The Jewish Publication Society of America |
1909 |

COLLATION: 12°. 307 p. (p. [1] Half-title; p. [3] Title; p. [4]
Copyright; p. 5–6, Translator's note by Henrietta Szold; p. 7,
Contents; p. [2, 8] blank; p. 9–17, Introduction; p. 18–288, Text;
p. 289–307, Index.)

Issued in green cloth; front cover: single rule box in black; back:
title, author, and publisher in black.

Original text, *La renaissance de la littérature hebraique* (Paris,
1903), was rendered into Hebrew by the author and published under
the title *Korot ha-Safrut ha-'Ibrit ha-Hadashah* (Warsaw, 1906–07).

"The present English translation, which has had the benefit of the author's revision, purports to be a rendition from the French. But the Hebrew recasting of the book has been consulted at almost every point, and the Hebrew works quoted by Dr. Slouschz were resorted to directly, though, as far as seemed practicable, the translator paid regard to the author's conception and Occidentalization of the Hebrew passages revealed in his translation of them into French." — Translator's note, p. 5–6.

1910

The Legends of the Jews

THE LEGENDS OF | THE JEWS | By | Louis Ginzberg | Translated from the German Manuscript by | Henrietta Szold | II | Bible Times and Characters | From Joseph to the Exodus | [*seal 2a*] | Philadelphia | The Jewish Publication Society of America | 1910 |

COLLATION: 8°. viii, 375 p. (p. [i–iv] same as v. 1; p. [v] Preface; p. [vi] blank; p. [vii]–viii, Contents; p. [1]–375, Text.)

See 1909, v. 1, for binding.

"My original intention was to continue Volume II up to the death of Moses, but the legendary. material clustering around the life and death of Moses is so abundant that practical considerations demanded the division of this material, in order not to make the second volume too bulky. The division chosen is a natural one. This volume closes with the Exodus, and contains the deeds of Moses in Egypt, while the following volume will deal with Moses in the desert." — Author's preface.

1913 edition: as above. Verso of title-page "Third edition Twelfth Thousand."

1940: "1,000 copies reprinted."— *AJYB*, 5702, p. 777.

5706–1946 edition: as above, with seal 3b. Verso of title-page: "Sixth Impression — 1946."

Philo-Judaeus of Alexandria

PHILO-JUDAEUS | OF ALEXANDRIA | By | Norman Bentwich |
Sometime Scholar of Trinity College, Cambridge | [*seal 2a*]
Philadelphia | The Jewish Publication Society of America | 1910 |

COLLATION: 12°. 273 p. (p. [1] Half-title; p. [3] Title; p. [4]
Copyright; p. [5] Dedication*; p. [7]–10, Preface; p. [11] Contents;
p. [2, 6, 12] blank; p. [13]–262, Text; p. [263]–265, Bibliography;
p. [266]–267; Abbreviations used for references; p. [268] blank;
p. [269]–273, Index.)

Issued in dark green cloth; front cover: title within double rule
box; back: title, design, author, publisher all in gilt.

*"To my mother | Θρεπτήρια | ."

"The third in our Jewish Worthies Series." — *AJYB*, 5671,
p. 360.

"It must be admitted that Philo has been greatly neglected by
Jews. To publish, then, an account of him, at once scholarly and
comprehensive, in research and fact, illuminated by discriminating
criticism of his point of view, is noteworthy. It is written in a charming and easy style. It is a book which will help to re-locate one of
our great men in the reverence and affections of the Jewish people.
To have accomplished the *multum* in the *parvo* of a small volume,
which not even the most indifferent will neglect, and glancing at,
can resist reading, is highly commendable." — *AJYB*, 5671, p. 367.

5708–1948 edition: title-page reset, with seal 3b. Verso of
title-page: "Reprinted 1940, 1948." Dedication page omitted.

The American Jewish Year Book
5671

The American Jewish | Year Book | 5671 | October 4, 1910,
to September 22, 1911 | Edited by | Herbert Friedenwald |
for the | American Jewish Committee | [*seal 2a*] | Philadelphia |
The Jewish Publication Society of America | 1910 |

COLLATION: 12°. x, 449 p. (p. [ii–iv] Advertisements; p. [v] Title; p. [vi] Copyright; p. [vii]–viii, Preface; p. [ix]–x, Special articles in previous issues; 1 l., Contents; p. [1]–337, Text; p. 338–354, 3rd annual report of the American Jewish Committee; p. [355]–445, Report of the 22nd year of the Jewish Publication Society of America 1909–1910; p. 446–449, Advertisements.)

Bound uniformly with 5660 (1899–1900) without seal. On front cover: title of special article in white.

"Only one important change has been made in this, the twelfth issue of the American Jewish Year Book. The article on The Year has been omitted, as the List of Events, arranged by countries, in itself constitutes an account of the year's activities, thus rendering any additional article unnecessary.

"The principal article is on immigration, as this has been one of the chief subjects of interest to the Jews of the United States during the year." — Preface, p. [vii].

Step by Step

STEP BY STEP | A Story of the Early Days | of | Moses Mendelssohn | By | Abram S. Isaacs | [seal 2a] | Philadelphia | The Jewish Publication Society of America | 1910 |

COLLATION: 12°. 160 p. (p. [1] Half-title; p. [3] Title; p. [4] Copyright; p. 5–6, Preface; p. 7, Contents; p. [2, 8] blank; p. 9–160, Text.) front. (colored port.), illus.

Issued in light green cloth; front cover: illustration, title in yellow; back: title, author and publisher in black.

Inscription on tissue cover of frontispiece: "Moses Mendelssohn, From an unpublished painting, dated 1784, in the possession of Hon. Mayer Sulzberger, Philadelphia, Pa. Copyright 1910, by The Jewish Publication Society of America."

Illustrations (facing p. 112 and on cover) by A[lfred] F[einberg].

"Written particularly for young people that have reached the threshold of maturer years." — Preface, p. 6.

1929 reprint, without port.

5703–1943 edition: title-page reset, with seal 3b, without port. Verso of title-page: "Reprinted, 1929; Reprinted, 1943."

Leon Gordon

LEON GORDON | An Appreciation | By | Abraham Benedict Rhine | [*seal 2a*] | Philadelphia | The Jewish Publication Society of America | 1910 |

COLLATION: 12°. 181 p. (p. [1] Half-title; p. [3] Title; p. [4] Copyright; p. [5] Dedication*; p. [2, 6] blank; p. 7–8, Preface; p. 9, Contents; p. 11–18, Introduction; p. 19–164, Text; p. [165]–176, Notes and Bibliography; p. [177]–181, Index.) front. (port.)

Issued in dark green cloth; back: rule, title, author, publisher, rule all in gilt.

*"To | my dear father | MEYER RHINE | whose scholarly attainments and love for the | Hebrew language and literature made it | possible for his son to enjoy and | appreciate poets like | LEON GORDON | this first attempt at authorship | is affectionately dedicated | ."

"This essay, originally written in 1902 as a thesis for the Rabbinical degree of the Hebrew Union College of Cincinnati, is an attempt to introduce the American Jewish public to the Hebrew literature of the nineteenth century. The study of this period, which constitutes one of the most pathetic chapters in Jewish history, will come in the nature of a revelation to the reader to whom the Hebrew language is a *terra incognita*. It will unfold to him a tale of the struggle between medievalism and modernity — a story of the longing of the Jewish soul for emancipation. He will meet with men of power and of genius, above all, with an array of heroes whose life was a constant battle in behalf of enlightenment and civilization. Incidentally, a study of nineteenth century Hebrew literature cannot but tend to raise the Russian Jew in the estimation of his American brother, and bring about a clearer understanding between them, which will inevitably result in closer fellowship and a firmer tie of sympathy."— Preface, p. 7.

1911

Selections for Homes and Schools

SELECTIONS | for | HOMES AND SCHOOLS | Compiled by | Marion L. Misch | [*seal 2a*] | Philadelphia | The Jewish Publication Society of America | 1911 |

COLLATION: 12°. 444 p. (p. [1] Half-title; p. [3] Title; p. [4] Copyright; p. [5]–6, Preface; p. [7]–9, Acknowledgments; p. [2, 10] blank; p. [11]–18, Contents; p. [19]–432, Text; p. [433]–444, Indexes.)

Issued in light green cloth; back: title, author and publisher in gilt.

CONTENTS: Tales from the Bible and the Talmud. — The Psalter. — The Holy days. — Miscellaneous. — Memory gems.

"The object is to provide material for home reading and for recitations in Jewish Religious Schools, Junior Sections of the Council of Jewish Women, and other Jewish organizations. It includes a number of short, simple verses for the younger children, and also some material familiar to the past generation, which will well bear repetition." — Preface, p. [7].

The American Jewish Year Book
5672

The American Jewish | Year Book | 5672 | September 23, 1911, to September 11, 1912 | Edited by | Herbert Friedenwald | for the | American Jewish Committee | [*seal 2a*] | Philadelphia | The Jewish Publication Society of America | 1911 |

COLLATION: 12°. x, 453 p. (p. ii–iv, Advertisements; p. [v] Title; p. [vi] Copyright; p. [vii]–viii, Preface; p. [ix]–x, Special articles in previous issues; 1 l., Contents; p. [1]–293, Text; p. 294–334, 4th annual report of the American Jewish Committee; p. [335]–

449, Report of the 23rd year of The Jewish Publication Society of America 1910–1911; p. 450–453, Advertisements.)

Bound uniformly with 5660 (1899–1900), without seal.

"In this, the thirteenth issue of The American Jewish Year Book, most of the lists which experience has proven to be useful, have been continued. ... The principal article this year, supplementing the Year Books of 5665 and 5670, gives the latest phases of the Passport Question." — Preface, p. [vii].

The Jewish Publication Society of America
What It Is

The Jewish Publication | Society of America | [*rule*] What It Is and What It | Has Done | [*seal 2a*] | 608 Chestnut Street | Philadelphia, Pa. | [1911]

[Note: The foregoing appears within a double rule box, with a small circle in each corner, all in black.]

COLLATION: nar. 24°. 5 l. (l. 1, Port.: The Board of Editors of the Bible Translation, verso [List of] The Board of Editors of the Bible Translation; l. 2–5, Text, verso l. 5, [List of] Publication Committee.)

Issued in light blue covers.

Cover-title, verso [List of] Officers.

The Legends of the Jews

THE LEGENDS OF | THE JEWS | By | Louis Ginzberg | Translated from the German Manuscript by | Paul Radin | III | Bible Times and Characters | From the Exodus to the Death of Moses | [*seal 2a*] | Philadelphia | The Jewish Publication Society of America | 1911 |

99

COLLATION: 8°. x, 481 p. (p. [i–iv] same as v. 1; p. [v] Dedication*; p. [vi] blank; p. [vii]–viii, Preface; p. [ix]–x, Contents; p. [1]–481, Text.)

See 1909, v. 1, for binding.

*"To | my mother | on the occasion of | her seventieth birthday | ."

"Reviser and proof-reader of Volume III, Doctor Isaac Husik." — p. [iv].

"The most natural way for the popular mind to connect existing conditions with the past is the symbolic method. The present volume contains, therefore, a number of symbolic explanations of certain laws, as for instance, the symbolical significance of the Tabernacle, which, properly speaking, do not belong to the domain of legend. The life of Moses, as conceived by Jewish legend, would, however, have been incomplete if the lines between Legend and Symbolism had been kept too strictly. With this exception the arrangement and presentation of the material in the third volume is the same as that in the two preceding ones." — Preface, p. vii–viii.

1942: "1,000 copies reprinted."— AJYB, 5704, p. 687.

5707–1947 edition: as above, with seal 3b. Verso of title-page: "Third Impression — 1947."

1912
Selected Essays by Ahad Ha-'Am

SELECTED ESSAYS | By | Ahad Ha-'Am [pseud. of Asher Ginzberg] | Translated from the Hebrew | By | Leon Simon | [seal 2a] | Philadelphia | The Jewish Publication Society of America | 1912 |

COLLATION: 8°. 347 p. (p. [1] Half-title; p. [3] Title; p. [4] Copyright; p. [5] Dedication*; p. [7]–8, Preface by L. S.; p. [9] Contents; p. [2, 6, 10] blank; p. [11]–40, Introduction by the translator; p. [41]–329, Text; p. [330] blank; p. [331]–347, Index.)

*"To my teacher | Ahad Ha-'Am | and to my friend | Asher Ginzberg | this volume of translations | is dedicated | ."

Issued in gray cloth; back: rules, title, author, publisher and rules in gilt.

CONTENTS: Sacred and profane. — Justice and mercy. — Positive and negative. — Anticipations and survivals. — Past and future. — Two masters. — Imitation and assimilation. — Priest and prophet. — Flesh and spirit. — Many inventions. — Slavery in freedom. — Some consolation. — Ancestor worship. — The transvaluation of values. — A new savior. — The spiritual revival. — Moses.

"The Essays included in the present volume are a comparatively small selection, but they will probably give an adequate idea of the author's attitude on Jewish questions . . . The translation has had the advantage of the author's revision . . ." — Preface, p. 7–8.

1936 edition: title-page reset, with seal 3b. Verso of title-page: "Reprinted, 1936."

5708–1948 edition: same as 1936. Verso of title-page: "Reprinted, 1936, 1944, 1948."

Yiddish Tales

YIDDISH TALES | Translated by | Helena Frank | [seal 2a] | Philadelphia | The Jewish Publication Society of America | 1912 |

[Note: Title, place of printing and date all in red.]

COLLATION: 12°. 599 p. (p. [1] Half-title; p. [2] blank; p. [3] Title; p. [4] Copyright; p. [5]–7, Preface; p. [8] Acknowledgment; p. [9]–10, Contents; p. [11]–587, Text; p. [588] blank; p. [589]–599, Glossary and Notes.)

Issued in green cloth; front cover: seal 2, blind stamped; back: rule, title, design, publisher and rule in gilt.

"This little volume [containing forty-eight tales by twenty different authors] is intended to be both companion and complement to 'Stories and Pictures,' by I. L. Perez, published by the Jewish Publication Society of America, in 1906. Its object was twofold: to introduce the non-Yiddish reading public to some of the many other Yiddish writers active in Russian Jewry, and — to leave it with a more cheerful impression of Yiddish literature than it receives from Perez alone." — Preface, p. [5].

CONTENTS: Reuben Asher Braudes: The misfortune. — Jehalel (Judah Löb Lewin): Earth of Palestine. — Isaac Löb Perez: A woman's wrath; The treasure; It is well; Whence a proverb. — Mordecai Spektor: An original strike; A gloomy wedding; Poverty. — Sholom-Alechem (Shalom Rabinovitz): The clock; Fishel the teacher; An easy fast; The Passover guest; Gymnasiye. — Eliezer David Rosenthal: Sabbath; Yom Kippur. — Isaiah Lerner: Bertzi Wasserführer; Ezrielk the scribe; Yitzchok-Yossel Broitgeber. — Judah Steinberg: A livelihood; At the matzes. — David Frischmann: Three who ate. — Micha Joseph Berdyczewski: Military service. — Isaiah Berschadski: Forlorn and forsaken. — Tashrak (Israel Joseph Zevin): The hole in the beigel; As the years roll on. — David Pinski: Reb Shloimeh. — S. Libin (Israel Hurewitz): A picnic; Manasseh; Yohrzeit for mother; Slack times they sleep. — Abraham Raisin: Shut in; The charitable loan; The two brothers; Lost his voice; Late; The Kaddish; Avrohom the orchard-keeper. — Hirsh David Naumberg: The Rav and the Rav's son. — Meyer Blinkin: Women; Löb Schapiro: If it was a dream. — Shalom Asch: A simple story; A Jewish child; A scholar's mother; The sinner. — Isaac Dob Berkowitz: Country folk; The last of them. — A folk tale: The clever rabbi.

1938 reprint. — *AJYB*, 5700, p. 675; 1943: "2,000 copies reprinted." — *AJYB*, 5705, p. 606.

5706–1945 edition: title-page reset, with seal 3b. Verso of title-page: "Reprinted 1945." "2,000 copies — 4th printing." — *AJYB*, 5707, p. 649.

1948: "3,000 copies reprinted." — *JPSA* [61st annual report] 1948, p. 3.

The Sign above the Door

THE | SIGN ABOVE THE DOOR | By | William W. Canfield | Author of | "Legends of the Iroquois," "Along the Way," | "The White Seneca," etc. | [*seal 2a*] | Philadelphia | The Jewish Publication Society | of America | 1912 |

COLLATION: 12°. 325 p. (p. [1] Half-title; p. [2] blank; p. [3] Title; p. [4] Copyright; p. [5] Contents; p. [6] [English text of Exodus 12, 21–24]; p. [7]–325, Text.)

Issued in blue cloth; back: rule, title, rules and publisher in gilt.

The American Jewish Year Book
5673

The American Jewish | Year Book | 5673 | September 12, 1912, to October 1, 1913 | Edited by | Herbert Friedenwald | for the | American Jewish Committee | [*seal 2a*] | Philadelphia | The Jewish Publication Society of America | 1912 |

COLLATION: 12°. viii, 453 p. (p. ii, Advertisement; p. [iii] Title; p. [iv] Copyright; p. [v]–vii, Preface; p. [viii] Special articles in previous issues; 1 l., Contents; p. [1]–290, Text; p. 291–314, 5th annual report of the American Jewish Committee; p. [315]–452, Report of the 24th year of The Jewish Publication Society of America 1911–1912; p. 453, Advertisement.)

Bound uniformly with 5660 (1899–1900) without seal.

"The leading article in this, the fourteenth, issue of the American Jewish Year Book is devoted to a survey, by Mr. Leonard G. Robinson, of the Agricultural Activities of the Jews in America, with special reference to the experiments, failures, and successes in the United States." — Preface, p. [v].

The Book of Delight

THE BOOK OF DELIGHT | And | Other Papers | By | Israel Abrahams, M.A. | Author of "Jewish Life in the Middle Ages," "Chapters on Jewish Literature," etc. | [*seal 2a*] | Philadelphia | The Jewish Publication Society of America | 1912 |

COLLATION: 8°. 323 p. (p. [1] Half-Title; p. [3] Title; p. [4] Copyright; p. 5–6, Preface; p. 7, Contents; p. [2, 8] blank; p. 9–300, Text; p. 301–315, Notes; p. [316] blank; p. 317–323, Index.)

Issued in light green cloth; back: rules, title, author and publisher in gilt.

CONTENTS: "The Book of delight". — A visit to Hebron. — The solace of books. — Medieval wayfaring. — The fox's heart. — "Marriages are made in heaven." — Hebrew love songs. — A handful of curiosities: George Eliot and Solomon Maimon; How Milton pronounced Hebrew; The Cambridge Platonists; The Anglo-Jewish Yiddish Literary Society; The mystics and saints of India; Lost Purim joys; Jews and letters; The shape of Matzoth.

1913
The Legends of the Jews

THE LEGENDS OF | THE JEWS | By | Louis Ginzberg | Translated from the German Manuscript | IV | Bible Times and Characters | From Joshua to Esther | [*seal 2a*] | Philadelphia | The Jewish Publication Society of America | 1913 |

COLLATION: 8°. vii, 448 p. (p. [i–iv] same as v. 1; p. [v]–vii, Contents; p. [1]–448, Text.)

See 1909, v 1, for binding.

1913 reprint. Verso of title-page: "Second Impression, Ninth Thousand."

1942: "1,000 copies reprinted."— *AJYB*, 5704, p. 687.

5707–1947 edition: as above, with seal 3b. Verso of title-page: "Fifth Impression, 1947."

The American Jewish Year Book
5674

The American Jewish | Year Book | 5674 | October 2, 1913, to September 20, 1914 | Edited by | Herbert Friedenwald | and | H. G. Friedman | for the | American Jewish Committee |

[*seal 2a*] | Philadelphia | The Jewish Publication Society of America | 1913 |

COLLATION: 12°. viii, 630 p. (p. [iii] Title; p. [iv] Copyright; p. [v]–vii, Preface by H. G. Friedman; p. [viii] Special articles in previous issues; 1 l., Contents; p. [1]–436, Text; p. 437–465, 6th annual report of the American Jewish Committee; p. [466] blank; p. [467]–625, Report of the 25th year of The Jewish Publication Society of America 1912–1913; p. 626–630, Advertisements.) ports., illus.

Bound uniformly with 5660 (1899–1900) without seal. On front cover: title of special article in white.

SPECIAL ARTICLES: The Twenty-Fifth Anniversary of the Founding of The Jewish Publication Society of America April 5 and 6 1913, pp. 19–187. — The Balkan Wars and the Jews, pp. 188–206. — The Levantine Jews in the United States, by D. De Sola Pool, pp. 207–220.

"This year marked the completion by the Society of twenty-five years of activity devoted to the spread of a knowledge of Jewish life and thought in the United States and among English-speaking Jews generally. ... It is, therefore, not inappropriate that the American Jewish Year Book, founded under its auspices and published by it, should give the leading place this year to the Quarter-Centenary Celebration of The Jewish Publication Society of America." — Preface, p. [v].

The Young Champion

THE YOUNG CHAMPION | One Year | in | Grace Aguilar's girlhood | By | Abram S. Isaacs | Author of "Step by Step" | [*seal 2a*] | Philadelphia | The Jewish Publication Society of America | 1913 |

COLLATION: 12°. 196 p. (p. [1] Half-title; p. [3] Title; p. [4] Copyright; p. 5–6, Preface; p. 7, Contents; p. [2, 8] blank; p. 9–196, Text.)

Issued in lilac cloth; front cover: miniature portrait of Grace Aguilar, title and author; back: title, rule, author, design, publisher all in white.

"A story having as its heroine Grace Aguilar, the little Spanish-Jewish girl in the England of Montefiore's and Disraeli's manhood."— *AJYB*, 5674, p. 472.

1929 edition: as above.

5706–1946 edition: as above, with seal 3b. Verso of title-page: "Reprinted 1940; Reprinted 1946."

The Haskalah Movement in Russia

THE | HASKALAH MOVEMENT | IN RUSSIA | By | Jacob S. Raisin, Ph.D., D.D. | Author of "Sect, Creed and Custom in Judaism," etc. | [*seal 2a*] | Philadelphia | The Jewish Publication Society of America | 1913 |

COLLATION: 8°. 355 p. (p. [1] Half-title; p. [2] [Quotation from] Dan. xii. 3–4; p. [3] Title; p. [4] Copyright, 1914; p. 5, Dedication*; p. 7, Contents; p. 9, List of Illustrations; p. 11–15, Preface; p. [6, 8, 10, 16] blank; p. 17–303, Text; p. [304] blank; p. 305–330, Notes; p. 331–337, Bibliography; p. [338] blank; p. 339–355, Index.) 6 ports. (including front.)

Issued in light green cloth; back: rule, title, author, publisher and rules in gilt.

*"To AARON S. RAISIN | Your name, dear father, will not be found in the following pages, for, like 'the waters of the Siloam that run softly,' you ever preferred to pursue your useful course in un-assuming silence. Yet, as it is your life, devoted entirely to meditat-ing, learning, and teaching, that inspired me in my effort, I dedicate this book to you; and I am happy to know that I thus not only dedicate it to one of the noblest of Maskilim, but at the same time offer you some slight token of the esteem and affection felt for you by | Your Son, | Jacob S. Raisin | ."

A Jewish Child's Book

A | JEWISH CHILD'S BOOK | By | Katherine Myrtilla Cohen | [*ornament*] | Philadelphia | [*double rule* | The Jewish Publication Society | of America | [Copyright 1913]

[Note: The foregoing appears within a black double rule box.]

COLLATION: 12°. 26 p. (p. [1] Title; p. [2]–25, Text and Colored Illustrations; p. 26, Copyright 1913 . . . Published with the co-operation of the David Sulzberger Memorial Fund of the Hebrew Education Society of Philadelphia; 1 l., seal 2a, verso The Acme Press.)

Issued with illustrated paper cover; front cover: title (in red), author and publisher in black.

"Issued by the Society in cooperation with the David Sulzberger Fund of the Hebrew Education Society of Philadelphia, is the first of a contemplated series of Kindergarten books. This little volume, with its quaint pictures of Jewish ceremonial life and the appropriate verses accompanying them, will attract young Jewish children." — *AJYB*, 5675, p. 424.

The Jewish Publication Society of America 25th Anniversary

THE JEWISH PUBLICATION | SOCIETY OF AMERICA | Twenty-fifth Anniversary | April fifth and sixth | nineteen hundred and thirteen | Philadelphia | [*seal 2a*] | Philadelphia | The Jewish Publication Society of America | 1913 |

COLLATION: 12°. 183 p. (p. [1] Half-title; p. [3] Title; p. [4] Copyright; p. [5] Contents; p. [7] Illustrations; p. [2, 6, 8] blank; p. [9]–173, Text; p. [174]–178, Charter and by-laws; p. [179]–183, List of publications.) illus., ports.

"First seal [1] used by The Jewish Publication Society of America." — p. 173.

Text on pp. [11]–173 identical with pp. [25]–187 in *AJYB*, 5674, from which it was reprinted.

1914

Zionism

... | ZIONISM | By | Richard J. H. Gottheil, | Professor of Semitic Languages in Columbia University, New York | Sometime President of the Federation of American Zionists | [*seal 2a*] | Philadelphia | The Jewish Publication Society of America | 1914 |

At head of title: Movements in Judaism | [*rule*] | .

COLLATION: 8°. 258 p. (p. [1] blank; p. [2] Movements in Judaism . . .; p. [3] Half-title; p. [4] לי מי לי אני אין אם; p. [5] Title; p. [6] Copyright; p. [7] Dedication: "To E. G."; p. 9, Contents; p. 11, List of Illustrations; p. 13–15, Foreword; p. [8, 10, 12, 16] blank; p. 17–216, Text; p. 217–231, Notes; p. [232] blank; p. 233–234, Bibliography; p. 235–258. Index.) 4 plates, 3 ports. (including front.)

Issued in light green cloth; back: rules, title, author, publisher and rules in gilt.

1939–5700 edition: as above, with seal 3b. Verso of title-page: "Reprinted 1939."

The Game of Doeg

The Game of Doeg | A Story of the | Hebrew People | By | Eleanor E. Harris | With illustrations by Alfred Feinberg | [*seal 2a*] | Philadelphia | The Jewish Publication Society of America | 1914 |

[Note: The foregoing appears within an ornamental box surrounded by a single rule box all in red. Title and imprint within single rule boxes and initial letters of title, author and publisher all in red.]

COLLATION: sq. 12°. 189 p. (p. [1] Half-title; p. [3] Title; p. [4] Copyright; p. 5, Contents; p. 7, List of Illustrations; p. [2, 6, 8] blank; p. 9–189, Text.) 5 illus. (including front.)

Issued in light blue cloth; front cover: title, rule, author, decoration within single rule box; back: decorations, title, rule, author, decorations, illustrated, publisher all in black.

CONTENTS: I. An unexpected guest. — II. The little one. III. A friend at court. IV. The minstrel. V. The game of Doeg. VI. A champion. VII. A jealous king. VIII. A broken pledge. IX. The school of the prophets. X. The sword of Goliath. XI. A partridge in the mountains. XII. The witch of Endor. XIII. The battle of Mount Gilboa.

The American Jewish Year Book
5675

The American Jewish | Year Book | 5675 | September 21, 1914, to September 8, 1915 | Edited by | Herman Bernstein | for the | American Jewish Committee | [*seal 2a*] | Philadelphia | The Jewish Publication Society of America | 1914 |

COLLATION: 12°. viii, 581 p. (p. [iii] Title; p. [iv] Copyright; p. [v]–vii, Preface; p. [viii] Special articles in previous issues; 1 l. Contents; p. [1]–378, Text; p. 379–418, 7th annual report of the American Jewish Committee; p. [419]–577, Report of the 26th year of The Jewish Publication Society of America 1913–1914; p. 578–581, Advertisements.)

Bound uniformly with 5660 (1899–1900) without seal. On front cover: titles of special articles in white.

SPECIAL ARTICLES: The Beilis Affair, pp. 19–89. — Jewish education in the United States, pp. 90–127. — Memoir of the Bureau of Jewish Statistics of the American Jewish Committee, by Joseph Jacobs, pp. 339–378.

Josephus

JOSEPHUS | By | Norman Bentwich | Author of "Philo-Judaeus of Alexandria" | [*seal 2a*] | Philadelphia | The Jewish Publication Society of America | 1914 |

COLLATION: 12°. 266 p. (p. [1] Half-title; p. [3] Title; p. [4], Copyright; p. [5]–6, Preface; p. [7] Contents; p. [9] Illustrations; p. [2, 8, 10] blank; p. [11]–259, Text; p. [260] blank; p. [261]–263, Bibliography and Abbreviations; p. [264] blank; p. [265]–266, Index.) 3 plates (including front.).

Issued in dark green cloth; front cover: title, within double rule box; back: title, design, author, publisher all in gilt.

"Another volume to our growing Biographical Series [the fourth in the Jewish Worthies Series]." — *AJYB*, 5676, p. 400.

"It has been my especial aim in this book to consider Josephus from the Jewish point of view. I have made no attempt to extenuate his personal conduct or his literary faults. My judgment may appear somewhat severe, but it is when tried by the test of faithfulness to his nation that Josephus is found most wanting; and I hope that while extenuating nothing I have not set down aught in malice." — Author's preface, p. 5–6.

1926 edition: as above.

1940–5700 edition: as above, with seal 3b. Verso of title-page: "Reprinted, 1940."

1945: "1,000 copies reprinted."— *AJYB*, 5707, p. 649.

1915

In Those Days

IN THOSE DAYS | The Story Of An Old Man | By | Jehudah Steinberg | Translated from the Hebrew by | George Jeshurun | [*seal 2a*] | Philadelphia | The Jewish Publication Society of America | 1915 |

COLLATION: 12°. 199 p. (p. [1] Half-title; p. [2] blank; p. [3] Title; p. [4] Copyright; p. 5–196, Text; p. 197–199, Notes.)

Issued in light blue cloth; front cover: florets, title and author in gilt, all within ornamental border; back: title, rule, author and publisher in gilt.

"A translation of Jehuda Steinberg's 'Ba-Yamim Ha-hem,' describes the life of Russian Jews in the time of Nicholas I, when Jewish children were snatched away from their homes in order that they might grow up as Christian soldiers. Steinberg has succeeded in narrating a serious story without continually lamenting and weeping, and throughout he preserves artistic good taste and sanity." — *AJYB*, 5676, p. 400.

This translation is the result of a Prize Competition held by the Jewish Publication Society of America, in 1912, for the best translation of the first two chapters of Steinberg's "Ba-Yamim Ha-hem."

The Power of Purim

THE POWER OF PURIM | And Other Plays | A series of one act plays | designed for Jewish religious schools | By | Irma Kraft | [*seal 2a*] | Philadelphia | The Jewish Publication Society of America | 1915 |

COLLATION: 12°. 189 p. (p. [1] Half-title; p. [2] (Note)*; p. [3] Title; p. [4] Copyright; p. [5] Contents; p. [7] Note**; p. [6, 8] blank; p. [9]–189, Text.) illus.

Issued in red cloth; front cover: illustration in black; title and author; back: title, rule, author and publisher all in white.

Illustrations by A[lfred] F[einberg].

*"The drama is ever more potent than the printed page, and the mind of the child is never more fired with religious enthusiasm than when he himself seems to be taking part in the great drama of Judaism which has come down to us through the centuries."

**"The plays occupy from twenty to thirty minutes in presentation, and are designed for children from the ages of six to sixteen . . ."

CONTENTS: The power of Purim (Purim). — A Maccabean cure (Hanukkah). — To save his country (Pesah). — Ambition in White-chapel (Shabuot). — Because he loved David so (Closing of school).

1929 edition: as above.

The American Jewish Year Book
5676

The American Jewish | Year Book | 5676 | September 9, 1915, to September 27, 1916 | Edited by Joseph Jacobs | for the | American Jewish Committee | [*seal 2a*] | Philadelphia | The Jewish Publication Society of America | 1915 |

COLLATION: 12°. ix, 559 p. (p. [iii] Title; p. [iv] Copyright; p. [v]–vii, Preface; p. [viii] Special articles in previous issues; p. [ix] Contents; p. [1]–355, Text; p. 356–393, 8th annual report of the American Jewish Committee; p. [394] blank; p. [395]–556, Report of the 27th year of The Jewish Publication Society of America 1914–1915; p. 557–559, Advertisements.) map.

Bound uniformly with 5660 (1899–1900) without seal. On front cover: title of special article in white.

"One result of the war will undoubtedly be to settle the fate of Palestine for a long time to come, and it seems therefore appropriate to devote the chief article of the present issue of the American Jewish Year Book to an account of the recent progress in Palestine as it has affected the Jewish inhabitants of the Holy Land. It has been written by Miss Henrietta Szold, and gives for the first time in English, at such length, an account of the upbuilding of the Jewish population of Palestine within recent years. Quite apart from its bearing upon future problems, the position of the Jews in the land of their fathers has an intrinsic interest of its own to every Jew, which Miss Szold's article cannot fail to satisfy." — Preface, p. vi.

SPECIAL ARTICLES: Recent Jewish progress in Palestine, by Henrietta Szold, pp. 25–158. — The Federation movement in American Jewish philanthropy, by Joseph Jacobs, p. 159–198.

112

The Jews among the Greeks and Romans

THE JEWS AMONG THE | GREEKS AND ROMANS | By | Max Radin |
[*seal 2a*] | Philadelphia | The Jewish Publication Society of
America | 1915 |

COLLATION: 8°. 421 p. (p. [1] Half-title; p. [3] Title; p. [4]
Copyright, 1916; p. [5] Dedication*; p. [7]–8, Preface; p. [9]
Contents; p. [11] Illustrations; p. [2, 6, 10, 12] blank; p. [13]–20,
Introduction; p. [21]–371, Text; p. [373]–413, Notes; p. [415]
Bibliography; p. [372, 414, 416] blank; p. [417]–421, Index.) 7 plates
(including front.).

Issued in light green cloth; back: rules, title, author, publisher
and rules in gilt.

*"Matri meae | pietatis ergo | hoc opusculum | D. D. D. | "

"Dr. Radin went to first sources for his information, and, writing
in a style that has been commented upon favorably, he traced the
various phases of Jewish life and thought in the classical world." —
AJYB, 5677, p. 416.

1916

History of the Jews in Russia and Poland

HISTORY OF THE JEWS | IN RUSSIA AND POLAND | From the
earliest times | until the present day | By | S. M. Dubnow |
Translated from the Russian | by | I. Friedlaender | Volume I |
From the beginning until the death of Alexander I | (1825) |
[*seal 2a*] | Philadelphia | The Jewish Publication Society of
America | 1916 |

COLLATION: 12°. 1 p. l., 413 p. (l. 1, Half-title, verso blank;
p. [1] Title; p. [2] Copyright; p. [3]–7, Translator's Preface; p.
[9]–11, Contents; p. [8, 12] blank; p. [13]–413, Text.)

Issued in black cloth; back: rule, title, rule, author, volume, publisher and rule in gilt.

Published in three volumes: v. 1, 1916; v. 2, 1918; v. 3, 1920.

"The translation is based upon a work in Russian which was especially prepared by Mr. Dubnow for The Jewish Publication Society of America ... The present publication may thus properly claim to give the first comprehensive and systematic account of the history of Russo-Polish Jewry." — Translator's preface, p. [3]–4.

5706–1946 edition: as above, with seal 3b. Verso of title-page: "Reprinted — 1946." Only vols. 1 and 2 reprinted.

The American Jewish Year Book
5677

The American Jewish | Year Book | 5677 | September 28, 1916, to September 16, 1917 | Edited by Cyrus Adler | for the | American Jewish Committee | [*seal 2a*] | Philadelphia | The Jewish Publication Society of America | 1916 |

COLLATION: 12°. ix, 599 p. (p. [iii] Title; p. [iv] Copyright; p. [v]–vii, Preface; p. [viii] Special articles in previous issues; p. [ix] Contents; p. [1]–287, Text; p. 288–410, 9th annual report of the American Jewish Committee; p. [411]–592, Report of the 28th year of The Jewish Publication Society of America 1915–1916; p. 593–599, Advertisements.) ports.

Bound uniformly with 5660 (1899–1900) without seal.

"The present issue of the American Jewish Year Book appears under untoward circumstances. Doctor Joseph Jacobs, who had undertaken its editorship, passed away on January 31, 1916, before any of his plans for the volume matured. As his own lamented demise, and that of Doctor Schechter a few months previously, removed from the Jewry of the world two of its greatest ornaments, the

Publication Committee of The Jewish Publication Society of America deemed it appropriate to publish biographies of these two distinguished men as the special articles of the volume.

". . . It seemed timely to print the estimate, though incomplete, of the number of Jews in the army and navy of the United States. This article, prepared by Lewis Landes, shows that there are 3741 Jews in the army and 844 in the navy, a total of 4585 Jewish officers and men, serving in the very modest regular military organization of our country." — Preface, p. [v].

SPECIAL ARTICLES: Solomon Schechter, a biographical sketch, by Cyrus Adler, pp. 25–67. — Joseph Jacobs, by Mayer Sulzberger, pp. 68–75. — Jews in the United States Army and Navy, by Lewis Landes, pp. 76–79.

A History of Mediaeval Jewish Philosophy

A HISTORY OF | MEDIAEVAL JEWISH PHILOSOPHY | By | Isaac Husik, A.M., Ph.D. | Assistant Professor of Philosophy in the University of Pennsylvania | New York | The Macmillan Company | 1916 | All rights reserved |

COLLATION: 8°. 1 p. l., l, 462 p. (l. 1, Half-title; verso The Macmillan Company . . .; p. [i] Title; p. [ii] Copyright, 1916, by The Macmillan Company; p. [iii] [Note]*; p. [v] Dedication**; p. vii–ix, Preface; p. xi, Table of Contents; p. [iv, vi, x, xii] blank; p. xiii–l, Introduction; 1 l. and p. 1–432, Text; p. 433–437, Bibliography; p. [438] blank; p. 439–448, Notes; p. 449, List of biblical and rabbinic quotations; p. [450] blank; p. 451–462, Index.)

Issued in brown cloth; back: title, author and publisher in gilt.

*"This book is issued by the Macmillan Company in conjunction with the Jewish Publication Society of America."

**"To | Solomon Solis Cohen, M.D. | as a token | of | gratitude and esteem | ."

115

"The Society considers it one of its legitimate functions to aid the publication of works by other agencies which for one reason or another it cannot undertake itself." — *AJYB*, 5677, p. 418.

"This is the first complete history of mediaeval Jewish rationalistic philosophy written in any modern tongue. Dr. Husik has done his work well, and has expressed profound reflections upon abstruse problems in a style limpid, fluent, and readily understood. The Society is proud that an American Jewish scholar produced this book, that the Society was the first one to suggest the preparation of such a work, and that it shared in its publication." — *AJYB*, 5678, p. 507.

1930 edition: title-page reset. Verso of title-page: "... Reprinted March 1930." p. ix: "This new edition is a reprint of that of 1916, corrected, and with Bibliography brought up to date."

5706–1946 edition: title-page reset, with seal 3b and the JPSA imprint. l, 466 p. Verso of title-page: "... Copyright, 1940, by The Jewish Publication Society of America. First Impression 1916; Second Impression 1930; Third Impression 1941; Fourth Impression 1944; Fifth Impression 1946." p. ix: "Professor Husik planned to make a number of minor changes in this volume; but he died (on March 22, 1939) without having realized this intention. The Jewish Publication Society of America thereupon decided to reprint the volume without change, except for bringing the bibliography up to date. To this task Professor Harry A. Wolfson of Harvard University lent his invaluable aid, and the Publication Committee herewith expresses to him its profound thanks. *December 1, 1941.*"

1948: "2,000 copies reprinted." — *JPSA* [61st annual report] 1948, p. 3.

1917

The Holy Scriptures

תורה נביאים וכתובים | THE HOLY SCRIPTURES | According to the Masoretic Text | A New Translation | with the aid of previous versions and with | constant consultation of Jewish authorities | Philadelphia | The Jewish Publication Society of America | 5677–1917 |

COLLATION: 12°. xvi, 1136 p. (p. [i] Title; p. [ii] Copyright, All rights reserved, The Lakeside Press, Chicago; p. iii–xii, Preface; p. xiii–xv, Table of Scriptural Readings; p. xvi, The order of the Books; p. [1]–1136, Text.)

Issued in black cloth; all edges red; front cover: title, blind stamped; back: rules, title, rules, publisher all in gilt.

A translation prepared by a Board of Editors, of which Max L. Margolis was editor-in-chief. — Cf. Preface, p. vi.

"The present translation is the first for which a group of men representative of Jewish learning among English-speaking Jews assume joint responsibility, all previous efforts in the English language having been the work of individual translators. It has a character of its own. It aims to combine the spirit of Jewish tradition with the results of biblical scholarship, ancient, mediaeval, and modern. It gives to the Jewish world a translation of the Scriptures done by men imbued with the Jewish consciousness, while the non-Jewish world, it is hoped, will welcome a translation that presents many passages from the Jewish traditional point of view. ... The sections of the Pentateuch as traditionally read on the Sabbath are indicated, and a table gives all Scriptural readings, both on the Sabbath and on feast days and fast days." — Preface, pp. vii, xi.

Reprints: Fourth Impression, 1922; Seventh Impression, August 1927; Ninth Impression, September 1931, all of which have 1917 imprint on the title-page.

5708–1948 edition. Verso of title-page: "Twenty-Second Impression March 1948, 415th thousand."

1950: "Reprinted, in a twenty-fourth impression, 19,700 copies ... making a total of 455,000 copies." — AJYB, 1952, p. 574.

Reprints: February 28, 1951 — 10,600 copies; September 6, 1951 — 11,250 copies; February 1, 1952 — 24,600 copies; October 1, 1952 — 6,400 copies. Information from Lesser Zussman, Executive Secretary, January, 1953.

117

An edition was also made available in 1931 as a "Bridal Bible."
21st printing see *AJYB*, 5709, p. 850.

The Holy Scriptures

תורה נביאים וכתובים | THE HOLY SCRIPTURES | According to
the Masoretic Text | A New Translation | With the aid of
previous versions and with | constant consultation of Jewish
authorities | Philadelphia | The Jewish Publication Society of
America | 5677–1917 |

COLLATION: 24°. xvi, 1136 p.

Issued in black grain leather, all edges red and gilt; front cover:
emblem of the Freemasons; back: title, publisher all in gilt.

Facsimile reproduction of *The Holy Scriptures*, 1917, Seventh
Impression, August, 1927.

Songs of a Wanderer

SONGS OF A WANDERER | By | Philip M. Raskin | [*seal 2a*] |
Philadelphia | The Jewish Publication Society of America |
1917 |

COLLATION: 16°. 234 p. (p. [1] Half-title; p. [3] Title; p. [4]
Copyright; p. [5] Dedication*; p. [2, 6] blank; p. [7]–10, Contents;
p. [11]–234, Text.)

Issued in gray cloth; front and back covers: title, design, author,
decoration and vertical lines in green; back: title, design, author,
decoration and publisher in gilt.

*"To | Louis D. Brandeis | As a mark of admiration and
respect | ."

"A volume of poems, many of which possess a delicate charm
and express simply and sincerely Jewish feelings with distinct Jewish
sentiments of pathos and despair." — *AJYB*, 5678, p. 508.

Abridged Prayer Book for Jews in the Army and Navy of the United States

Abridged | Prayer Book | for | Jews in the Army and Navy | of the | United States | Philadelphia | The Jewish Publication Society of America | 5678–1917 |

COLLATION: 24°. 3 p. l., 85 p. (l. 1, Title, verso Copyright; l. 2, Preface; l. 3, Contents, verso blank; p. [1]–80 (paged in duplicate), Hebrew and English text (on opposite pages); p. 81–84, Prayer for the government, America, The Star-Spangled Banner, Hail! Columbia; p. 85, Calendar for 5678 (1917)–5680 (1920).)

Issued in tan cloth; rounded edges; front cover: title in black.

"In April, 1917, the Central Conference of American Rabbis, the Union of American Hebrew Congregations, the Union of Orthodox Jewish Congregations, the Council of Young Men's Hebrew and Kindred Associations, the Jewish Publication Society of America, the Agudath ha-Rabbonim, and the United Synagogue of America joined in forming a Board to minister to the religious welfare of Jews in the Army and Navy of the United States. The Jewish Publication Society of America offered to publish an abridged Prayer Book for these men if an agreement as to the text could be reached . . . . The present volume has been prepared under their direction." — Preface.

This Prayer Book has been reprinted again and again as the need for it arose, especially during World Wars I and II. Obviously the calendar at the end underwent revision in order to render it up-to-date as far as practical needs necessitated it. It was distributed by the National Jewish Welfare Board.

The Story of Bible Translations

THE STORY OF | BIBLE TRANSLATIONS | By | Max L. Margolis | [*seal 2a*] | Philadelphia | The Jewish Publication Society of America | 1917 |

COLLATION: 1 p. l., 135 p. (l. 1, Half-title, verso blank; p. [1] Title; p. [2] Copyright; p. [3] Dedication*; p. [5] Contents; p. [7] Illustrations; p. [4, 6, 8] blank; p. [9]–129, Text; p. [130] blank; p. [131]–135, Index.) 8 facsim. (part double)

Issued in light blue cloth; front cover: seal 2a, blind stamped; back: decoration, title, author, decoration, publisher, decoration, all in gilt.

*"To | Philip N. and Carrie G. Aronson | in filial love | ."

"Dr. Margolis presents in popular style the story of Bible translations from the earliest times to our own, tells how these translations spread throughout the world, how some of them were epoch making, and how new movements of thought were born as a result." — *AJYB*, 5678, p. 511.

"Traces the history of the most important translations and the influence they exerted. He tells us how the translations spread throughout the world, how some were epoch making, and how new reforms of thought resulted from them. The author's mastery enabled him to treat the subject with authority and in a style at once attractive and popular. Following within a few weeks after the publication of the monumental new translation of the Bible, this volume served well to explain to Jew and non-Jew the importance of our version and the influence it would exert upon Jewish life in English-speaking countries." — *AJYB*, 5679, p. 414.

5708–1948 edition: as above, with seal 3b. Verso of title-page: "Reprinted 1943, 1948."

Report of the Jewish Publication Society
Past Present Future

Past | Present | Future | [Report of the Annual Meeting | of the | Jewish Publication Society of America | March 25, 1917] |

COLLATION: 8°. 23 p.

This report has been reset and republished in the *AJYB*, 5678, pp. 506–538.

The American Jewish Year Book
5678

The American Jewish | Year Book | 5678 | September 17, 1917, to September 6, 1918 | Edited by Samson D. Oppenheim | for the | American Jewish Commitee | [*seal 2a*] | Philadelphia | The Jewish Publication Society of America | 1917 |

COLLATION: 12°. x, 722 p. (p. [iii] Title; p. [iv] Copyright; p. [v]–vi, Preface; p. [vii]–viii, Special articles in previous issues; p. [ix]–x, Contents; p. [1]–433, Text; p. 434–500, 10th annual report of the American Jewish Committee; p. [501]–715, Report of the 29th year of The Jewish Publication Society of America 1916–1917; p. [716] blank; p. 717–722, Advertisements.) front. (port. of Moses Jacob Ezekiel)

Bound uniformly with 5660 (1899–1900) without seal.

"Due to the painstaking labor of Dr. Julius Greenstone, there is now contained in the Year Book for the first time a hundred-year calendar. It has also been felt by the editor that a complete list of the rabbis of the United States would be in the highest degree desirable; and accordingly every effort has been made to obtain the names and addresses of all rabbis." — Preface, p. vi.

SPECIAL ARTICLES: The Jews of Latin America, by Harry O. Sandberg, pp. 35–105. — Jewish rights at international congresses, by Max J. Kohler, pp. 106–160. — The new English translation of the Bible, pp. 161–193. — Jewish war relief work, pp. 194–226. — Moses Jacob Ezekiel, by Samson D. Oppenheim, pp. 227–232.

Jewish Calendar for One Hundred Years

JEWISH CALENDAR | for | ONE HUNDRED YEARS | 5585–5684 | 1824–1924 | [*rule*] The Jewish Publication Society of America | Philadelphia | [1917]

COLLATION: 12°. 2 l., 13 tables.

Issued in gray cloth; front cover: title in black.

Reprinted from *AJYB*, 5678, p. 24–34.

Jewish Rights at International Congresses

Jewish Rights at | International Congresses | by | Max J. Kohler | <Reprint from the American Jewish Year Book 5678 > | Philadelphia | The Jewish Publication Society of America | 1917 |

COLLATION: 12°. 55 p.

Cover-title.

The Breakfast of the Birds

The Breakfast of the Birds | And Other Stories | From the Hebrew of Judah Steinberg | By | Emily Solis-Cohen, Jr. | With four illustrations in colors | [*seal 2a*] | Philadelphia | The Jewish Publication Society of America | 1917 |

COLLATION: 4°. 175 p. (p. [1] Half-title; p. [3] Title; p. [4] Copyright; p. [5] (Translator's) dedication*; p. 7. Author's dedication**; p. 9–10, Foreword; p. 11, Contents; p. [2, 6, 8, 12] blank; p. 13–175, Text.) 4 colored plates (including front.).

Issued in brown cloth; colored illustration by Alfred Feinberg pasted on front cover; back: rules, title, rule, author, decoration, publisher, rules all in black.

*"To our yet living master | Solomon Schechter | I dedicate in reverence and love | the work he bade me do | ."

**"To three lovely flowerets: | Nahum, my son, my first-born, my pride; | Zionah, my daughter, my only, my treasure; | Malkah, darling daughter of my friend Isaac Edelman . . . | "

"A child was chosen to illustrate this book that the child point of view might find expression and the value of the book be enhanced for all readers. The artist is Edith Rudin." — Foreword, p. 10.

CONTENTS: The breakfast of the birds. — The face on the clouds. — The swallow. — Service. — The messengers of spring. —

The magic top. — Stay-at-homes and wanderers. — The holy dust. — The last farthing. — The spoiled holiday. — Two judges. — The friend in the sky. — The painter-lad and the princess. — Hemdan. — The eagle and the cat. — Simeon by-my-head. — Simple Joseph. — Gentlemen and churls.

"Some of these tales of Steinberg are mere bits of fancy, some delightful satires or pleasant allegories, but all of them possess a literary and ethical quality that makes them well worth rendering into any tongue." — *AJYB*, 5678, p. 513.

"These delightful tales of Steinberg are fanciful, allegorical, and some satirical, but all of them are possessed of literary quality well worth rendering into any tongue. The make-up of the book as to format and type, particularly the four charming illustrations in color, prepared especially for the book by a girl fourteen years of age, and the attractive cover design, make this volume as fine a juvenile as could be desired." — *AJYB*, 5679, p. 415.

1936 edition: as above, with seal 3a. Verso of title-page: Third Edition, 1936."

1941: "1,400 copies reprinted."— *AJYB*, 5703, p. 508.

1944: "3,000 copies — 4th printing" — *AJYB*, 5706, p. 741. Changed cover in 1944.

5707–1947 edition: same as 1936. Verso of title-page: "Fifth Impression — 1947." "5,000 copies."— *AJYB*, 5709, p. 850.

The New English Translation of the Bible

The New English Translation | of the Bible | [*seal 2a*] Philadelphia | The Jewish Publication Society of America | 1917 |

Collation: 12°. 33 p.

This represents a considerably revised reprint of a contribution by Max L. Margolis to the *AJYB*, 5678, pp. 161–193.

1918

Readings from the Holy Scriptures for Jewish Soldiers and Sailors

Readings from the | HOLY SCRIPTURES | for | Jewish Soldiers and Sailors | [*seal 2b*] | Prepared and issued for | The Jewish Welfare Board | United States Army and Navy | The Jewish Publication Society of America | Philadelphia | 5678–1918 |

COLLATION: 24°. iv, 276 p. (p. [i] Title; p. [ii] Copyright; p. iii–iv, Contents; p. 1–276, Text.)

Issued in tan cloth, rounded edges; front cover: title in black.

These Readings have been reprinted again and again as the need for them arose, especially during World Wars I and II.

History of the Jews in Russia and Poland

HISTORY OF THE JEWS | IN RUSSIA AND POLAND | From the earliest times | until the present day | By | S. M. Dubnow | Translated from the Russian | by | I. Friedlaender | Volume II | From the death of Alexander I. until the death of Alexander III. | (1825–1894) | [*seal 2a*] | Philadelphia | The Jewish Publication Society of America | 1918 |

COLLATION: 12°. 429 p. (p. [1] Half-title; p. [3] Title; p. [4] Copyright; p. [5]–7, Translator's Preface; p. [2, 8] blank; p. [9]–12, Contents; p. [13]–429, Text.)

See 1916, v. 1, for binding and reprints.

"The dates given in this volume are those of the Russian calendar, except for the cases in which the facts relate to happenings outside of Russia." — Translator's preface, p. 7.

"The want of a work of this kind has long been keenly felt by those interested in Jewish life. Dubnow's power of grasping and presenting the broad aspects of general Jewish history and his life-long, painstaking labors in the particular field of Russian-Jewish history fit him in a singular measure to cope with this task.

"Dubnow's work limits itself to the history of the Jewish population in the Russian empire and it throws a lurid light on conditions in that country in pre-revolutionary times. The attitude of a country towards its Jewish citizens may be said to serve as the barometer of its civilization. Those who are amazed by the collapse of the colossal empire of the Czar will find an answer in Dubnow's account of the incessant barbarities inflicted by them upon their Jewish subjects." — *AJYB*, 5680, p. 693.

The American Jewish Year Book
5679

The American Jewish | Year Book | 5679 | September 7, 1918, to September 24, 1919 | Edited by | Samson D. Oppenheim | for the | American Jewish Committee | [*seal 2a*] | Philadelphia | The Jewish Publication Society of America | 1918 |

COLLATION: 12°. x, 613 p. (p. [iii] Title; p. [iv] Copyright; p. [v]–vi, Preface; p. [vii]–viii, Special articles in previous issues; p. [ix]–x, Contents; p. [1]–361, Text; p. 362–407, 11th annual report of the American Jewish Committee; p. [408] blank; p. [409]–609, [Report of the 30th year of] The Jewish Publication Society of America [1917–1918]; p. 610–613, Advertisements.)

Bound uniformly with 5660 (1899–1900) without seal.

"This volume contains an admirable survey of the inner life of the Jews of Serbia from the pen of Dr. I. Alcalay, chief rabbi of Serbia, and a brief but illuminating account of the formation of the New York City Federation for the Support of Jewish Philanthropic Societies, written by I. Edwin Goldwasser. As this is the twentieth volume of the American Jewish Year Book, it was deemed advisable to print an Index to the articles hitherto published in the Year Books. This Index was compiled by Miss Minnie Baum." — Preface, p. vi.

SPECIAL ARTICLES: The Jewish population of the United States, by Samson D. Oppenheim, pp. 31–74. — The Jews of Serbia, by I. Alcalay, pp. 75–87. — The Jewish Welfare Board, by Chester Jacob Teller, pp. 88–102. — The collection of Jewish war statistics, by Julian Leavitt, pp. 103–112. — Federation for the Support of Jewish Philanthropic Societies of New York City, by I. Edwin Goldwasser, pp. 113–146. — Index to articles in first twenty volumes, pp. 353–361.

The Jewish Publication Society of America
What it is

The | Jewish Publication | Society of America | [*two rules*] | What it is | and | What it has done | [*two rules*] | "Formed for the publication | and dissemination of literary, scien- | tific and religious works, giving | instruction in the principles of the | Jewish religion and in Jewish his- | tory and literature." | — *From the Charter.* | [*two rules*] | Executive Office | Broad Street and Girard Avenue | Philadelphia | [*seal 2a*] | [1918]

[Note: The foregoing appears within a black single rule box. Rules and seal in orange.]

COLLATION: 8°. 12 l., including ports.

Cover-title. Verso of title: list of officers; back cover: illustration of Society's headquarters.

1919
Jewish Contributions to Civilization

JEWISH CONTRIBUTIONS | TO CIVILIZATION | An Estimate | By | Joseph Jacobs | [*seal 2a*] | Philadelphia | The Jewish Publication Society of America | 1919 |

COLLATION: 12°. 2 p. l., 3–334 p. (l. 1, Half-title, verso blank; l. 2, Title, verso Copyright; p. 3–6, Prefatory Statement; p. 7, Contents; p. [8] blank; p. 9–323, Text; p. [324] blank; p. 325–334, Index.)

Issued in dark blue cloth; back: rules, title, rule, author, rule, publisher and rule all in gilt.

". . . Studies which appeared in the *Journal of the Anthropological Institute* and were afterwards republished as *Studies in Jewish Statistics*, 1891." — Preface, p. 3.

"It is a justification and explanation of the Jew's position in history, and is an answer to the insidious assumption of the higher anti-Semites of modern times." — *AJYB*, 5679, p. 416.

"Without being apologetic, Dr. Jacobs has pointed out the share of the Jews in the world's progress, and puts forth his claims substantiated by facts." — *AJYB*, 5680, p. 694.

Trade edition: with seal 2a. Imprint reads: The Conat Press | Philadelphia | . On verso of t.-p.: "Copyright, 1919." Another edition, with "1920" on t.-p.

1944: "1,000 copies reprinted."— *AJYB*, 5706, p. 741.

5706–1945 edition: as above, with seal 3c. Verso of title-page: "Reprinted, 1945."

The Holy Scriptures

תורה נביאים וכתובים | THE HOLY SCRIPTURES | According to the Masoretic Text | A New Translation | with the aid of previous versions | and with constant consultation | of Jewish authorities | [*ornament*] | Philadelphia | The Jewish Publication Society of America | 5679–1919 |

COLLATION: f°. xvi, 1136 p., 4 l. (p. [i] Title; p. [ii] Copyright, 1917, All rights reserved; p. iii–xii, Preface; p. xiii–xv, Table of Scriptural Readings; p. xvi, The order of the Books; p. [1]–1136, Text; 4 l. for records of The Family Register, Births, Marriages, Deaths.)

Issued in black seal grain leather; all edges red and gilted; front and back covers: tooled border; back: rule, title, rule, in gilt.

The Pulpit and Family Bible.

"This is probably the finest specimen of book-making found in any Bible issued in America. It is hoped that no synagogue pulpit, no Sabbath-School platform, no lodge-rostrum, and no family which treasures the old tradition of recording family events in their Family Bible will be without it." — *AJYB*, 5681, p. 471.

Under the Sabbath Lamp

UNDER THE SABBATH | LAMP | Stories of our time | for old and young | By | Abram S. Isaacs | [*seal 2a*] | Philadelphia | The Jewish Publication Society of America | 1919 |

COLLATION: 12°. 259 p. (p. [1] Half-title; p. [3] Title; p. [4] Copyright; p. [5] Dedication*; p. 7-8, Preface; p. 9, Contents; p. [2, 6, 10] blank; p. 11-259, Text.)

Issued in gray cloth; front cover: Sabbath lamp, title, author; back: title, author, publisher all in black.

*"To | Father and Mother | in grateful memory of happy years | under their Sabbath Lamp | reverently dedicated | ."

CONTENTS: Introduction. — The old Shofar. — Born again. — Before dawn. — The trendelé. — The children's gift. — The happy family. — A voice for freedom. — From land to land. — A rabbi's wife. — How the debt was paid. — Only a child. — The rabbi's romance. — Just from Jerusalem. — The children's revolt. — At grandmother's school.

"This volume contains sixteen short stories depicting idyllic aspects in simple, charming language, will prove of interest to young and old. Each tale may be said to be an echo of the not distant past." — *AJYB*, 5680, p. 694.

"A collection of stories intended to provide entertaining reading to the average Jewish household. In these stories, associated chiefly with the atmosphere of the Sabbath lamp, and written in the guise of fiction, the author has managed to discuss problems of Jewish religious and spiritual interest with an eagerness and light-heartedness of joyous children." — *AJYB*, 5681, p. 468.

The American Jewish Year Book
5680

The American Jewish | Year Book | 5680 | September 25, 1919, to September 12, 1920 | Volume 21 | Edited by | Harry Schneiderman | for the | American Jewish Committee |[*seal 2a*] | Philadelphia | The Jewish Publication Society of America | 1919 |

COLLATION: 12°. xii, 894 p. (p. [iii] Title; p. [iv] Copyright; p. [v]–vii, Preface; p. [viii]–x, Special articles in previous issues; p. [xi]–xii, Contents; p. [1]–617, Text; p. 618–684, 12th annual report of the American Jewish Committee; p. [685]–890, Report of the 31st year of The Jewish Publication Society of America 1918–1919; p. 891–894, Advertisements.)

Bound uniformly with 5660 (1899–1900) without seal.

"The volume contains a new Directory of Local Jewish Organizations in the United States, which supersedes the Directory published in The American Jewish Year Book 5668." — Preface, p. vi.

SPECIAL ARTICLES: The participation of the Jews of France in the Great War, by Sylvain Halff, pp. 31–97. — The story of British Jewry in the War, by Michael Adler, pp. 98–119. — The Jewish battalions and the Palestine campaign, by Joshua H. Neumann, pp. 120–140. — American Jews in the World War, by Julian Leavitt, pp. 141–155.

Hellenism

... | HELLENISM | By | Norman Bentwich | Author of "Philo-Judaeus of Alexandria," etc. | [*seal 2a*] | Philadelphia | The Jewish Publication Society of America | 1919 |

At head of title: Movements in Judaism | [*rule*] | .

COLLATION: 8°. 386 p. (p. [1] blank; p. [2] Movements in Judaism . . .; p. [3] Half-title; p. [5] Title; p. [6] Copyright, 1920; p. [7] Dedication*; p. 9, Contents; p. 11–14, Preface; p. [4, 8, 10] blank; p. 15–359, Text; p. [360] blank; p. 361–375, Notes; p. [376] blank; p. 377–379, Bibliography; p. [380] blank; p. 381–386, Index.)

Issued in light green cloth; back: rules, title, author, publisher and rules in gilt.

*"To my wife | Helen | who represents for me the perfect union of | Hebraism and Hellenism | in love | 'I remember for thee the kindness of | thy youth, the love of thine espousals; | how thou wentest after me in the wilderness, | in a land that was not sown.' | ."

"The title of this book should be rather Hellenisticism — if one might coin the word — than Hellenism, since it is concerned not with all the culture which produced the brilliant civilization of classical Hellas, but with its debasement which was spread over the world during the three centuries immediately preceding the Christian era." — Preface, p. 11.

"This book deals with one of the most fascinating phases of Jewish history. The author has skilfully handled the difficult material, and has presented an excellent sketch of Jewish life and activity during the two centuries that preceded the destruction of the Temple and the subsequent periods." — *AJYB*, 5680, p. 694.

"Mr. Bentwich treats of an important and fascinating period in Jewish history, which not only affected the Jewish people in Palestine and in the diaspora, but determined to a considerable degree the future development of the religious history not alone of the Jews, but of the world generally." — *AJYB*, 5681, p. 469.

5703–1943 edition: title-page reset, with seal 3b. Verso of title-page: "Reprinted, 1943."

130

1920

By-Paths in Hebraic Bookland

BY-PATHS | IN HEBRAIC BOOKLAND | By | Israel Abrahams,
D.D., M.A., | Author of "Jewish Life in the Middle Ages,"
"Chapters on Jewish Literature," etc. | [*seal 2a*] | Philadelphia |
The Jewish Publication Society of America | 1920 |

COLLATION: 8°. 371 p. (p. [1] Half-title; p. [2] blank; p. [3]
Title; p. [4] Copyright; p. 5–10, Preface; p. 11–13, Contents; p. 14,
Illustrations; p. [15]–364, Text; p. 365–371, Index.) 6 ports., facsim.

Issued in dark blue cloth; back: rules, title, author, publisher
and rules in gilt.

Originally written in 1913 for serial publication and considerably revised for this volume. — Cf. Preface p. 5.

CONTENTS: Part I: The story of Ahikar. — Philo on the "Con-
templative Life." — Josephus against Apion. — Caecilius on the
sublime. — The phoenix of Ezekielos. — The letter of Sherira. —
Nathan of Rome's dictionary. — The sorrows of Tatnu. — Part II:
Ibn Gebirol's "Royal Crown." — Bar Hisdai's "Prince and Der-
vish." — The Sarajevo Haggadah. — A piyyut by Bar Abun. —
Isaac's lamp and Jacob's well. — "Letters of Obscure Men." —
De Rossi's "Light of the Eyes." — Guarini and Luzzatto. — Hahn's
note book. — Leon Modena's "Rites." — Part III: Menasseh and
Rembrandt. — Lancelot Addison on the Barbary Jews. — The
Bodenschatz pictures. — Lessing's first Jewish play. — Isaac Pinto's
prayer-book. — Mendelssohn's "Jerusalem." — Herder's anthology.
— Walker's "Theodore Cyphon." — Horace Smith of the "Re-
jected Addresses." — Part IV: Byron's "Hebrew Melodies." —
Coleridge's "Table Talk." — Blanco White's sonnet. — Disraeli's
"Alroy." — Robert Grant's "Sacred Poems." — Gutzkow's "Uriel
Acosta." — Grace Aguilar's "Spirit of Judaism." — Isaac Leeser's
Bible. — Landor's "Alfieri and Salomon." — Part V: Browning's
"Ben Karshook." — K. E. Franzos' "Jews of Barnow." — Herz-

berg's "Family Papers." — Longfellow's "Judas Maccabaeus." — Artoms's sermons. — Salkinson's "Othello." — "Life Thoughts" of Michael Henry. — The poems of Emma Lazarus. — Conder's "Tent work in Palestine." — Kalisch's "Path and Goal." — Franz Delitzsch's "Iris.". — "The Pronaos" of I. M. Wise. — A Baedeker litany. — Imber's song.

"This book is written in the usual charming style of that distinguished Jewish savant. The volume touches upon some very interesting items of Jewish literature which are usually neglected, but Dr. Abrahams brilliantly points out their charm and quaintness . . . The attractiveness of the volume is increased by illustrations of Rembrandt's etching of Menasseh ben Israel, portraits of Isaac Leeser, Emma Lazarus, Grace Aguilar, Isaac M. Wise, and Naphtalie Hertz Imber." — *AJYB*, 5681, p. 469.

5703–1943 edition: title-page reset, with seal 3b. Verso of title-page: "Reprinted, 1943."

The Jewish Classics Series

THE | JEWISH CLASSICS | SERIES | General Statement and in- | structions to contributors | The Jewish Publication Society of America | Philadelphia | 1920 |

[Note: The foregoing appears within a black single rule box.]

COLLATION: 16°. 24 p.

Issued in blue paper covers: title as above.

Playmates in Egypt

PLAYMATES | IN EGYPT | And Other Stories | By | Elma Ehrlich Levinger | [*seal 2a*] | Philadelphia | The Jewish Publication Society of America | 1920 |

COLLATION: 12°. 130 p. (p. [1] Half-title; p. 3, Title; p. [4] Copyright; p. 5, Dedication*; p. 7–10, Preface; p. 11, Contents; p. [2, 6, 12] blank; p. 13–130, Text.)

132

Issued in light green cloth; front cover: illustration, title, rule, author; back: title, author all in white.

*"To Dr. S. Benderly | friend and teacher | I dedicate this little | volume of stories | with admiration and | gratitude | ."

CONTENTS: Playmates in Egypt (Passover). — In the tents of Israel (Sukkot.) — The dawn of freedom (Rosh ha-Shanah). — The borrowed garment (Yom Kippur). — The lad who brought no offering (Shabu'ot). — The silent harp (Tish'ah be-Ab). — The sprig of myrtle (Purim). — Friends (Hanukkah). — The great hope (Sabbath of Consolation). — The golden ring (Lag be-'Omer).

"A number of short stories, each one dealing with some phase of Jewish history and centering around some Jewish occasion or festival." — *AJYB*, 5682, p. 392.

5706–1946 edition: title-page reset, with seal 3b. Verso of title-page: "Reprinted 1940, Reprinted 1946."

Address of Simon Miller

Address of | SIMON MILLER, Esq. | President of | The Jewish Publication Society | At Annual Meeting | Sunday, March 21, 1920 | at Philadelphia |

COLLATION: 8°. 4 l.

Cover-title.

This address has been reset and published in the *AJYB*, 5681, pp. 464–473.

The American Jewish Year Book
5681

The American Jewish | Year Book | 5681 | September 13, 1920, to October 2, 1921 | Volume 22 | Edited by | Harry Schneiderman | for the | American Jewish Committee | [*seal 2a*] | Philadelphia | The Jewish Publication Society of America | 1920 |

COLLATION: 12°. x, 504 p. (p. [i] Title; p. [ii] Copyright; p. [iii]–v, Preface; p. [vi]–viii, Special articles in previous issues; p. [ix]–x, Contents; p. [1]–393, Text; p. [394]–458, 13th annual report of the American Jewish Committee; p. [459]–498, Report of the 32nd year of The Jewish Publication Society of America 1919–1920; p. 499–504, Advertisements.)

Bound uniformly with 5660 (1899–1900) without seal.

SPECIAL ARTICLES: Jewish social research in United States, by Hyman Kaplan, pp. 31–52. — The Jews of Alsace-Lorraine (1870–1920), by Sylvain Halff, pp. 53–79. — The Falashas, by Jacques Faitlovitch, pp. 80–100. — The Peace Conference and Rights of Minorities, pp. 101–130. — Professional tendencies among Jewish students in colleges, universities, and professional schools, pp. 383–393.

Announcement of a Popular Commentary

ANNOUNCEMENT OF A | POPULAR COMMENTARY | on the Holy Scriptures | and suggestions to | contributors | Philadelphia | 1920 |

At head of title: Jewish Publication Society | of America | .

[Note: The foregoing appears within a black double rule box.]

COLLATION: nar. 24°. 22 p.

Issued in light blue paper covers; front cover: title as above; back cover: seal 2a.

History of the Jews in Russia and Poland

HISTORY OF THE JEWS | IN RUSSIA AND POLAND | From the earliest times | until the present day | By | S. M. Dubnow | Translated from the Russian | by | I. Friedlaender | Volume III | From the accession of Nicholas II. | until the present day |

with bibliography and index | [*seal 2a*] | Philadelphia | The Jewish Publication Society of America | 1920 |

COLLATION: 12°. 1 p. l., 411 p. (l. 1, Half-title, verso blank; p. [1] Title; p. [2] Copyright; p. [3] Note*; p. [4] blank; p. [5]–6, Contents; p. [7]–169, Text; p. [171]–203, Bibliography; p. [170, 204] blank; p. [205]–411, Index.)

See 1916, v. 1, for binding.

*"The present volume . . . [which deals with the reign of Nicholas II., the last of the Romanovs] contains, in addition to the text, an extensive bibliography and an index to the entire work."

Rosh Ha-Shanah and Yom Kippur

. . . | ROSH HA-SHANAH | and | YOM KIPPUR | The Jewish Publication Society of America | Philadelphia | 1920 |

At head of title: Little Studies | in Judaism | 1 | .

Title from cover.

COLLATION: 24°. 16 p. (front cover: title, verso Copyright, The Lord Baltimore Press; back cover: Note*, verso Note**.)

Issued in light blue paper covers.

*"In addition to its regular publications the Jewish Publication Society of America proposes to issue from time to time 'Little Studies in Judaism,' which it is hoped will spread the knowledge of Jewish belief and practice and deepen Jewish conviction."

**"The Jewish Publication Society of America is devoted to 'the publication and dissemination of literary, scientific and religious works, giving instruction in the principles of the Jewish religion and in Jewish history and literature' . . ."

Written by Samuel Schulman.

No more published.

1921

Post-Biblical Hebrew Literature

POST-BIBLICAL | HEBREW LITERATURE | An Anthology | ★
Texts, Notes, and Glossary | [and ★ ★ | English Translation] |
By | B. Halper, M.A., Ph.D. | Dropsie College, Philadelphia |
[*seal 2a*] | Philadelphia | The Jewish Publication Society of
America | 1921 |

COLLATION: 8°. 2 v. (v. 1, xviii, 300 p.: p. [i] Half-title; p. [ii]
blank; p. [iii] Title; p. [iv] Copyright*; p. v–xiv, Preface; p. xv–
xviii, Contents; 1 l., and p. [1]–202, Hebrew texts; p. [203]–270,
Notes; p. [271]–300, Glossary; v. 2, 251 p.: p. [1] Half-title; p. [2]
blank; p. [3] Title; p. [4] Copyright; p. 5–13, Preface; p. [14] blank;
p. 15–18, Contents; p. 19–251, English translations.)

Issued in dark blue cloth; back: rule, title, volume, editor,
publisher and rule in gilt.

‏*„מלאכת סדור האותיות נעשתה על ידי משה אלפירוביץ".‏

"In preparing the selections for this *Anthology* I have been guided
by two principles: the literary merit of the extract and its pedagogic
value. I have endeavored to incorporate what I considered the best
sections from the best works . . . The texts are arranged chronologically as far as possible . . . The glossary at the end of the volume
is confined to words and phrases not occurring in the Bible and to
biblical words invested with a new shade of meaning." — Author's
preface, v. 1.

"This volume of translations is a companion to the Hebrew
texts printed in a separate book . . . Wherever possible, I have
attempted to retain the flavor of the original, and the translation is
literal as far as the English idiom would allow." — Ibid., v. 2.

"The plan of the work is designed to familiarize students and
the general reader with the growth and development of post-Biblical
Hebrew literature. The extracts are arranged chronologically and are
prefaced by brief entries giving the salient facts of the authors and
their works. It is thus a history of Hebrew literature by examples.

The author of the work, Dr. B. Halper, who is also the Editor of the Society, has succeeded admirably in presenting the gems of post-biblical Hebrew literature, incorporating practically all its branches within the compass of 200 pages. Viewing the work in its entirety, it may be said that the extracts have been carefully selected, cleverly annotated and gracefully rendered into English. The English volume contains the translations, brief introductions and only such notes as are absolutely necessary for the study of the text." — *AJYB*, 5682, p. 394.

"A volume which, as an anthology of Jewish literary treasures, gives a glimpse into the vast storehouse of Hebrew literature from the conclusion of the biblical period down to recent times." — *AJYB*, 5683, p. 387.

Volume 1: 5707–1946 edition, title-page reset, with seal 3b. Verso of title-page: "Second Impression, 1946."

Volume 2: 5704–1943 edition, title-page reset, with seal 3b. Verso of title-page: "Second Impression, 1943." "2,000 copies reprinted." — *JPSA* [61st annual report] 1948, p. 3.

The American Jewish Year Book
5682

The American Jewish | Year Book | 5682 | October 3,1921, to September 22, 1922 | Volume 23 | Edited by | Harry Schneiderman | for the | American Jewish Committee | [*seal 2a*] | Philadelphia | The Jewish Publication Society of America | 1921 |

COLLATION: 12°. x, 423 p. (p. [i] Title; p. [ii] Copyright; p. [iii]–v, Preface; p. vi–viii, Special articles in previous issues; p. [ix]–x, Contents; p. [1]–299, Text; p. [300]–379, 14th annual report of the American Jewish Committee; p. [380] blank; p. [381]–423, Report of the 33rd year of The Jewish Publication Society of America 1920–1921.) front. (port. of Jacob Henry Schiff)

Bound uniformly with 5660 (1899–1900) without seal.

"The leading article in the present volume is a biographical sketch of the late Jacob H. Schiff . . . from the pen of Doctor Cyrus Adler, who was a close personal friend of Mr. Schiff and his enthusiastic co-worker in many an enterprise, especially those dealing with the promotion of Jewish education and learning." — Preface, p. [iii], iv.

SPECIAL ARTICLES: Jacob Henry Schiff, a biographical sketch, by Cyrus Adler, pp. 21–64. — Israel Friedlaender, a biographical sketch, by Jacob Kohn, pp. 65–79. — Abram S. Isaacs, by Lewis M. Isaacs, pp. 80–83. — Jewish Americanization agencies, by Charles S. Bernheimer, pp. 84–111.

Saadia Gaon His Life and Works

. . . | SAADIA GAON | His Life and Works | By | Henry Malter, Ph.D. | Professor of Rabbinical Literature at the Dropsie | College for Hebrew and Cognate learning | [*seal 2a*] | Philadelphia | The Jewish Publication Society of America | 1921 |

At head of title: The Morris Loeb Series | [*rule*] | .

COLLATION: 8°. 446 p. (p. [1] Half-title; p. [2] (Note)*; p. [3] Title; p. [4] Copyright; p. [5] [Quotation in Hebrew and English translation from] Saadia, *Sefer ha-Galui*; p. [7] Dedication**; p. 9–14, Preface; p. 15–20, Introduction; p. [21] Contents; p. [6, 8, 22] blank; p. [23]–446, Text.)

Issued in brown cloth; back: title, author and publisher in gilt.

*"Professor Morris Loeb, of New York, the distinguished chemist, scholar and public worker, who died on October 8, 1912, by his last Will and Testament, created a Fund under the following terms: 'I give and bequeath to the Jewish Publication Society of America the sum of Ten Thousand Dollars as a permanent fund, the income of which alone shall, from time to time, be utilized for and applied to the preparation and publication of a scholarly work devoted to the interests of Judaism.'

"The present volume is the first issued under this Fund."

**"To | Solomon Solis Cohen, M.D. | in token of | high esteem and sincere friendship | ."

138

CONTENTS: Part I. Life of Saadia Gaon. Part II. The works of Saadia Gaon. Part III. Bibliography. — Postscript. — Addenda. — List of Abbreviations. — Indices.

"Dr. Henry Malter's investigation into the life and literary activity of Saadia, have produced a book which, in the opinion of those qualified to judge, says the last word on the numerous moot questions connected with the great Gaon." — *AJYB*, 5677, p. 418.

"This book, one of considerable proportions, represents the first complete appreciation of the life and works of the greatest Babylonian scholar and head of an academy (during the first half of the tenth century), who is generally recognized as the father and founder of Jewish scientific research, as it developed during the Middle Ages down to our own time. Dr. Malter's book contains also a minute historical account of the amazing amount of intellectual work that has been done by Jews and Christians in editing and translating, describing and elucidating the numerous writings of this phenomenal Jewish scholar. This book forms the first of the scientific series issued under the Loeb foundation." — *AJYB*, 5682, p. 395.

"In interpreting for modern times the life and works of the greatest of the Gaonim, Professor Malter has brought to his task a love for his subject and a rare familiarity with all the literature on Saadia. Professor Malter has taken into account everything known that bears upon his topic, and he thus has succeeded in drawing not only a vivid picture of the man Saadia — the founder of Jewish science, the revivifier of Jewish faith and learning — but also in depicting the historical background and throwing new light upon an obscure period in Jewish history. While the chief value of the book is to students and teachers, its interest is not confined to these alone. As a contribution to the history of culture it appeals with special force to Jews who wish to become better acquainted with the life and times of the great Gaon." — *AJYB*, 5683, p. 388.

5702–1942 edition: as above, with seal 3b. Verso of title-page: "Second Impression — 1942."

1922

The Hebrew Scriptures in the Making

THE | HEBREW SCRIPTURES | IN THE MAKING | By | Max L. Margolis | [*seal 2a*] | Philadelphia | The Jewish Publication Society of America | 1922 |

COLLATION: 16°. 131 p. (p. [1] Half-title; p. [3] Title; p. [4] Copyright; p. [5] Dedication*; p. [7] Contents; p. [2, 6, 8] blank; p. [9–10] Chronological Table; p. [11]–126, Text; p. [127]–131, Index.)

Issued in blue-gray cloth; front cover: seal 2a, blind stamped; back: design, title, author, design, publisher all in gilt.

*"To the memory of | Israel Friedlaender | scholar teacher martyr | ."

"It gives a remarkable account of the problems connected with the Bible, traditional and untraditional. Needless to say that this subject treated by such a scholar as Professor Margolis may be regarded as authoritative and accurate. Though small in size, it is full of valuable information and will be welcomed by those who seek reliable information about the Bible." — *AJYB*, 5683, p. 388.

"It is . . . full of information, giving an admirable account of the problems connected with the Bible from a traditional and untraditional point of view." — *AJYB*, 5684, p. 436.

5708–1948 edition: as above, with seal 3b. Verso of title-page: "Reprinted 1943, 1948."

FRENCH TRANSLATION: La formation de la bible hébraique, trad. de M. Liber, Paris, 1953.

The American Jewish Year Book
5683

The American Jewish | Year Book | 5683 | September 23, 1922, to September 10, 1923 | Volume 24 | Edited by | Harry Schneiderman | for the | American Jewish Committee | [*seal*

2a] | Philadelphia | The Jewish Publication Society of America |
1922 |

COLLATION: 12°. ix, 570 p. (p. [i] Title; p. [ii] Copyright,
Printed by The Conat Press; p. [iii]–iv, Preface; p. [v]–vii, Special
articles in previous issues; p. [viii]–ix, Contents; p. [1]–322, Text;
p. [323]–376, 15th annual report of the American Jewish Committee;
p. [377]–570, Report of the 34th year of The Jewish Publication
Society of America 1922–1923.)

Bound uniformly with 5660 (1899–1900) without seal.

"The greater part of the contents of this, the twenty-fourth
volume of the American Jewish Year Book, was prepared in the office
of the Bureau of Jewish Social Research under the supervision of
Dr. H. S. Linfield.

"In addition to the usual Directories and Lists, two special
features are presented with these pages. The first is a Survey of the
Year 5682, prepared by Doctor Linfield. This is a substitute for the
Record of Events published in former volumes . . . . The other
special feature in this volume is a list of Jews in the United States
who are prominent in the various professions, in the arts, in science,
or in other walks in the public life of our country . . . compiled by
Mr. I. George Dobsevage." — Preface, p. [iii].

SPECIAL ARTICLE: Jews of prominence in the United States,
compiled by I. George Dobsevage, pp. 109–218.

1923

The Feet of the Messenger

The | Feet of the Messenger | By | Yehoash | <Solomon
Bloomgarden > | Translated from the Yiddish by | Isaac
Goldberg | [*seal 2a*] | Philadelphia | The Jewish Publication
Society of America | 1923 |

COLLATION: 12°. 296 p. (p. [1] Half-title; p. [3] Title; p. [4]
Copyright; p. [5] [Quotation from] Isaiah 52.7.; p. [2, 6] blank;
p. [7–8] Contents; p. [9]–296, Text.)

Issued in colored illustrated cloth; front cover: title in yellow, author in green, on blue; back: title, author within rule box in blue, on tan.

"Impressions of Jewish life in Palestine at the beginning of the World War. It is a description of the Holy Land as it appears to an eminent poet and keen observer. The original was published in Yiddish." — *AJYB*, 5683, p. 389.

"With a pleasant sense of humor the author described the various types of settlers of the Holy Land, as well as their surroundings and their relations with their Arab neighbors. The narrative reads smoothly and pleasantly and displays fine sensibilities. Since Robert Hichens wrote his colorful book on the Holy Land, it is doubtful whether such charming descriptions dealing with this subject have appeared in any language. The author has succeeded in introducing to the reader the real atmosphere of Palestine, particularly of Jewish Palestine. The quaint life and customs of the immigrant Jews are effectively and sympathetically portrayed.

"There is a good deal of Jewish folk-lore given in the pages of this volume. The entire book is written in a festive spirit which the author succeeds in communicating to the reader, who is spell-bound by the beauty of the atmosphere. A very pathetic picture is given at the end, portraying the chaos and uncertainty which filled the atmosphere at the beginning of the War. At first the old settlers felt that the work of a life-time had been destroyed, but gradually this wore off as conditions began to be more or less stabilized. A very complimentary account is given of the conduct of American sailors towards poor refugees who were transported to safety." — *AJYB*, 5684, p. 437–438.

The American Jewish Year Book
5684

The American Jewish | Year Book | 5684 | September 11, 1923, to September 28, 1924 | Volume 25 | Edited by | Harry Schneiderman | for the | American Jewish Committee | [*seal 2a*] | Philadelphia | The Jewish Publication Society of America | 1923 |

COLLATION: 12°. ix, 593 p. (p. [i] Title; p. [ii] Copyright; p. [iii]–iv, Preface; p. [v]–vii, Special articles in previous issues; p. [viii]–ix, Contents; p. [1]–364, Text; p. [365]–425, 16th annual report of the American Jewish Committee; p. [426] blank; p. [427]–593, Report of the 35th year of The Jewish Publication Society of America 1922–1923; 1 p., Advertisement.) front. (port. of Mayer Sulzberger), plates.

Bound uniformly with 5660 (1899–1900) without seal.

"This issue contains an index to the principal contents of the twenty-five volumes of the American Jewish Year Book. During the past quarter of a century the American Jewish Year Book has acquired a firm, useful, and honorable status in the field of reference books in general and of Jewish hand-books in particular. It is a valuable source book of information on matters of Jewish interest. It is frequently referred to and quoted, and it has been used as a model for other works of this nature." — Preface, p. iv.

SPECIAL ARTICLES: Portraits of early American Jews, by Hannah R. London, pp. 147–162. — The Jewish method of slaying animals, by Moses Hyamson, pp. 163–179. — Kol Nidre, by Israel Davidson, pp. 180–194. — Jews who have received the Nobel Prize, by Benjamin Harrow, pp. 195–203. — A classified list of standard books in English on Jewish subjects, by I. George Dobsevage, pp. 204–255. — Index to articles in the first twenty-five volumes of American Jewish Year Book (5660–5684), pp. 354–364. — A response to the question "Whether unfermented wine may be used in Jewish ceremonies," by Louis Ginzberg, pp. 401–425.

Selected Religious Poems of Solomon Ibn Gabirol

Selected Religious Poems | of | Solomon Ibn Gabirol | Translated into English verse | by | Israel Zangwill | From a critical text edited | by | Israel Davidson, Ph.D. | Professor of Mediaeval Hebrew Literature in the Jewish Theological | Seminary of America | [*seal 2c*] | Philadelphia | The Jewish Publication Society of America | 1923 |

143

COLLATION: 16°. 5, [iii]–lix, 247 p. (5 p., Advertisement [or Series of Jewish Classics]; p. [iii] Series title: "The Schiff Library of Jewish Classics;" p. [vi] Title; p. [vii] Hebrew title*; p. [viii] Copyright; p. [ix] Dedication**; p. [iv–v, x] blank; p. [xi–xii] Contents; p. xiii–xliv, Introduction by Israel Davidson; p. xlv–lix, "On translating Gabirol" by Israel Zangwill; p. 1–123 (paged in duplicate), Text and Translation (on opposite pages); p. [124] blank; p. [125]–136, Notes on Introduction; p. [137]–186, Notes on Text; p. [187]–245, המקורות ושנויי נוסחאות; p. 246, Technical Payyetanic terms; p. 247, מפתח הפיוטים על סדר הא"ב.)

Issued in blue cloth; top edges gilted; front cover: SJC, in lower right hand corner; back: designs, author, translator, rule, editor, publisher, designs all in gilt.

* מחברת משירי קדש | אשר | לשלמה בן יהודה אבן גבירול |
לקטו נערכו והוגהו | על ידי | ישראל דאווידזאן | פרופיסור בבית
מדרש הרבנים דנו־יורק | עם תרגום אנגלי | מאת | ישראל זאנגוויל |
פילאדלפיא | החברה היהודית להוצאת ספרים אשר [seal 2c]
באמיריקה | תרפ"ג |

**"Dedicated | by the translator | to his old friend, | The Hon. Louis Marshall, LL.D., | President of the American Jewish Committee | and of the Committee of the Jewish Delegations | at the Peace Conference, | in gratitude, personal and impersonal, | to a tireless and fearless worker for oppressed Jewries | and for Jewish and American ideals, | a doctor of Hebrew Law, | a lover of Hebrew poetry, | and a Jew after Ibn Gabirol's own heart. | "

"It was decided to inaugurate the Series with a selection from the religious poetry of Solomon ibn Gabirol, the greatest of mediaeval Jewish poets, who flourished in the golden age of the Spanish-Jewish period, and the Committee deem themselves especially fortunate in being able to present a translation in English verse by so eminent a poet and writer as Israel Zangwill, who has performed his task with the utmost devotion. The Committee believe, too, that through the painstaking labors of Professor Israel Davidson, a distinguished authority on Hebrew poetry and Jewish liturgy, they are able to

144

present a text greatly surpassing in accuracy any hitherto published."
— Advertisement, p. 4–5.

"This handy volume beautifully printed, artistically bound, containing an accurate vocalized Hebrew text prepared by the greatest authority on Hebrew poetry with an English translation by the foremost Jewish literary figure of today, is certainly a fitting and auspicious beginning of 'The Schiff Library of Jewish Classics.'

"Gabirol and Zangwill are great names in Jewish literature. In both burns the unquenchable flame of the Jewish spirit. Heine called Gabirol a nightingale of piety, the thinker among poets and the poet of thinkers. This book is instinct with high religious fervor and breathes in glowing faith in the wisdom, justice and graciousness of God; they utter the most authentic note in Jewish song since the days when the Psalms were written." — *AJYB*, 5685, p. 680.

1923 reprint. Verso of title-page: "Second Printing."

5705–1944 edition: as above, with seal 3b. Verso of title-page 'Third Printing 1944."

1924

Thirty-five Years of Jewish Endeavor

Thirty-five Years | of Jewish Endeavor | [*rule*] | Being a Brief Statement of the Purposes of the | Jewish Publication Society of America, together | with an Account of What it has Done and an | Appeal to American Jews to Help Further its Plans | [*rule*] | [*seal 2 in green*] | [*rule*] | Type set by The Jewish Publication | Society Press at Philadelphia, in May, Nineteen | Hundred and Twenty-four |

[Note: The foregoing appears within a single rule box and an ornamental border both in black on tan paper.]

COLLATION: 24°. 122 p., 16 1.

Issued in paper boards. Cover-title.

At end: "This little volume of which 250 copies have been printed especially for the friends of the Society contains the title-pages of over one hundred and twenty books issued by the Society of which over 1,500,000 copies have been distributed . . ."

The American Jewish Year Book
5685

The American Jewish | Year Book | 5685 | September 29, 1924, to September 18, 1925 | Volume 26 | Edited by | Harry Schneiderman | for the | American Jewish Committee | [*seal 2a*] | Philadelphia | The Jewish Publication Society of America | 1924 |

COLLATION: 12°. x, 813 p. (p. [i] Title; p. [ii] Copyright; p. [iii]–v, Preface; p. [vi]–viii, Special articles in previous issues; p. [ix]–x, Contents; p. [1]–602, Text; p. [603]–672, 17th annual report of the American Jewish Committee; p. [673]–813, Report of the 36th year of The Jewish Publication Society of America 1923–1924.) facsim., ports.

Bound uniformly with 5660 (1899–1900) without seal.

"Aside from the biographical notices, only one special article is given in this issue, namely: 'The Yiddish Press — An Americanizing Agency,' by Doctor Mordecai Soltes, Director of Extension Education of the Bureau of Jewish Education, New York City. This article was written by Doctor Soltes as his doctorate thesis at Teachers College, Columbia University, and it was regarded as suitable for publication in the American Jewish Year Book, because it gives a vivid and fascinating picture of the role of the Yiddish press in that process of the adjustment of the immigrant to his new environment which has come to be called 'Americanization.'" — Preface, p. [iii].

SPECIAL ARTICLES: The Yiddish press — an Americanizing agency, by Mordecai Soltes, pp. 165–372. — Mayer Sulzberger, by Louis Marshall and Solomon Solis-Cohen, pp. 373–403. — Simon

Wolf, by Max J. Kohler, pp. 404–419. — Rabbi Joseph Krauskopf, a biographical sketch, by Abraham J. Feldman, pp. 420–447. — Henry Berkowitz, by William Rosenau, pp. 448–458. —Benzion Halper, by Cyrus Adler, pp. 459–471.

The Yiddish Press — an Americanizing agency, by Mordecai Soltes, reprinted in separate form by Teachers College, Columbia University, New York City, 1925.

Studies in Judaism
Third Series

STUDIES IN JUDAISM | Third Series | By | S. Schechter, M.A., Litt.D. | [*seal 2a*] | Philadelphia | The Jewish Publication Society of America | 1924 |

COLLATION: 8°. vii, 336 p. (1 l., Half-title, verso blank; p. [i] Title; p. [ii] Copyright; p. [iii] Contents; p. [iv] blank; p. [v]–vii, Foreword by Alexander Marx and Frank I. Schechter [editors]; p. [1]–276, Text; p. [277]–305, Notes; p. [306] blank; p. [307]–336, Index.)

Issued in light green cloth; back: rules, title, author, publisher and rules in gilt.

CONTENTS: Jewish saints in mediaeval Germany. — "As others saw him" a retrospect, A. D. 54. — Abraham Geiger. — Leopold Zunz. — On the study of the Talmud. — The Talmud. — Notes of lectures on Jewish philanthropy.

Rabbi Jacob Bosniak collated the "Notes of lectures on Jewish philanthropy" taken by himself and other students of the Jewish Theological Seminary of America with the notebook of the lecturer. — Cf. Foreword, p. [v].

"In offering these essays to the public the editors feel that comment by them on the subject matter would be superfluous. It is the vigor of style, the originality of thought and the depth of learning displayed in these papers that will speak for themselves, and that, the

147

editors believe, will insure for this third series of 'Studies in Judaism' the same cordial welcome, which greeted both of its predecessors." — Foreword, p. vi–vii.

"Though a posthumous publication it is alive with the genius of the master Jewish essayist, and covers a number of subjects."— *AJYB*, 5684, p. 438.

"The volume covers the full range of Professor Schechter's literary activity from the early years of his life in England to his last days in the New World. It contains a mine of information and fresh ideas, and combines great learning with literary charm.

"Jewish literature is richer for these Studies . . ., which are models of the manner in which a scholar can select from dry-as-dust materials, just those characteristics which give vivid reality to the human lives of the past and the present. Prof. Schechter comments upon scholarly facts with the wide culture and sympathetic outlook of a Matthew Arnold. He had the art of reviving the past in its human aspects and of bringing before our eyes a whole system of life which has passed into the far distant centuries. The essays are fresh, full of energy and life." — *AJYB*, 5686, p. 489–491.

5706–1945 edition: title page reset, with seal 3b. Verso of title page: "Reprinted 1945." 6 l., 328 p. For this reprint the text was subjected to considerable revision and correction.

Selected Poems of Jehudah Halevi

Selected Poems | of | Jehudah Halevi | Translated into English | By | Nina Salaman | Chiefly from the critical text | edited by | Heinrich Brody, Ph.D. | [*seal 2c*] | Philadelphia | The Jewish Publication Society of America | 1924 |

COLLATION: 16°. xxviii, 192 p. (6 p., Advertisement [of Series of Jewish Classics]; p. [vii–viii omitted in numbering]; p. [xi] Series title: "The Schiff Library of Jewish Classics;" p. [xiv] Title;

p. [xv] Hebrew title*; p. [xvi] Copyright; p. [xvii] Dedication**; p. [ix–x, xii–xiii, xviii] blank; p. [xix]–xxiii, Contents; p. [xxiv] blank; 1 l. | אני כנור לשירין | "I am a harp for thy songs" |) verso blank; p. xiii–xxviii (repeated in numbering), Introduction by Nina Salaman; p. 1–147 (paged in duplicate), Text and Translation (on opposite pages); p. [148] blank; p. [149]–174, Rhymed Translations; p. [175]–186, Notes on Text; p. [187]–190, מקורות השירים; p. [191]–192, מפתח השירים על סדר הא״ב.)

Bound uniformly with Gabirol, *Selected religious poems*, 1923.

This is the second book in the Series.

*מחברת משירי | יהודה בן שמואל הלוי | נערכו והוגהו | על ידי | חיים בראדי | רב הכולל בעיר פראג | עם תרגום אנגלי | מאת | נינה אשת ר' נתן בן מאיר שלמה | [*seal 2c*] | פילאדלפיא | החברה היהודית להוצאת ספרים אשר באמריקה | תרפ״ד |

**"Dedicated | by the translator | to the memory of her father |."

"The present, the second volume of the Series, is based largely upon the critical text of the *Diwan* of Jehudah Halevi, prepared by the distinguished Rabbi Heinrich Brody of Prag, and published under the auspices of the Mekize Nirdamim Society. Doctor Brody has graciously permitted the use of these selections, and has made certain alterations in his published text, and supplied several notes for the present volume. The translation is due to Mrs. Nina Salaman, who has for a decade been the medium through which many English readers have had glimpses into medieval Jewish poetry." — Advertisement, p. 5.

"The selections and translations were made by Nina Salaman, who occupies a distinguished place as a translator of Hebrew poetry . . . The Hebrew text of this volume, upon which the translation is based, was taken with his permission from H. Brody's edition of Halevi, and has been revised by him for this series. The volume contains an introduction by Mrs. Salaman in which she sketches the life of Halevi and his work, together with brief illuminating notes and other features intended to aid the reader and the student in the use of the book . . . Mrs. Salaman's translation is accurate, yet retains at the same time the poetic charm of the original. The rendering is in prose, with a tendency toward rhythm, and follows the metrical original line for line. Some of Mrs. Salaman's previous versions of Halevi's poems in rhyme are also included at the end of the book." — *AJYB*, 5686, p. 491 f.

1925 edition: London: George Routledge and Sons, Limited | 1925, also on title-page. Verso of title-page: "Copyright 1925 by The Jewish Publication Society of America | London: George Routledge and Sons, Limited | All rights reserved."

1928 edition: same as 1924, with seal 2b. Verso of title-page: "Second Impression 1928."

1942: "1,100 copies reprinted."— *AJYB*, 5704, p. 687.

5706–1946 edition: as above, with seal 3b. Verso of title-page: "Fourth Impression, 1946."

1925

Moses Montefiore

MOSES MONTEFIORE | By | Paul Goodman | [*seal 2a*] | Philadelphia | The Jewish Publication Society of America | 1925 |

COLLATION: 12°. 255 p. (p. [1] Title; p. [2] Copyright; p. [3] Dedication*; p. [5] Contents; p. [7] Illustrations; p. [9] Preface; p. [4, 6, 8, 10] blank; p. [11]–21, Introduction; p. 22–227, Text; p. 228, Genealogical table; p. [229]–250, Bibliography; p. [251]–255, Index.) 8 plates and ports. (including front.)

Issued in dark green cloth; back: title, design, author and publisher in gilt.

*"To the Yehidim and Elders | of the | Spanish and Portuguese Jews' Congregation | "Shaar Ashamaim" | Bevis Marks, London | which was the source of inspiration | and centre of activity | of its former | Senior Yahid and Elder | Sir Moses Montefiore, Bart. | This book is | dedicated | on his semi-jubilee of office (1895–1920 | by their devoted secretary | the author.]"

"Fifth volume in the Jewish Worthies Series." — *AJYB*, 5687, p. 527.

"The life of Sir Moses Montefiore is in itself a chapter of the history of the Jews in modern times, and it was only his great skill that the author, Paul Goodman, of London, was enabled in the limited space of 260 pages to deal so minutely with the large amount of material available in connection with the subject. It is attractively illustrated with several portraits of Sir Moses Montefiore, Judith Lady Montefiore, East Cliff Lodge, Lady Judith Montefiore College at Ramsgate, and other illustrations." — *AJYB*, 5687, pp. 527–528.

1925 reprint, without illustrations.

5703–1943 edition: title-page reset, with seal 3b, without illustrations. Verso of title-page: "Reprinted, 1943."

The American Jewish Year Book 5686

The American Jewish | Year Book | 5686 | September 19, 1925, to September 8, 1926 | Volume 27 | Edited by | Harry Schneiderman | for the | American Jewish Committee | [*seal 2a*] | Philadelphia | The Jewish Publication Society of America | 1925 |

COLLATION: 12°. x, 621 p. (p. [i] Title; p. [ii] Copyright; p. [iii]–iv, Preface; p. [v]–viii, Special articles in previous issues; p. [ix]–x, Contents; p. [1]–411, Text; p. [413]–479, 18th annual report of the American Jewish Committee; p. [412, 480] blank; p. [481]–621, Report of the 37th year of The Jewish Publication Society of America 1924–1925.) front. (plate: Emil G. Hirsch from the Memorial Tablet by Jules L. Butensky)

Bound uniformly with 5660 (1899–1900) without seal.

"It is . . . in harmony with the practice of presenting in the Year Book articles on Jewish life in various lands, that we publish in this volume an article on the Jewish Community of Canada by Martin Wolff, Esq., of Toronto, a writer who has had unusual opportunities to become conversant with the facts." — Preface, p. [iii].

Kasriel the Watchman

KASRIEL | THE WATCHMAN | And Other Stories | By | Rufus Learsi [pseud. of Israel Goldberg] | [*seal 2a*] | Philadelphia | The Jewish Publication Society of America | 1925 |

COLLATION: 12°. 3 p. 1., 311 p. (1. 1, Title, verso Copyright; 1. 2, Dedication*, verso (Note)**; 1. 3, Contents, verso blank; p. [1]–311, Text.) plates (including front.).

Issued in red and black illustrated paper boards; back: black cloth; title, author and publisher in gilt.

Illustrations by Reuben Leaf.

*"This medley of childhood memories I | dedicate to my mother. | The Author |."

**"The Jewish Publication Society of America is indebted to Nathan H. Shrift, of New York, for aiding in the publication of this volume."

CONTENTS: Kasriel the watchman. — Perl the peanut woman. — Benjy and Reuby. — Feivel the fiddler. — Phantasies.

"Stories dealing with homely incidents in the Jewish life of the lower East Side have all the quaintness of a generation that is fast passing away under modern influences." — *AJYB*, 5687, p. 530.

1936 edition: title-page reset, with seal 3b, without illustrations. Verso of title-page:. . . "Reprinted, 1936."

5708–1948 edition: same as 1936. Verso of title-page: "Reprinted, 1936, Reprinted, 1948."

152

The Legends of the Jews

<small>THE LEGENDS OF</small> | <small>THE JEWS</small> | By | Louis Ginzberg | V | Notes to Volumes I and II | From the Creation to the Exodus | [*seal 2a*] | Philadelphia | The Jewish Publication Society of America | 1925 |

COLLATION: 8°. xi, 446 p. (p. [i–iv] same as v. 1; p. [v] Dedication*; p. [vi] blank; p. vii–xi, Preface; p. [1]–439, Notes; p. [440] blank; p. 441–446, List of Abbreviations.)

*"To the memory of | Judge Mayer Sulzberger | ."

See 1909, v. 1, for binding.

"The Fifth volume of 'The Legends of the Jews' consists entirely of Professor Louis Ginzberg's notes covering the text of Volumes I and II of his monumental work, dealing with Bible characters and incidents from Creation to Moses in Egypt ... In the notes will be found the sources from which the material was drawn, and they will be seen to be co-extensive with Rabbinical, Apocryphal, and Pseudo-epigraphic literature, and to cover also a considerable portion of mediaeval Jewish literature. . . . Throughout, the notes supplement the text by giving variant legends which for the sake of continuity could not be incorporated in the text and has to be given separately in the notes." — *AJYB*, 5687, p. 529.

1939: "1,000 copies reprinted."— *AJYB*, 5701, p. 685.

5707–1947 edition: as above, with seal 3b. Verso of title-page: "Sixth Impression — 1947."

The Book of Psalms

תהלים | The | Book of Psalms | [*design*] | 5685–1925 | The Jewish Publication Society | of America, Philadelphia |

[Note: The foregoing appears with a black single rule box. Each page, including text and title-page, within a black single rule box, and running captions are underlined.]

COLLATION: 32°. 3–289 p. (p. [3] Title; p. [4] Copyright . . .
London: George Routledge and Sons, Limited. All rights reserved,
(Note) *; p. [5]–289, Text (in English).)

Issued in black cloth; front cover: title; back: six double rule
boxes; title in English and in Hebrew, all in gilt.

*"This edition of the Psalms is reprinted from 'The Holy
Scriptures, according to the Masoretic Text, a New Translation,
with the aid of previous versions and with constant consultation of
Jewish authorities.' Published by The Jewish Publication Society
of America in 1917 at Philadelphia."

5689–1929 edition: as above. Verso of title-page: "Second
Impression — 1929."

1943: "11,000 copies reprinted."— *AJYB*, 5705, p. 606.

1926

The American Jewish Year Book

5687

The American Jewish | Year Book | 5687 | September 9, 1926,
to September 26, 1927 | Volume 28 | Edited by | Harry
Schneiderman | for the | American Jewish Committee | [*seal
2a*] | Philadelphia | The Jewish Publication Society of Amer-
ica | 1926 |

COLLATION: 12°. x, 645 p. (p. [i] Title; p. [ii] Copyright;
p. [iii]–iv, Preface; p. v–viii, Special articles in previous issues;
p. [ix]–x, Contents; p. [1]–428, Text; p. 429–520, 19th annual
report of the American Jewish Committee; p. [521]–645, Report
of the 38th year of The Jewish Publication Society of America
1925–1926.) plates, ports.

Bound uniformly with 5660 (1899–1900) without seal.

"In view of the incidence in 1925 of the one hundred and
fiftieth anniversary of the Declaration of Independence, and in 1926
of the tercentenary of the purchase from its Indian inhabitants of
Manhattan Island by the Dutch, an article on the Jews of Colonial

154

times was deemed to be timely, and we present a brief resumé of the most important events of Jewish interest of that period by Albert M. Friedenberg, the Corresponding Secretary of the American Jewish Historical Society." — Preface, p. [iii].

SPECIAL ARTICLES: The architecture of the synagogue, by William G. Tachau, pp. 155–192. — The Jews of America, 1654–1787, by Albert M. Friedenberg, pp. 193–218. — Israel Abrahams, by Herbert Loewe, pp. 219–234. — Kaufmann Kohler, by H. G. Enelow, pp. 235–260. — Henry Malter, by Alexander Marx, pp. 261–272. — Ephraim Lederer, by Julius H. Greenstone, pp. 273–285.

Kiddush Ha-Shem

KIDDUSH HA-SHEM | An epic of 1648 | By | Sholom Ash | Translated by | Rufus Learsi [pseud. of Israel Goldberg] | [seal 2c] | Philadelphia | The Jewish Publication Society of America | 1926 |

COLLATION: 12°. 4 p. 1., 227 p. (1. 1, Title, verso Copyright; 1. 2, Dedication*; 1. 3, [Quotation] from an old Chronicle; verso of 1. 2 and 3 blank; 1. 4 and p. [1]–227, Text.)

Issued in black cloth; front cover: title, author; back: title, author and publisher all in red.

*"To Dr. J. L. Magnes | in token of esteem and affection | ."

"It is a historical novel of great power and deals with a period of Cossack outrages, not of the twentieth, but of the seventeenth century." — AJYB, 5683, p. 389.

"It treats of the times of the Chmelnitzki atrocities in Poland. In a masterful manner this distinguished Yiddish writer portrays the struggles endured by our people who lived as Jews in intensely hostile environments, how their little joys were blasted and how these humble Jews of Poland lived and died for their faith. It is verily an epic of 1648." — AJYB, 5687, p. 530.

5707–1946 edition: title-page reset, with seal 3b. Verso of title-page: "Reprinted, 1936, Reprinted, 1943, Reprinted, 1946."

Hebrew Ethical Wills

Hebrew Ethical Wills | Selected and edited | By | Israel
Abrahams | Reader in Talmudic in the University of Cam-
bridge, | formerly Senior Tutor at Jews' College, London. |
Part One [and Two] | [*seal 2c*] | Philadelphia | The Jewish
Publication Society of America | 1926 |

COLLATION: 16°. 2 v. (paged continuously). v. 1: 6, [vii]–xxvi,
161 p. (6 p., Advertisement [of Series of Jewish Classics]; p. [vii]
series title: "The Schiff Library of Jewish Classics;" p. [x] Title;
p. [xi] Hebrew title*; p. [xii] Copyright; p. [xiv] Dedication**;
p. [xv] [Quotation in Hebrew and English from] Genesis 18.19;
p. [viii–ix, xiii, xvi] blank; p. [xvii]–xviii, Contents; p. xix–xxvi,
Introduction; p. 1–161 (paged in duplicate), Text and Translation
(on opposite pages); v. 2: 3 p. l., 162–348 p. (1. 1–3, same as v. 1,
p. [vii–xii]; p. 162–348 (paged in duplicate), Text and Translation
(on opposite pages.)

Bound uniformly with Gabirol, *Selected religious poems*, 1923.

This is the third book (in two volumes) in the Series.

‏* צואות גאוני ישראל | לקטו נערכו הוגהו ונעתקו | על ידי | ישראל
בן ברוך בר אברהם | חלק א [–בן | [*seal 2c*] | פילאדלפיא | החברה
היהודית להוצאת ספרים אשר באמיריקא | תרפ"ז |‏

‏** "מנחת אהבה | לזכרון | מוהר"ר שניאור זלמן שעכטער | זצ"ל | ."‏

"Abrahams' volume of Ethical Wills has brought to the attention of the world a type of literature which is almost exclusively
Jewish and of the finest import." — *AJYB*, 5689, p. 347.

The Hebrew translation of the editor's bibliographical descriptive notes prefixed to each of the wills comprising the volume was
made by Dr. Joseph Reider.

1926 reprint. Verso of title-page: "Second Impression 1936."

5708–1948 edition: as above, with seal 3b. Verso of title-page:
"Second Impression, 1936; Third Impression, 1948."

1927

A History of the Jewish People

A HISTORY OF | THE JEWISH PEOPLE | By | Max L. Margolis
and Alexander Marx | [*seal 2a*] | Philadelphia | The Jewish
Publication Society of America | 1927 |

COLLATION: 8°. xxii, 823 p., 1 1. (p. [i] Half-title; p. [ii] Note*;
p. [iii] Title; p. [iv] Copyright, All rights reserved; p. v–vi, Preface;
p. vii–xxii, Table of Contents; p. [1]–737, Text; p. [738] blank;
p. 739–752, Bibliography; p. 753–773, Chronological Tables (part
folded); p. [774 omitted in numbering]; p. 775–823, Index; 1 1.,
(List of) Maps.) At end colored maps (part double).

Issued in dark blue cloth; front cover: title, authors; back:
title, authors, publisher all in gilt.

*"This book is published at the desire of the late Rosetta M.
Ulman of Williamsport, Pennsylvania, from funds contributed from
her estate by her executor, Mr. Abraham Erlanger. Miss Ulman
wished the publication of this volume for the furtherance of truth
and equity."

"The present work is intended for the layman and the student.
A short Bibliography at the end of the volume has likewise in mind
these two classes of readers who may seek to obtain further information. It is not accordingly a register of source-works, and books and
articles in the English language wherever obtainable have been given
preference. A Chronological Table will enable the reader to survey
contemporaneous events synchronously. The Index was prepared
by Dr. Louis L. Kaplan.
"This volume is the conjoint labor of the two authors. The
writing was done by the first of the undersigned, and a good part
of it during his year's sojourn in Palestine, and he gratefully records
his obligation to his fellow-author for his valuable Lecture Notes
on the history of the talmudic and mediaeval periods. Moreover, the
manuscript was gone over repeatedly by the two authors in joint
conference, every fact and date and expression was scrutinized, and

'that which we had hammered was again and again brought back to the anvil'." — Preface, p. vi.

1934 edition: as above. Verso of title-page: "First Printing, March 1927; Second Printing, October 1929; Third Printing, November 1934."

5707–1947 edition: as above, with seal 3b. Verso of title-page: ". . . Fourth Printing, November 1938; Fifth Printing, March, 1941; Sixth Printing, January 1944; Seventh Printing, April, 1945; Eighth Printing, June, 1947."

Translations into French and Spanish:

Histoire du peuple juif traduit de l'Anglais par J. Robillot Licencié ès-lettres. Paris, Payot, 1930.

Historia del pueblo Judío, Buenos Aires, Editorial Israel 1945 / 5705. Verso of title-page: Traduccion directa del ingles por Román Jiménez; indices de nombres por Salvador Alonso.

Travels in North Africa

TRAVELS | in | NORTH AFRICA | By | Nahum Slouschz | [*seal 2b*] | Philadelphia | The Jewish Publication Society of America | 1927 |

COLLATION: 12°. x, 488 p. (p. [i] Title; p. [ii] Copyright, All rights reserved; p. iii–iv, Contents; p. v–x, Foreword; p. [1]–488, Text.)

Issued in green cloth; back: title, rule, author and publisher in gilt.

CONTENTS: Part 1. Tripoli. — Part II. The three Jebels of the Sahara. — Part III. Carthage and Tunis. — Part IV. The Jews in Algeria. — Part V. The Jews of Morocco.

"The present volume is the result of ten years of travel amongst the Jews of Africa and much of study and research into their history and ethnography." — Foreword, p. v.

Translated by Miss Amy E. Schechter. — *AJYB*, 5677, p. 417.

"Dr. Slouschz has made several journeys through Morocco, Libya, and Tunis, and penetrated the edge of the Great Sahara Desert. In the course of his travels he made valuable discoveries, adding vastly to our knowledge of the history and customs of a region which was once densely populated by active communities of Jews, and which is still the abode of no inconsiderable number of our race." — *AJYB*, 5677, p. 417.

5704–1944 edition: title-page reset, with seal 3b, and provided with a new title "The Jews of North Africa." Verso of title-page: "Reprinted, 1944."

The American Jewish Year Book
5688

The American Jewish | Year Book | 5688 | September 27, 1927, to September 14, 1928 | Volume 29 | Edited by | Harry Schneiderman | for the | American Jewish Committee | [*seal 2a*] | Philadelphia | The Jewish Publication Society of America | 1927 |

COLLATION: 12°. 2 l., x, 445 p., 10 l. (2 l. of Advertisements; p. [i] Title; p. [ii] Copyright; p. [iii]–iv, Preface; p. v–viii, Special articles in previous issues; p. [ix]–x, Contents; p. [1]–281, Text; p. [282] blank; p. [283]–382, Report of the 39th year of The Jewish Publication Society of America 1926–1927; p. 383–389, "Statement by Henry Ford regarding charges against Jews made in . . . The Dearborn Independent and . . .'The International Jew' . . . together with an explanatory statement by Mr. Louis Marshall . . . and his reply to Mr. Ford;" p. [390] blank; p. 391–445, 20th annual report of the American Jewish Committee; 10 l. of Advertisements.)

Bound uniformly with 5660 (1899–1900) without seal.

"The only special feature in the present volume is an article on the Jews of Hungary based on the census of 1920, by Doctor Harry S. Linfield, which is appended to his article on Statistics of Jews. The data included in the article on Hungary will be found of great interest, as reflecting the life of Jews in another country, especially those statistics which bear upon births, marriage and divorce, conversion

159

and apostasy, deaths, and in view of the existence of a legal *numerus clausus*, those bearing upon the enrollment of Jews in colleges and universities." — Preface, p. [iii].

SPECIAL ARTICLES: Israel Zangwill, a biographical sketch, by Harry Schneiderman, pp. 121–143. — Oscar S. Straus, a biographical sketch, by Cyrus Adler, pp. 145–155. — The Jews of Hungary, Census of 1920, pp. 265–281.

1928

The Treatise Ta'anit of the Babylonian Talmud

The Treatise | TA'ANIT | of the | Babylonian Talmud | Critically edited on the basis of manuscripts | and old editions and provided with | a translation and notes | by | Henry Malter, Ph.D. | Professor of Rabbinical Literature at Dropsie College | [*seal 2c*] | Philadelphia | The Jewish Publication Society of America | 1928 |

COLLATION: 16°. 7, [vii]–xlvii, 243 p. (7p., Advertisement [of Series of Jewish Classics]; p. [vii] Series title: "The Schiff Library of Jewish Classics;" p. [x] Title; p. [xi] Hebrew title*; p. [xii] Copyright; p. [xiii] Contents; p. [viii–ix, xiv] blank; p. xv–xlvii, Introduction; p. 1–240 (Paged in duplicate), Text and Translation (on opposite pages); p. 241–243, Index of names.)

Bound uniformly with Gabirol, *Selected religious poems*, 1923.

This is the fourth in the Series.

* מסכת תענית | מן | תלמוד בבלי | הוגהה על פי כתבי יד שונים

והוצאות עתיקות ונעתקה | לשפת אנגלית | על ידי | צבי מלטער |

מורה ספרות התלמודית בדרופסי קוליג | [*seal 2c*] | פילאדלפיא |

החברה היהודית להוצאת ספרים אשר באמיריקא | תרפ"ח |

"Textually an epoch-making work, whilst the translation itself is charming and gives the reader an insight into one of the most interesting tractates of the Talmud." — *AJYB*, 5689, p. 347.

The Legends of the Jews

THE LEGENDS OF | THE JEWS | By | Louis Ginzberg | VI | Notes to Volumes III and IV | From Moses in the Wilderness to Esther | [*seal 2a*] | Philadelphia | The Jewish Publication Society of America | 1928 |

COLLATION: 8°. 4 p. l., 490 p. (l. 1–2, same as v. 1 p. [i–iv]; l. 3, Dedication*; l. 4, Contents; verso of l. 3–4, blank; p. 1–481, Notes; p. [482] blank; p. 483–490, List of Abbreviations.)

See 1909, v. 1, for binding.

*"To the memory of my dear friend | and colleague | Israel Friedlaender | לקדושים אשר בארץ המה ואדירי כל חפצי בם |."

1942: "1,000 copies reprinted."— *AJYB*, 5704, p. 687.

5706–1946 edition: as above, with seal 3b. Verso of title-page: "Second Impression, 1939; Third Impression, 1946."

Students Scholars and Saints

STUDENTS | SCHOLARS AND SAINTS | By Louis Ginzberg | [*seal 2b*] | Philadelphia | The Jewish Publication Society of America | 1928 |

COLLATION: 12°. 2 p. l., vii–xiii, 291 p. (l. 1, Title, verso Copyright; l. 2, Dedication*, verso blank; p. vii–xi, Preface; p. [xii] blank; p. xiii, Contents; p. 1–262, Text; p. [263]–282, Notes; p. [283]–291, Index.)

Issued in purple cloth; front cover: title, rule, author; back: title, rule, author, publisher all in gilt.

*"To my wife | תנו לה מפרי ידיה |."

161

CONTENTS: The Jewish primary school. — The disciple of the wise. — The rabbinical student. — The religion of the Pharisee. — Jewish thought as reflected in the halakah. — The Gaon, Rabbi Elijah Wilna. — Rabbi Israel Salanter. — Zechariah Frankel. — Isaac Hirsch Weiss. — Solomon Schechter. — David Hoffman.

"The lectures . . . give the reader some insight into the cultural life of the Jew." — Preface, p. vii.

1943: "1,000 copies reprinted."— *AJYB*, 5705, p. 606.

5706–1945 edition: title-page reset, with seal 3b. Verso of title-page: "Reprinted, 1945."

Worlds that Passed

WORLDS | THAT PASSED | By | A. S. Sachs | [*seal 2b*] | Philadelphia | The Jewish Publication Society | of America | 1928 |

COLLATION: 12°. v, 289 p. (p. [i] Title; p. [ii] Copyright; p. iii–iv, Contents; p. v, Prefatory Note*; p. 1–282, Text; p. 283–289, Glossary.)

Issued in red cloth; top edges red; front cover: title, rule, author; back: title, rule, author, publisher all in black.

*"I wish to express my thanks to Mr. Harold Berman for translating this book into English and to Mr. Judah Joffe for his collaboration in the English version." — The author.

Stories of the customs and institutions of Jewish life in Lithuania before World War I. They perpetuate "a life and thought that have disappeared and would have been forgotten had it not been for this publication." — *AJYB*, 5690, p. 404.

5703–1943 edition: title-page reset, with seal 3b. Verso of title-page: "Reprinted, 1943."

School Days in Home Town

SCHOOL DAYS | [*rule*] IN [*rule*] | HOME TOWN | By | Abram S. Isaacs | [*seal 2a*] | Philadelphia | The Jewish Publication Society of America | 1928 |

COLLATION: 12°. 162 p. (p. [1] Title; p. [2] Copyright; p. 3,
[Poem] "School days in home town;" p. 5–6, Preface; p. 7, Contents;
p. [4, 8] blank; p. 9–162, Text.)

Issued in light green cloth; top edges green; front cover: title,
author within tooled box; back: title, rule, author, publisher all in
dark green.

"The story of a Jewish school whose atmosphere was undoubtedly old-fashioned." — Preface, p. 5.

The American Jewish Year Book
5689

The American Jewish | Year Book | 5689 | September 15,
1928, to October 5, 1929 | Volume 30 | Edited by | Harry
Schneiderman | for the | American Jewish Committee |
[*seal 2a*] | Philadelphia | The Jewish Publication Society of
America | 1928 |

COLLATION: 12°. x, 446 p. (p. [i] Title; p. [ii] Copyright;
p. [iii]–iv, Preface; p. v–viii, Special articles in previous issues;
p. [ix]–x, Contents; p. [1]–270, Text; p. 271–335, 21st annual
report of the American Jewish Committee; p. [336] blank; p.
[337]–446, Report of the 40th year of The Jewish Publication
Society of America 1927–1928.)

Bound uniformly with 5660 (1899–1900) without seal.

"The leading special feature in this volume is an article by
Dr. H. S. Linfield on the Jewish population of the United States,
based upon information gathered by him as director of the Statistical
Department of the American Jewish Committee.

"Only one change has been made in the recurrent features of
the year book, — in place of the article consisting of a survey of
the year, which has been a feature of this publication for the past
six years, there has been substituted a briefer review of the year,
presenting only the most important and outstanding matters of Jewish
interest which engaged public attention during the period. To this
is appended, partly in abstract and partly in *extenso*, the report of

the Joint Palestine Survey Commission appointed last year by Dr. Chaim Weizmann on behalf of the World Zionist Organization, in conjunction with Mr. Louis Marshall, chairman of a non-partisan conference to discuss Palestine affairs which had several meetings in the United States." — Preface, p. [iii]–iv.

SPECIAL ARTICLES: Ahad Ha-Am, by Leon Simon, pp. 87–99. — Jewish population in the United States 1927, by H. S. Linfield, pp. 101–198. — Jewish congregations in the United States, a preliminary statement, by H. S. Linfield, pp. 199–201. — Joint Palestine Survey Commission, pp. 326–333.

1929

Letters of Rebecca Gratz

Letters of | Rebecca Gratz | Edited with an introduction and notes | By Rabbi David Philipson, D.D. | Author of "The Reform Movement in Judaism," | "The Jew in English Fiction," etc., etc. | [*seal 2 b*] | Philadelphia | The Jewish Publication Society of America | 1929 |

COLLATION: 8°. xxiv p., 1 1., 454 p. (p. [i] Title; p. [ii] Copyright; p. [iii] Dedication*; p. [iv] blank; p. v–vi, Foreword by D. P.; p. vii–xxiv, Introduction; 1 1. and p. 1–439, Text; p. [440] Editor's Note**; p. 441–454, Index.) 2 ports. (including front.), facsims.

Issued in brown cloth; front cover: blind stamped miniature portrait of Rebecca Gratz; back: design, title, design, editor, seal 2a, and design all in gilt.

*"Dedicated | to the | Sisterhood | of the | Bene Israel Congregation | Cincinnati | ."

**"No letters remain to be added. This epistolary output, extending over well-nigh sixty years [1808–1866], presents a vivid picture of the lovely personality who stands forth as one of the glories of American Jewish womanhood."

164

"In editing the letters I have omitted such portions as are of too intimate a family nature to be paraded before the public eye. I have not edited the language nor the punctuation. The writer of the letters wrote in a flowing manner and employed usually a small dash in place of commas and semi-colons. This peculiarity is characteristic and does not at all interfere with the charm and effectiveness of the style." — Introduction, p. viii.

"The publication of these letters was made possible by the generosity of the Sisterhood of the Bene Israel Congregation (Rockdale Avenue Temple) of Cincinnati, Ohio, who supplied the funds for a memento of the fortieth anniversary of the service of Rabbi David Philipson as the rabbi of the Congregation." — *AJYB*, 5690, p. 405.

The American Jewish Year Book
5690

The American Jewish | Year Book | 5690 | October 5, 1929, to September 22, 1930 | Volume 31 | Edited by | Harry Schneiderman | for the | American Jewish Committee | [*seal 2a*] | Philadelphia | The Jewish Publication Society of America | 1929 |

COLLATION: 12°. ix, 502 p. (p. [i] Title; p. [ii] Copyright; p. [iii] Preface; p. v–vii, Special articles in previous issues; p. [iv, viii] blank; p. [ix] Contents; p. [1]–334, Text; p. 335–395, 22nd annual report of the American Jewish Committee; p. [396] blank; p. [397]–502, Report of the 41st year of The Jewish Publication Society of America 1928–1929.) front. (port. of Louis Marshall)

Bound uniformly with 5660 (1899–1900) without seal.

"Dr. H. S. Linfield, Director of the Statistical Department of the American Jewish Committee, presents in the present volume the results of a study of the organization of the Jewish Community in the United States. . . . In connection with the article are presented many tables and lists which will be found very useful by Jewish social and communal workers." — Preface.

SPECIAL ARTICLE: The communal organization of the Jews in the United States, 1927, by H. S. Linfield, pp. 99–254.

The Rise of a New and Cultural American Jewry

The Rise of a New and Cultural | American Jewry | The Jewish Publication Society recog- | nizes all shades of Judaism, averting | all narrowness. The Society has succeeded | in perhaps a greater degree than any other | organization that was ever started among | the Jews in the United States in welding | into one body Jews whose interpretation | of Judaism differ most widely, and yet | consciously or sub-consciously recognize | that in some way, somehow, they | are related to each other by | a common tradition. | [*design*] | The Jewish Publication Society of America | 219 North Broad Street | Philadelphia | [1929]

COLLATION: 8°. 20 p. ports.

Issued in tan paper covers; front cover: title within ornamental border; back cover: seal 2b, all in brown.

Frankfort

... | FRANKFORT | By | A. Freimann and F. Kracauer | Translated from the German manuscript | by | Bertha Szold Levin | [*seal 2b*] | Philadelphia | The Jewish Publication Society of America | 1929 |

At head of title: Jewish Communities Series.

COLLATION: 16°. 3 p. 1., 285 p. (1. 1, Title, verso Copyright; 1. 2, Illustrations; 1. 3, Table of Contents; verso of 1. 2–3, blank; p. 1–274, Text; p. 275, Bibliography; p. [276] blank; p. 277–285, Index.) plates (including front.), plan.

166

Issued in dark blue cloth; front cover: title, within double rule box, and series in gilt, all within ornamental tooled border; back: design, title "History of Jews in Frankfort", rule, author, publisher, design, all in gilt.

The Life of the People in Biblical Times

THE | LIFE OF THE PEOPLE | IN BIBLICAL TIMES | By | Max Radin, Ph.D. | Professor of Law in the | University of California | [*seal 2b*] | Philadelphia | The Jewish Publication Society of America | 1929 |

COLLATION: 16°. 236 p. (p. [1] Half-title; p. [3] Title; p. [4] Copyright; p. [5] Contents; p. [7] Dedication*; p. [2, 6, 8] blank; p. [9]–14, Introduction; p. [15]–230, Text; p. [231]–236, Index.)

Issued in blue-gray cloth; front cover: seal 2a, blind stamped; back: design, title, author, design and publisher in gilt.

*"Uxori Meae | hunc libellum qualiscumque est | quem eius ope et consilio scripsi | grato animo acceptum refero | ."

5708–1948 edition: title-page reset, with seal 3b. Verso of title-page: "Reprinted 1943, 1948."

Sefer Ha-'Ikkarim Vol. I

SEFER HA-'IKKARIM | Book of Principles | By | Joseph Albo | Critically edited on the basis of manuscripts | and old editions and provided with | a translation and notes | By | Isaac Husik, LL.B., M.A., Ph.D. | Professor of Philosophy | at the University of Pennsylvania | Volume One | [*seal 2c*] | Philadelphia | The Jewish Publication Society of America | 1929 |

COLLATION: 16°. 2, [iii]–xxviii, 204 p. (2 p., Advertisement [of Series of Jewish Classics]; p. [v] Series title: "The Schiff Library of Jewish Classics;" [viii] Title; p. [ix] Hebrew title*; p. [x] Copyright; p. [xi] Dedication**; p. [xiii] Contents; p. [iii–iv, vi–vii, xii, xiv] blank; p. xv–xxviii, Introduction by Isaac Husik; p. 1–203 (paged in duplicate), Text and Translation (on opposite pages); p. 204, Additional note.) front. (facsim.)

Bound uniformly with Gabirol, *Selected religious poems*, 1923.

This is the fifth book (in five volumes) in the Series. v. 1–2, issued in 1929; v. 3–4, parts 1–2, in 1930.

CONTENTS: Book One.

* ספר העקרים | לרבי | יוסף אלבו | הוגה על פי כתבי יד שונים

והוצאות עתיקות ונעתק | לשפת אנגלית | מאת | יצחק הוזיק |

פרופיסור לפילוסופיא באוניורסיטא דפינסילוניא | מאמר ראשון

ו-מאמר רביעי | חלק שני [seal 2c] | פילאדלפיא | החברה היהודית

להוצאת ספרים אשר באמיריקא | תר"ץ |

**"To the memory | of | William Romaine Newbold | ."

"The work was composed in the early part of the fifteenth century and has remained a popular work among the Jews. Modern students and readers may, through it, get an insight into the mediaeval Jewish mind far removed, no doubt, from thoughts of the present day, and yet in many things surprisingly modern. It would appear that concerning the eternal verities, the problems besetting the human mind have changed but little." — Advertisement, p. 1.

5706–1946 edition: as above, with seal 3b. Verso of title-page: "Second Impression, 1946."

Sefer Ha-'Ikkarim
Vol. II

SEFER HA'IKKARIM | Book of Principles | By | Joseph Albo | Critically edited on the basis of manuscripts | and old editions and provided with | a translation and notes | By | Isaac Husik, LL.B., M.A., Ph.D. | Professor of Philosophy | at the Uni-

168

versity of Pennsylvania | Volume Two | [*seal 2c*] | Philadelphia |
The Jewish Publication Society of America | 1929 |

COLLATION: 16°. 4 p. l., 219 p. (1. 1–3, same as v. 1, p. [v–x];
1. 4, Contents; p. 1–219 (paged in duplicate), Text and Translation
(on opposite pages).) front. (facsim.)

See v. 1, 1929, for Hebrew title and binding note.

CONTENTS: Book two.

Outlines of Jewish History

Outlines | of | JEWISH HISTORY | From B. C. E. 586 to C. E.
1929 | By | Lady Magnus | Revised by M. Friedländer, Ph.D. |
With additional chapters by | Solomon Grayzel, Ph.D. |
[*seal 2b*] | Third revised American edition | Philadelphia |
The Jewish Publication Society of America | 1929 |

COLLATION: 12°. xxiii, 418 p. (p. [i] Half-title; p. [iii] Title;
p. [iv] Copyright; p. [v] Preface to the Society's edition, by The
Committee; p. [ii, vi] blank; p. [vii]–viii, Preface by Katie Magnus;
p. [ix]–xxiii, Contents; p. [1]–397, Text; p. 398–407, Chronological
Table; p. [408] blank; p. 409–418, Index.) Colored maps (including
front.).

Issued in red cloth; front cover: title and author within single
rule box; back: title, author, publisher, all in black.

See 1890 for earlier editions.

A new Preface to the Society's edition, dated September, 1929,
replaces the one in the earlier editions.

"As an aid to teachers and pupils there have been incorporated
in this edition five maps, originally prepared for 'A History of the
Jewish People,' by Max L. Margolis and Alexander Marx, published
by the Society in 1927." — Society's preface, p. [v].

1939: "1,000 copies reprinted."— *AJYB*, 5701, p. 685; 1942:
"1,400 copies." — *AJYB*, 5704, p. 687; 1945: "1,000 copies."—
AJYB, 5707, p. 649.

5708–1948 edition: as above, with seal 3b.

Wonder Tales

[*Line of florets*] | WONDER TALES | Of Bible Days | [*line of florets*] | Rabbinic legends | retold for Jewish children | by | Elma Ehrlich Levinger | Author of "Playmates in Egypt," etc. | [*seal 2b*] | Philadelphia | The Jewish Publication Society of America | 1929 |

COLLATION: 12°. viii, 348 p. (p. [i] Title; p. [ii] Copyright; p. [iii] Dedication*; p. [iv] Acknowledgments; p. [v] Table of Contents; p. [vi] blank; p. vii–viii, A word to the children who will read this book; p. [1]–348, Text.) plates (including front.).

Issued in tan cloth; front cover: title, author; back: title, author, publisher all in brown.

*"This collection | of stories for children | is dedicated in memory of | a happy childhood | to the memory of | My Father | ."

CONTENTS: I. Abraham. The boy who broke the idols. II. Joseph. The slave who became a prince. III. Moses. The shepherd of the wilderness. IV. David. The cave where David slept. V. Solomon. The king who became a beggar. VI. Elijah. The friend of the needy.

Illustrated by Todros Geller.

5707–1947 edition: title-page reset, with seal 3b. Verso of title-page: "Reprinted, 1943; Reprinted, 1947."

1930

The American Jewish Year Book
5691

The American Jewish | Year Book | 5691 | September 23, 1930, to September 11, 1931 | Volume 32 | Edited by | Harry Schneiderman | for the | American Jewish Committee | [*seal 2a*] | Philadelphia | The Jewish Publication Society of America | 1930 |

COLLATION: 12°. ix, 436 p. (p. [i] Title; p. [ii] Copyright; p. [iii] Preface; p. v–vii, Special articles in previous issues; p. [iv, viii] blank; p. [ix] Contents; p. [1]–281, Text; p. 283–333, 23rd annual report of the American Jewish Committee; p. [282, 334] blank; p. [335]–436, Report of the 42nd year of The Jewish Publication Society of America 1929–1930.) front. (port. of Louis Marshall) Bound uniformly with 5660 (1899–1900) without seal.

"Some additions have been made to the group of directories and lists which appear recurrently in this series; lists of Jewish hospitals, homes for indigent children, and homes for the aged have been included, and the other lists have been carefully revised and brought up to date." — Preface.

SPECIAL ARTICLE: Louis Marshall, a biographical sketch, by Cyrus Adler, pp. 21–55.

London

... | LONDON | By | Elkan Nathan Adler | [*seal 2b*] | Philadelphia | The Jewish Publication Society of America | 1930 |

At head of title: Jewish Communities Series.

COLLATION: 16°. xv, 255 p. (p. [i] Title; p. [ii] Copyright; p. [iii] Illustrations; p. [v] Dedication*; p. [iv, vi] blank; p. vii–xv, Table of Contents; p. 1–224, Text; p. 225–227, Bibliography; p. [228] blank; p. 229–239, Chronological Annals; p. 240, Additional Note; p. 241–255, Index.) plates, ports., map.

Bound uniformly with Aron Freimann, *Frankfort*, 1929.

*"To | Philip S. Henry | Schoolfellow, Friend, and Fellow-Traveller, | This Sketch is affectionately inscribed | ."

Sabbatai Zevi

SABBATAI ZEVI | A tragedy in three acts | and six scenes with | a prologue and | an epilogue | By | Sholom Ash | Authorized Translation from the Russian Version | By | Florence Whyte |

and | George Rapall Noyes | [*seal 2b*] | Philadelphia | The Jewish Publication Society of America | 1930 |

COLLATION: 12°. 131 p. (p. [1] Half-title; p. [2] blank; p. [3] Title; p. [4] Copyright; p. [5] Illustrations; p. [6] [Quotation from] Babylonian Talmud; p. [7]–131, Text.) 4 plates (including front.).

Issued in gray cloth; front cover: illustration, title; back: title, rule, author, publisher all in black.

Venice

... | VENICE | By | Cecil Roth | [*seal 2b*] | Philadelphia | The Jewish Publication Society of America | 1930 |

At head of title: Jewish Communities Series.

COLLATION: 16°. x, 380 p. (p. [i] Title; p. [ii] Copyright; p. [iii] Illustrations; p. [v] [Quotation from] Childe Harold, IV.iv.; p. [vii] Table of Contents; p. [iv, vi, viii] blank; p. ix–x, Preface; p. 1–358, Text; p. 359–369, Epilogue; p. [370] blank; p. 371–372, Bibliography; p. 373–380, Index.) plates (including front.), folded plan.

Bound uniformly with Aron Freimann, *Frankfort*, 1929.

Sefer Ha-'Ikkarim
Vol. III

SEFER HA-'IKKARIM | Book of Principles | By | Joseph Albo | Critically edited on the basis of manuscripts | and old editions and provided with | a translation and notes | By | Isaac Husik,

172

LL.B., M.A., Ph.D. | Professor of Philosophy | at the University of Pennsylvania | Volume Three | [*seal 2c*] | Philadelphia | The Jewish Publication Society of America | 1930 |

COLLATION: 16°. 4 p. 1., 351 p. (1. 1–3, same as v. 1, p. [v–x]; 1. 4, Contents; p. 1–351 (pages in duplicate), Text and Translation (on opposite pages).) front. (facsim.)

See v. 1, 1929, for Hebrew title and binding note.

CONTENTS: Book three.

Sefer Ha-'Ikkarim
Vol. IV

SEFER HA-'IKKARIM | Book of Principles | By | Joseph Albo | Critically edited on the basis of manuscripts | and old editions and provided with | a translation and notes | By | Isaac Husik, LL.B., M.A., Ph.D. | Professor of Philosophy | at the University of Pennsylvania | Volume Four | Part One [and Part Two] | [*seal 2c*] | Philadelphia | The Jewish Publication Society of America | 1930 |

COLLATION: 16°. 2 v. (paged continuously). (v. 4; part 1: 4 p. 1., 272 p. (1. 1–3, same as v. 1, p. [v–x], 1. 4, Contents; p. 1–272 (paged in duplicate), Text and Translation (on opposite pages); v. 4, part 2: 4 p. 1., 273–597 p. (1. 1–4, same as v. 4, part 1; p. 272–498 (paged in duplicate), Text and Translation (on opposite pages); p. [499]–597, Indices.) front. (facsims.)

See v. 1, 1929, for Hebrew title and binding note.

CONTENTS: v. 4, part 1: Book Four (chapters 1–28). — v. 4, part 2: Book Four (chapters 29–51). — Index of sources. — Bibliography. — List of Biblical passages. — List of rabbinical passages. — List of Aristotelian passages. — Additions and Corrections. — General Index.

173

1931

The American Jewish Year Book
5692

The American Jewish | Year Book | 5692 | September 12, 1931, to September 30, 1932 | Volume 33 | Edited by | Harry Schneiderman | for the | American Jewish Committee | [*seal 2a*] | Philadelphia | The Jewish Publication Society of America | 1931 |

COLLATION: 12°. ix, 512 p. (p. [i] Title; p. [ii] Copyright; p. [iii]–iv, Preface; p. [v–vii] Special articles in previous issues; p. [viii] blank; p. [ix] Contents; p. [1]–338, Text; p. 339–402, 24th annual report of the American Jewish Committee; p. [403]–512, Report of the 43rd year of The Jewish Publication Society of America 1930–1931; 6 l., Advertisements.)

Bound uniformly with 5660 (1899–1900) without seal.

" We present several interesting lists — Jews who have served or are serving as Governors of States, as Judges of United States and State Courts, and as Ambassadors and Ministers of the United States in foreign lands; we present also a complete list of Jews who have won the Nobel Prize, in view of additions to their number since the article on that subject appeared in Volume 25." — Preface, p. [iii].

SPECIAL ARTICLES: Nathan Straus, by David de Sola Pool, pp. 135–154. — Ben Selling, by Henry J. Berkowitz, pp. 155–163. — Jewish women's organization in the United States, by Rebekah Kohut, pp. 165–201. — Jewish inmates of the State Prisons of the United States 1920–1929, by H. S. Linfield, pp. 203–211.

The Holy Scriptures

THE HOLY SCRIPTURES | An Abridgment | for use in the | Jewish school and home | [*seal 2b*] | Philadelphia | The Jewish Publication Society of America | 1931–5691 |

174

COLLATION: 8°. xxiv, 795 p. (p. [i] Half-title; p. [ii] (Note)*;
p. [iii] Title; p. [iv] Copyright, All rights reserved; p. v–vi, Preface;
p. vii–xxiv, Table of Contents; p. 1–795, Text.)

Issued in light blue cloth; front cover: title, blind stamped;
back: title and publisher in gilt.

*"This book is published from The Minnie, Katharine and Julia
Mayer Fund bequeathed by Julia Mayer to The Hebrew Sunday
School Society of Philadelphia which gratefully dedicated this volume
to the memory of Minnie, Katharine and Julia Mayer."

"This book is an abridgment of the Holy Scriptures and is
based upon the translation of the Hebrew Bible issued by the Jewish
Publication Society of America.

"The publication of this volume has been made possible by the
Hebrew Sunday School Society of Philadelphia.

"This book has been compiled, edited and prepared for the press
by Miss Emily Solis-Cohen who worked in cooperation with a
committee which represented jointly the Hebrew Sunday School
Society of Philadelphia and the Jewish Publication Society of America." — Preface, p. v.

5705–1945 edition: as above, with seal 3b. Verso of title-
page: "3rd Impression, 1945 19th Thousand."

Introduction to the Talmud and Midrash

INTRODUCTION | to | THE TALMUD AND MIDRASH | By | Hermann
L. Strack | Authorized Translation on the Basis | of the
Author's Revised Copy of the | Fifth German Edition | [*seal
2a*] | Philadelphia | Jewish Publication Society of America |
1931 |

COLLATION: 8°. xvii, 374 p. (p. [i] Half-title; p. [iii] Title;
p. [iv] Copyright; p. v, The Translator's Preface; p. vi–vii, From
the Author's Preface and Foreword to the First and Fourth Editions;
p. viii–ix, Foreword to the Fifth Edition; p. [ii, x] blank; p. xi–xiii,
Table of Contents; p. xv–xvii, Preliminary remarks; p. [1]–234,

Text; p. [235]–349, Notes; p. [350] blank; p. [351]–362, Indexes; p. [363]–374, Appendices.)

Issued in dark blue cloth; back: title, author and publisher in gilt.

"This English translation of the ... work is to all intents and purposes a sixth edition of the original. It was prepared, according to instructions of the author as transmitted by his widow, from a copy of the fifth German edition revised by the author and marked: 'Manuscript ready for the Printer. For the English translation'." — Translator's preface, p. v.

Translator: Max L. Margolis.

5705–1945 reprint. "4,000 copies — 2nd printing." *AJYB,* 5707, p. 649.

Rules for The Jewish Publication Society Press

RULES | for | The Jewish Publication | Society Press | [*seal 2c*] | Philadelphia | Jewish Publication Society of America | 1931 |

COLLATION: nar. 12°. 13 p., 2 unnumbered pages.

Issued in light green paper covers; title as above, within black double rule box.

"The suggestions contained in this pamphlet are prepared for the use of the Jewish Publication Society Press." — p. 3.

1932
Legends of Palestine

LEGENDS OF PALESTINE | By | Zev Vilnay | [*seal 2a*] | Philadelphia | The Jewish Publication Society of America | 1932 |

COLLATION: 8°. xiii, 492 p. (p. [i] Title; p. [ii] Copyright; p. iii–iv, Preface by The Publication Committee; p. v–x, Table of

Contents; p. xi–xiii, List of Illustrations; p. [1]–430, Text; p. 431–480, The sources of the legends; p. 481–492, Classification of the legends.) illus. (including maps)

Issued in light blue cloth; front cover: title, blind stamped; back: title, rule, author, and publisher in gilt.

"A translation with additions and re-arrangements, of a Hebrew volume published . . . under the title *Agadot Erez Yisrael*, which appeared in London in 1929." — Preface, p. iii.

The American Jewish Year Book 5693

The American Jewish | Year Book | 5693 | October 1, 1932 to September 20, 1933 | Volume 34 | Edited by | Harry Schneiderman | for the | American Jewish Committee | [*seal 2a*] | Philadelphia | The Jewish Publication Society of America | 1932 |

COLLATION: 12°. ix, 438 p. (p. [i] Title; p. [ii] Copyright; p. iii, Preface; p. [iv] blank; p. v–viii, Special articles in previous issues; p. [ix] Contents; p. [1]–275, Text; p. 277–343, 25th annual report of the American Jewish Committee; p. [276, 344] blank; p. [345]–438, Report of the 44th year of The Jewish Publication Society of America 1931–1932.) front. (port. of Julius Rosenwald)

Bound uniformly with 5660 (1899–1900) without seal.

"The lists of Jews who have been or are Governors of States, Judges of United States and State Courts, Ambassadors and Ministers of the United States, and of Jews who have won the Nobel prize, are repeated in this volume to permit the correction of errors in the preceding issue, or the addition of new names made necessary by recent appointments or elections. The recurrent features of the Year Book have been carefully brought up to date." — Preface.

SPECIAL ARTICLES: Dr. Lee K. Frankel 1867–1931, by Solomon Lowenstein, pp. 121–140. — Julius Rosenwald, by Pauline K. Angell, pp. 141–176.

A History of the Marranos

A HISTORY OF THE | MARRANOS | By | Cecil Roth | [*seal 2a*] | Philadelphia | The Jewish Publication Society of America | 1932 |

COLLATION: 8°. xii, 422 p. (p. [i] Title; p. [ii] Copyright; p. [iii] Dedication: "For | Irene | 6.VI.31. | "; p. [v] "Contra la verdad no ay fuerça;" p. vii, Table of Contents; p. ix, List of illustrations; p. [iv, vi, viii, x] blank; p. xi–xii, Foreword; p. 1–376, Text; p. [377]–400, Notes; p. 401–407, Bibliography; p. [408] blank; p. 409–422, Index.) illus.

Issued in red cloth; front cover: title, blind stamped; back: title, rule, author and publisher in gilt.

"It is not . . . its importance which gives the history of the Marranos its appeal, but its incredible romance. The submerged life which blossomed out at intervals into such exotic flowers; the unique devotion which could transmit the ancestral ideals unsullied, from generation to generation, despite the Inquisition and its horrors; the figures of rare heroism which every now and again emerged to burst upon the world; the extraordinary climax in our own days — all combine to make a story unparralleled in history for sheer dramatic appeal." — Foreword, p. xi–xii.

Hebrew translation:

ססיל רות | תולדות האנוסים | נתירגם שמואל גילאין | "דעת" — הוצאת "עם עובד", תל־אביב, תשי"ב.

5707–1947 edition: title-page reset, with seal 3b. Verso of title-page: "Revised edition, 1941; Second Impression, 1947." "2,000 copies — 3rd printing."— *AJYB*, 5709, p. 850.

Woman in Jewish Law and Life

. . . | Woman in Jewish Law and Life | An inquiry and a guide to literary sources of | information concerning the nature of Jewish law, and the status accorded woman | [Quotation from] Genesis 5.1, 2. | By | Emily Solis-Cohen, Jr. | [*seal of J WB*] | Published by the | Jewish Publication Society of America | for the | Jewish Welfare Board | 71 West 47th Street | New York City | [1932]

At head of title: Jewish Welfare Board Publications | [*rule*].

COLLATION: 12°. viii, 73 p. (p. [i] Title; p. [ii] Copyright, 1932 by The Jewish Welfare Board, Printed at The Jewish Publication Society Press . . .; p. [iii] In Acknowledgment; p. [iv] blank; p. v–vi, Special Acknowledgments; p. vii–viii, Contents; p. 1–63, Text; p. [64] blank; p. [65]–73, Bibliography.)

Issued in gray paper covers; on front: title as above, without imprint, all within double rule box.

1933

Purim or the Feast of Esther

PURIM | or | The Feast of Esther | An historical study | By | N. S. Doniach | Sometime Hody Scholar of Wadham College, Oxford. | [*seal 2b*] | Philadelphia | The Jewish Publication Society of America | 1933 |

COLLATION: 12°. 5 p. l., 277 p. (1. 1, Title, verso Copyright; 1. 2, Dedication: "To my mother;" l. 3, [Quotation from] Racine, Preface to *Esther*; l. 4, Contents; l. 5, Preface; verso of 1. 2–5, blank; p. 1–5, Introduction; p. [7]–245, Text; p. [6, 246] blank; p. [247]–266, Notes; p. 267–268, Bibliography . . .; p. 269–277, Index.)

Issued in red cloth; back: line, title, rule, sub-title, rule, author, rule, publisher, line all in blue on silver paper label.

An "attempt not only to describe Purim but also to solve the problems of its origin and history. . . . to the best of my knowledge, this is the first attempt to give so detailed a portrayal of a Jewish festival." — Author's preface.

The American Jewish Year Book
5694

The American Jewish | Year Book | 5694 | September 21, 1933 to September 9, 1934 | Volume 35 | Edited by | Harry Schneiderman | for the | American Jewish Committee | [*seal 2a*] | Philadelphia | The Jewish Publication Society of America | 1933 |

COLLATION: 12°. ix, 401 p. (p. [i] Title; p. [ii] Copyright; p. iii–iv, Preface; p. v–viii, Special articles in previous issues; p. [ix] Contents; p. [1]–278, Text; p. [279]–315, The American Jewish Committee 26th annual report 1932; p. [316] blank; p. [317]–401, Report of the 45th year of The Jewish Publication Society of America 1932–1933; 4 l., Advertisements.)

Bound uniformly with 5660 (1899–1900) without seal.

"The year 5693 will stand out in the post-Exilic history of the Jewish people as the year in which a country universally regarded as an outpost of civilization and culture permitted itself to be led astray by a malicious race mania onto a path of the most degrading mass persecution. A great part of the Review of the Year 5693, contained in this volume, the thirty-fifth of the series, is, therefore, devoted to a description of recent events in Germany and their repercussions in other lands. In an appendix to the Review, we present the text of the petition of Franz Bernheim to the League of Nations, and the minutes of the discussions of the League Council regarding that petition which was based on the minority clauses of the German-Polish convention of 1922 in respect of German Upper Silesia." — Preface, p. iii.

SPECIAL ARTICLES: Bernheim Petition to the League of Nations, pp. 74–101. — Max Leopold Margolis, a sketch by Cyrus Adler, pp. 139–144. — Cyrus L. Sulzberger, by Morris D. Waldman, pp. 145–156. — The Synagogue and Jewish Communal Activities, by Horace Stern, pp. 157–170.

180

Mekilta de-Rabbi Ishmael
Vol. I

MEKILTA | de-Rabbi Ishmael | A critical edition on the basis
of the | manuscripts and early editions with | an English
translation, introduction | and notes | By | Jacob Z. Lauterbach,
Ph.D. | Professor at the | Hebrew Union College, Cincinnati |
Volume One | [*seal 2b*] | Philadelphia | The Jewish Publication
Society of America | 1933 |

COLLATION: 16°. 3, [iv]–lxv, 255 p. (3 p., Advertisement (of
Series of Jewish Classics); p. [v] Series title: "The Schiff Library of
Jewish Classics;" p. [viii] Title; p. [ix] Hebrew title*; p. [x] Copy-
right; p. [xi] Contents; p. [iv, vi–vii, x, xii] blank; p. xiii–lxiv,
Introduction; p. lxv, Sigla used in apparatus criticus; p. 1–255 (paged
in duplicate), Text and Translation (on opposite pages).)

Bound uniformly with Gabirol, *Selected religious poems*, 1923.

This is the sixth book (in three volumes) in the Series. Volumes
1–2 issued in 1933; v. 3, in 1935.

CONTENTS: Pisḥa. — Beshallaḥ.

* מכילתא | דרבי ישמעאל | הוצאה חדשה על פי כתבי יד
ודפוסים ישנים עם שינויי נוסחאות | ומראה מקומות ותרגום והערות
בשפת אנגלית | מאת | יעקב בצלאל הכהן לויטערבאך | פרופיסור
בבית מדרש הרבנים בסינסינאטי | ספר ראשון [שני] [ושלישי] |
[*seal 2b*] פילאדלפיא | החברה היהודית להוצאת ספרים אשר
באמיריקא | תרצ"ד]-תרצ"ה[|

1950: "Reprinted 2,450 copies of each of the three volumes . . .
making a total of 3,750 copies of each volume." — *AJYB*, 1952,
p. 574.

Mekilta de-Rabbi Ishmael
Vol. II

MEKILTA | de-Rabbi Ishmael | A critical edition on the basis of the | manuscripts and early editions with | an English translation, introduction | and notes | By | Jacob Z. Lauterbach, Ph.D. | Professor at the | Hebrew Union College, Cincinnati | Volume Two | [*seal 2b*] | Philadelphia | The Jewish Publication Society of America | 1933 |

COLLATION: 16°. 4 p. l., 292 p. (l. 1–4, same as v. 1, p. [v–xi]; p. 1–292 (paged in duplicate), Text and Translation (on opposite pages).)

See Volume 1, 1933, for Hebrew title and binding note.

CONTENTS: Shirata. — Vayassa. — Amalek. — Baḥodesh.

Additament to Peniné Ha-Zohar

ADDITAMENT | TO PENINÉ HA-ZOHAR | Containing saws, bon mots | controversies, and parables | culled from the Zohar and | annotated | by | Nehemiah S. Libowitz | [*seal 2a*] | Printed by the Hebrew Press of | The Jewish Publication Society of America | Philadelphia | 1933 |

COLLATION: 8°. [64 p.] סד ע'.

Cover-title.

Text and added title-page in Hebrew: תשלום פניני הזהר.

[Note: Although it bears its seal, the book is not a publication of The Society.]

1934

A Life of Menasseh ben Israel

A LIFE OF MENASSEH | BEN ISRAEL | Rabbi, Printer, and Diplomat | By | Cecil Roth | [*seal 2a*] | Philadelphia | The Jewish Publication Society of America | 1934 |

COLLATION: 12°. xii, 373 p. (p. [i] Title; p. [ii] Copyright; p. [iii] Dedication: "For mother;"; p. [v] [Quotation from] De Barrios, Vida de Isaac Usiel, p. 46; p. [vii] Table of Contents; p. ix, List of Illustrations; p. [iv, vi, viii, x] blank; p. xi–xii, Preface; p. 1–287, Text; p. [289]–307, Bibliography; p. [309]–355, Notes; p. [288, 308, 356] blank; p. 357–373, Index.) plate, ports. (including front. facsims.)

Issued in gray cloth; back: title, design, author and publisher in gilt.

5705–1945 edition: as above, with seal 3b. Verso of title-page: "Second Printing, 1945." Facsimiles only reproduced.

The American Jewish Year Book
5695

The American Jewish | Year Book | 5695 | September 10, 1934 to September 27, 1935 | Volume 36 | Edited by | Harry Schneiderman | for the | American Jewish Committee | [*seal 2a*] | Philadelphia | The Jewish Publication Society of America | 1934 |

COLLATION: 12°. ix, 594 p. (p. [i] Title; p. [ii] Copyright; p. [iii]–iv, Preface; p. v–viii, Special articles in previous issues; p. [ix] Contents; p. [1]–403, Text; p. [404] blank; p. [405]–474, The American Jewish Committee 27th annual report 1933; p. [475]–594, Report of the 46th year of The Jewish Publication Society of America 1933–1934.)

Bound uniformly with 5660 (1899–1900) without seal.

"The continuing crisis in the lives of the Jews of Germany is reflected in the present volume, as it was in its predecessor. Not only is a considerable part of the List of Events given over to occurrences affecting the Jews of that country, but some of the tragic effects are indicated also in the Necrology which includes the names of a number of distinguished German Jews who died by their own hands, and in the notices of appointments of scholars and teachers, ousted from the laboratories and the lecture halls of German colleges and universities, to positions of honor in the schools of foreign countries, where they were cordially welcomed. The present volume also contains a special article [by Melvin M. Fagen] dealing with discussions of minority and refugee questions at the 1933 Assembly of the League of Nations, evoked by Germany's degradation of Jews and Christian descendants of Jews, one of whose effects was the flight from Germany of some sixty thousand refugees from a campaign of persecution which has outraged the conscience of mankind." — Preface, p. [iii].

SPECIAL ARTICLES: Hyman Gerson Enelow, by David Philipson, pp. 23–53. — George Alexander Kohut, by Alexander Marx, pp. 55–64. — The Federation in the changing American scene, by B. M. Selekman, pp. 65–87. — Minority and refugee questions before the League of Nations, pp. 89–119. — Index to volumes 1–35 of the American Jewish Year Book, pp. 561–580.

Ma'aseh Book

MA'ASEH BOOK | Book of Jewish Tales and Legends | Translated from the Judeo-German | By | Moses Gaster | Late Chief Rabbi of the Sephardic Community | of England | Volume One [and Two] | [*seal 2b*] | Philadelphia | The Jewish Publication Society of America | 1934 |

COLLATION: 16°. 2 v. (paged continuously). v. 1: 2, [iii]–xliii, 316 p. (2 p., Advertisement [of Series of Jewish Classics]; p. [v] Series title: "The Schiff Library of Jewish Classics;" p. [vii] Title; p. [viii] Copyright; p. ix–xv, Contents; p. [iii–iv, vi, xvi] blank; p. xvii–xliii, Introduction; p. 1–316, Text.); v. 2: x, 317–694 p. (p. [i–iv] same as v. 1, p. [v–viii]; p. v–x, Contents; p. 317–

657, Text; p. [658] blank; p. 659–662, Appendix; p. [663]–694, Notes.)

Bound uniformly with Gabirol, *Selected religious poems*, 1923.

This is the seventh book (in two volumes) in the Series.

1945: "4,000 sets — 2nd printing."— *AJYB*, 5707, p. 649.

Selected Poems of Moses Ibn Ezra

Selected poems | of | Moses Ibn Ezra | Translated into English | by | Solomon Solis-Cohen | M.D., D.H.L., Sc.D. | From a critical text | edited and annotated by | Heinrich Brody, Ph.D. | [*seal 2b*] | Philadelphia | The Jewish Publication Society of America | 1934 |

COLLATION: 12°. 2, xxxv, 401 p. (2 p., Advertisement [of Series of Jewish Classics]; 1 l., Series title: "The Schiff Library of Jewish Classics," verso blank; p. [ii] Title; p. [iii] Hebrew title*; p. [iv] Copyright; p. [v] [Editor's] Dedication**; p. [vii] [Translator's] Dedication***; p. [ix] Contents; p. [i, vi, viii, x] blank; p. xi–xviii, Concerning the translation a foreword by Solomon Solis-Cohen; p. xix–xxxv, Introduction by H. Brody; p. [1]–171 (paged in duplicate), Text and Translation (on opposite pages); p. [173]–192, Notes to introduction; p. [193]–347, Notes on text; p. [349]–391, Notes on translation; p. 393, List of sources; p. [172, 348, 392, 394] blank; p. 395–398, Index of first lines of poems; p. 399–401, Index of selections from Tarshish.)

Bound uniformly with Gabirol, *Selected religious poems*, 1923.

This is the eighth book in the Series.

* מחברת משירי | משה בן יעקב אבן עזרא | מוגהים ומבוארים על ידי | חיים בראדי | עם תרגום אנגלי | מאת | שלמה דא סילוא סוליס־כהן | [*seal 2b*] | פילאדלפיא | החברה היהודית להוצאת ספרים אשר באמריקה | תרצ"ד |

** מגש. | לידידו החכם | דר. ישראל דאווידזאן | מאת | העורך | .

***"To his sister | Charity | teacher incomparable | his first

185

instructor in the | sacred tongue | the translator brings in love | these
fruits of the latter harvest | ."

5706–1945 edition: as above, with seal 3b. Verso of title-page:
"Second Edition, 1945."

1935

The Decay of Czarism

THE DECAY OF CZARISM | The Beiliss Trial | A contribution
to the history of the political | reaction during the last years |
of Russian Czarism. | Based on unpublished materials in the |
Russian archives | By | Alexander B. Tager | Translated from
the Russian original | [*seal 2a*] | Philadelphia | The Jewish
Publication Society of America | 1935 |

COLLATION: 8°. xxi, 297 p. (p. [i] Half-title; p. [iii] Title;
p. [iv] Copyright; p. [v] Dedication: "To my children;" p. vii–x,
Table of Contents; p. xi, List of Photostats [i. e. facsimiles]; p. [ii,
vi, xii] blank; p. xiii–xvi, Foreword by The Publication Committee;
p. xvii–xxi, Introduction; p. 1–231, Text; p. [232] blank; p. [233]–
270, Appendices; p. [271]–297, Index.) facsims.

Issued in dark green cloth; back: title, rule, author and publisher
in gilt.

Mendel Beiliss was tried in the Kiev Circuit court (Okriuzh-
noi sud) September-October 1913, for the murder of Andrei Iush-
chinskii.

"This book has appeared in the Russian language [Tsarskaya
Rossiya i Dielo Beilisa, Moscow, 1933]. The Russian edition differs
from this one in two respects: first, it contains more details about the
Czaristic regime and the Beiliss case, and second, it has a complete
list of the sources upon which this work is based." — Appendix,
p. 235.

P. 235–250: "Archive cases ... which served as the foundation
of this book."

The American Jewish Year Book
5696

The American Jewish | Year Book | 5696 | September 28, 1935 to September 16, 1936 | Volume 37 | Edited by | Harry Schneiderman | for | The American Jewish Committee | [*seal 2a*] | Philadelphia | The Jewish Publication Society of America | 1935 |

COLLATION: 12°. ix, 546 p. (p. [i] Title; p. [ii] Copyright; p. iii–iv, Preface; p. v–viii, Special articles in previous issues; p. [ix] Contents; p. [1]–385, Text; p. [387]–461, The American Jewish Committee 28th annual report 1935; p. [386, 462] blank; p. [463]– 546, Report of the 47th year of The Jewish Publication Society of America 1934–1935.)

Bound uniformly with 5660 (1899–1900) without seal.

"In recording the leading events of Jewish interest which have taken place throughout the world during the past year, we have, in response to many requests, reverted to the medium of an article. The review in the present volume was prepared jointly by the Editor and Mr. Melvin M. Fagen." — Preface, p. iv.

SPECIAL ARTICLES: Max J. Kohler, by Irving Lehman, pp. 21–25. — Adolph S. Ochs, by Louis Rich, pp. 27–53. — Edwin Wolf, by Simon Miller, pp. 55–60. — Maimonides, by Solomon Zeitlin, pp. 61–97. — The Jew in agriculture in the United States, by Gabriel Davidson, pp. 99–134.

Mekilta de-Rabbi Ishmael
Vol. III

MEKILTA | de-Rabbi Ishmael | A critical edition on the basis of the | manuscripts and early editions with | an English translation, introduction | and notes | By | Jacob Z. Lauterbach, Ph.D. | Professor at the | Hebrew Union College, Cincinnati |

Volume Three | [*seal 2b*] | Philadelphia | The Jewish Publication Society of America | 1935 |

COLLATION: 16°. 4 p. l., 272 p. (l. 1–4, same as v. 1, p. [v–xi]; p. 1–211 (paged in duplicate), Text and Translation (on opposite pages); p. [213]–257, Indices; p. [212, 258] blank; p. [259]–271, Page Concordance; p. 272, Corrigenda.)

See Volume 1, 1933, for Hebrew title and binding note.

CONTENTS: Nezikin. — Kaspa. — Shabbatta.

1936

Vienna

... | VIENNA | By | Max Grunwald | [*seal 2b*] | Philadelphia | The Jewish Publication Society of America | 1936 |

At head of title: Jewish Communities Series.

COLLATION: 16°. xxiv, 557 p. (p. [i] Title; p. [ii] Copyright; p. [iii] List of Illustrations; p. [v] (Note)*; p. [vii] [Four lines of verse from] Edwin Arlington Robinson; p. ix–xv, Table of Contents; p. [xvii] Foreword by The Publication Committee; p. [iv, vi, viii, xvi, xviii] blank; p. xix–xxiv, Introduction; p. 1–478, Text; p. [479]–530, Appendices; p. 531–538, Bibliography; p. 539–557, Index.) 8 plates (including ports., facsims.).

Bound uniformly with Aron Freimann, *Frankfort*, 1929.

Verso of p. 557: "Text set in Scotch Roman Type by the Jewish Publication Society Press."

*"The publication of this volume has been made possible through the generosity of the late Abraham Erlanger who died October 1, 1929, and who left a bequest to the Jewish Publication Society of America to be used 'to defray the cost of writing or editing and publication of a specific work or works'."

"The manuscript of this book on the history of the Jews of Vienna was prepared by Dr. Max Grunwald in German. The translation into English was made by Dr. Solomon Grayzel." — Foreword.

The Jews of Germany

The Jews of Germany | A Story of Sixteen Centuries | by Marvin Lowenthal | [*seal 3a*] | Philadelphia | The Jewish Publication Society of America | 1936 |

COLLATION: 8°. 1 p. l., xi, 444 p. (l. 1, Half-title, verso blank; p. [i] Title; p. [ii] Copyright; p. [iii] Dedication*; p. [iv] blank; p. v–vi, Contents; p. vii–xi, Preface; 1 l. and p. 1–421, Text; p. 422–427, Selected Bibliography; p. [428] blank; p. 429–444, Index.)

Issued in dark blue cloth; top edges blue; front cover: title, author within square rule box; back: title, author, within square rule box; rule, publisher, rule all in gilt.

At end: "Text set in Granjon type."

*"In memory of | Henry and Diana L. Gitterman | ."

"Like most histories the present book tells more than its title is likely to suggest. For one thing the experience of the Jews in Germany was, until recent years, largely a counterpart of their experience elsewhere. Except for dates, personalities, and local circumstance, its story is the story of all Jewry." — Preface, p. vii.

Trade edition: New York, Longmans, Green and Co., 1936. 1938 reprint. — *AJYB*, 5700, p. 675; 1939: "2,000 copies."— *AJYB*, 5701, p. 685.

5705–1944 edition: as above, with seal 3b. Verso of title-page: "Sixth Impression, 1944."

The American Jewish Year Book 5697

The American Jewish | Year Book | 5697 | September 17, 1936 to September 5, 1937 | Volume 38 | Edited by | Harry Schneiderman | for | The American Jewish Committee | [*seal 3a*] | Philadelphia | The Jewish Publication Society of America | 1936 |

COLLATION: 12°. ix, 737 p. (p. [i] Title; p. [ii] Copyright; p. iii–iv, Preface; p. v–viii, Special articles in previous issues; p.

[ix] Contents; p. [1]–585, Text; p. [587]–651, The American Jewish Committee 29th annual report 1936; p. [586, 652] blank; p. [653]–737, Report of the 48th year of The Jewish Publication Society of America 1935–1936; 20 l., Catalogue.) front. (port. of Julius Stern Weyl)

Bound uniformly with 5660 (1899–1900) without seal. On front cover: titles of special articles in gilt.

"It has been deemed timely to present in this volume also an annotated list of the most important writings in the English language, produced as a result of the Nazi revolution in Germany, and especially the impact of that revolution on the Jews in that country, and on Jews everywhere else. We are fortunate in having, as the compiler and annotator of this list, Dr. Joshua Bloch, Chief of the Jewish Division of the New York Public Library.

". . . There is one new departure in the recurrent features of the Year Book. This is a completely revised directory of Jewish federations and welfare funds, prepared in the office of the Council of Jewish Federations and Welfare Funds. The other recurrent features, namely, the various directories and lists, and the article on statistics of Jews, have also been carefully revised and brought up to date on the basis of the latest available authoritative data." — Preface, p. iii, iv.

SPECIAL ARTICLES: Julius S. Weyl, A biographical appreciation, by David J. Galter, pp. 21–26. — Twenty-five years of Jewish education in the United States, by Israel S. Chipkin, pp. 27–116. — The migration of Jews in recent years, by John L. Bernstein, pp. 117–134. — Nazi-Germany and the Jews, an annotated bibliography, by Joshua Bloch, pp. 135–174.

Major Noah

MAJOR NOAH: | American-Jewish Pioneer | by Isaac Goldberg | Sometime Special Lecturer on Hispano-American Literature, | Harvard University | [*seal 3a*] | Philadelphia | The Jewish Publication Society of America | 1936 |

COLLATION: 8°. xvii, 316 p. (p. [i] The Life of Mordecai M. Noah (1785–1851); p. [iii] Title; p. [iv] Copyright; p. [v] By the same author . . .; p. vii–ix, Contents; p. [xi] List of Illustrations; p. [ii, vi, x, xii] blank; p. xiii–xvii, Foreword and Acknowledgments; p. 1–280, Text; p. 281–286, Appendix I "Addenda to Noah's Plays;" p. 287–293, Appendix II "Noah's wife and children;" p. [294] blank; p. 295–308, Bibliography; p. 309–316, Index.) 3 ports. (including front.), plate.

Issued in gray and light blue cloth; top edges blue; front cover: blue horizontal lines; decorations and title in black, sub-title and author in gray; back: title in gray on black; author, seal 3b, and publisher in gray on blue.

At end: "Text set in Caslon Old Style Type . . ."

"In preparing this biography of Mordecai Manuel Noah, one of the first United States, as distinguished from Colonial, Jews, I have in every possible instance gone back to the available documents, — his own writings, contemporary reports, official records, letters, magazines, newspapers and even consultation with descendants." — Author's foreword, p. xiii.

"Written in clear, vigorous English, the early period of American Jewish life, and the Jewish problems common to that day and to ours become alive; they are made part of our present day American Jewish heritage." — Mortimer J. Cohen, in *AJYB*, 5698, p. 869.

Trade edition: New York, Alfred A. Knopf, 1937.

5705–1944 edition: as above, with seal 3b. Verso of title-page: "Third Impression, 1944."

Mesillat Yesharim

MESILLAT YESHARIM | The Path of the Upright | By | Moses Hayyim Luzzatto | A critical edition provided with | a translation and notes | By | Mordecai M. Kaplan | [*seal 3c*] | Philadelphia | The Jewish Publication Society of America | 1936 |

COLLATION: 16°. 2, xxxvii, 230 p. (2 p., Advertisement [of Series of Jewish Classics]; p. [i] Series title: "The Schiff Library of Jewish Classics;" p. [iv] Title; p. [v] Hebrew title*; p. [vi] Copyright; p. [vii] Dedication: "To my mother;" p. [ii–iii, viii] blank; p. ix–x, Contents; p. xi–xxxvii, Introduction; p. 1–230 (paged in duplicate), Text and Translation (on opposite pages).

Bound uniformly with Gabirol, *Selected religious poems*, 1923.

This is the ninth book in the Series.

* מסלת ישרים | לרבי | משה חיים לוצאטו | הוצאה חדשה עם
שינויי נוסחאות ומראה מקומות ותרגום | והערות בשפת אנגלית |
מאת | מרדכי מנחם קפלן | [*seal 3c*] פילאדלפיא | החברה היהודית
להוצאת ספרים אשר באמיריקא | תרצ"ז |

5708–1948 edition: as above, with seal 3b. Verso of title-page: "Second Impression, 1948."

1937

Brand Plucked from the Fire

BRAND PLUCKED | FROM THE FIRE | אוּד מֻצָּל מֵאֵשׁ| By | Jessie Sampter | [*seal 3a*] | Philadelphia | The Jewish Publication Society of America | 1937 |

COLLATION: 8°. 1 l., xi, 211 p. (l. 1, Half-title, verso blank; p. [i] Title; p. [ii] Copyright; p. [iii] Dedication: "To you who are myself;" p. v–vii, Preface; p. [ix] Contents; p. [iv, viii, x] blank; p. [xi] Black and white drawings by Maxim B. Gottlieb; p. [1]–211, Text.) illus.

Issued in light blue paper boards with dark blue cloth back and corners; front cover: white label containing title and author within double rule box, in black; back: title and author within double rule box, publisher all in gilt.

Verso of p. 211: "The text of this book was set in the composing rooms of the Press of the Jewish Publication Society of America on the monotype in Garamont. This fine traditional letter was designed by Frederic W. Goudy exclusively for casting on the monotype machine."

CONTENTS: I. Land of Israel. II. Little songs of big and little things. III. Coming of peace. IV. Psalms in struggle. V. Diaspora.

"A number of these poems have appeared or been reprinted in collections, anthologies and year books of American or Jewish poetry ... The arrangement of these poems is not chronological. The book begins with the end, with Palestine, and ends with the longing for it. The 'Little Songs' were written over a period of many years, earlier and later than any of the other poems.

" 'The Psalms' were all written within one year, the 'Coming of Peace' a few years later, during the World War of 1914–18. Anyone interested in "dating" may care to know that those poems in which God is named were written before 1925. Each section is, on the whole, chronologically arranged." — Preface, p. v, vii.

"Interprets for us, in poetry, the struggles of a sensitive, Jewish spirit in these tumultuous, uncertain times for a faith by which to live. Despite the windy darkness of the world, she still sings the old songs of faith ... she sings of things, little and big, of the coming of peace among the nations, and she finds her redemption in the land of Israel. There, she summons her people not to despair. Under the poetic symbol of the little red flowers, the anemones, that bloom faithfully each Spring, she calls Israel to face the harsh realities involved in building the ancient homeland." — Mortimer J. Cohen, in *AJYB*, 5698, p. 869–870.

Hebrew translation with a preface by Henrietta Szold:

ישע סמפטר | אוד מצל מאש | שירים [עברית: פנחס לנדר] הוצאת

„עדי" תל־אביב, תש"ה. |

193

The American Jewish Year Book
5698

The American Jewish | Year Book | 5698 | September 6, 1937 to September 25, 1938 | Volume 39 | Edited by | Harry Schneiderman | for | The American Jewish Committee | [*seal 3a*] | Philadelphia | The Jewish Publication Society of America | 1937 |

COLLATION: 12°. x, 937 p. (p. [i] Title; p. [ii] Copyright; p. iii–iv, Preface; p. v–viii, Special articles in previous issues; p. ix–[x] Contents; p. [1]–780, Text; p. [781]–844, The American Jewish Committee 30th annual report 1937; p. [845]–937, Report of the 49th year of The Jewish Publication Society of America 1936–1937; 25 l., Catalogue.) front. (illus. from the painting by Leopold Pilichowski of the Dedication of the Hebrew University).

Bound uniformly with 5697 (1936–1937).

"The Review of the Year presented in this volume is again voluminous, owing largely to the unusually numerous events of Jewish interest which occurred during the period . . . As an appendix to the Review, there is given the official summary of the report of the British Royal Commission which investigated Arab-Jewish relations in Palestine. Inasmuch as the recommendations of that Commission will probably be the subject of discussion for many months to come, the inclusion of this summary will, it is hoped, be helpful to those interested.

"Aside from some changes in typography, the only other departure in connection with the recurrent features is the method of presentation of the directory of national Jewish organizations. It is believed that the new method will be found to have many advantages over that in use for so many years." — Preface, p. iv.

SPECIAL ARTICLES: Simon Wolfe Rosendale, A biographical sketch by G. Herbert Cone, pp. 25–28. — Richard J. H. Gottheil, A biographical sketch, by Louis I. Newman, pp. 29–46. — Jewish community organization in the United States. An outline of types

194

of organizations, activities and problems, by Maurice J. Karpf, pp. 47–148. — The Jewish Welfare Board — twenty years old, by Cyrus Adler, pp. 149–177. — The Hebrew University in Jerusalem, by Joseph Klausner, pp. 179–192. — American Jews and the Hebrew University, by Samuel B. Finkel, pp. 193–201.

Deuteronomy

... | DEUTERONOMY | with commentary | By | Joseph Reider, Ph.D. | Professor of Biblical Philology, Dropsie College | [*seal 3a*] | Philadelphia | The Jewish Publication Society of America | 5697–1937 |

At head of title: The Holy Scriptures | [rule] | .

COLLATION: 8°. xliv, 355 p. (p. [i] Half-title; p. [iii] Title; p. [iv] Copyright; p. [v] Foreword; p. vii–viii, Preface; p. ix, Table of Contents; p. [ii, vi, x] blank; p. xi–xliv, Introduction; p. 1–346, Text and Commentary; p. 347–355, Index.) 3 maps at end.

Issued in dark blue cloth; back: rules, series title, rule, title, rule, commentator, publisher and rules in gilt.

Verso of p. 355: "The text of this book was set in the composing rooms of the Press of the Jewish Publication Society of America on the monotype in Binny Old Style. The basis of this useful letter was a type cut in Scotland, and it was first put on the Monotype Machine in 1908."

See Margolis, *Micah*, 1908 for note on Series. This volume is the second in the series.

"The present Commentary on Deuteronomy reflects in the main, though not in every detail, the traditional point of view concerning the origin and composition of the Pentateuch." — Preface, p. vii.

5708–1948 edition: as above, with seal 3b. Verso of title-page: "Second Impression, 1948."

Hanukkah
The feast of lights

HANUKKAH | The feast of lights | Compiled and edited by | Emily Solis-Cohen, Jr. | [*seal 3a*] | Philadelphia | The Jewish Publication Society of America | 1937 |

COLLATION: 8°. xvii, 374 p. (p. [i] Half-title; p. [iii] Title; p. [iv] Copyright; p. [v] [Acknowledgments]; p. vii–x, Contents; p. [xi] List of Illustrations; p. [xii] "The victory of the spirit" by Louis D. Brandeis; p. xiii, To the reader by The Contributors; p. [ii, vi, xiv] blank; p. xv–xvii, Foreword; p. [1]–362, Text; p. 363–372, Bibliography; p. 373–374, Acknowledgments.) plates (including front.), music.

Issued in light blue cloth; top edges blue; front cover: title, rule, and compiler within single rule box; back: design, rule, compiler, rule, title, rule, publisher, rule, design, all in gilt.

Verso of l. at end: "The text of this book was set in the composing rooms of the Press of the Jewish Publication Society of America on the monotype in Binny Old Style. The basis of this useful letter was a type cut in Scotland, and it was first put on the Monotype Machine in 1908."

"History . . . poetry; plays and riddles with synagogue music, excerpts from the Apocrypha, the Talmud, and the Prayer-book . . . stories . . . for young and old." — To the reader, p. xiii.

"The covers of The Hanukkah Book [p. 308–334] have been spread apart to admit stories for the little ones [Book III "For the Young"] — for children in the nursery, for children growing into their teens, for all who like to hear Mother read tales from the long ago. These stories have been written especially for this Book." — 2nd ed., p. 311.

5708–1947 edition: as above, with seal 3b. Verso of title-page: "Revised Second edition, 1940; Reprinted, 1945; Reprinted, 1947." xix, 400 p.

1951: "Reprinted 1,500 copies . . . bringing the total to 7,500 copies." — *AJYB*, 1953, p. 595.

1938
Tomorrow's Bread

TOMORROW'S | BREAD | by | Beatrice Bisno | [*seal 3b*] | The Jewish Publication Society | of America | Philadelphia | 1938 |

[Note: The foregoing appears within a black single rule box.]

COLLATION: 8°. 4 p. l., 328 p. (l. 1, Half-title, l. 2*; l. 3, Title, verso Copyright, All rights reserved; l. 4, Dedication: "To Francis J. Oppenheimer"; verso of l. 1, 2, 4, blank; p. [1]–326, Text; p. 327–328, Yiddish, Hebrew, German and Russian words.)

Issued in gray cloth; front cover: title in gilt; back: rules, designs; rules, title, rule, and author on black; rules, designs, publisher, and rules in gilt.

*"The novel was chosen for the Edwin Wolf Award for the best novel of Jewish interest. The Award was given in memory of Edwin Wolf, a former President of the Jewish Publication Society of America, by his children. The judges of the contest were Dorothy Canfield Fisher, Fannie Hurst, and Edwin Wolf, 2nd."

Trade edition: New York, Liveright, 1938.

The Legends of the Jews

THE LEGENDS OF | THE JEWS | By | Louis Ginzberg | VII | INDEX | By | Boaz Cohen | [*seal 3a*] | Philadelphia | The Jewish Publication Society of America | 1938

COLLATION: 8°. ix, 612 p. (p. [i–iv] same as v. 1; p. [v] Contents; p. [vi] blank; p. vii–ix, Preface by Boaz Cohen; p. 1–515,

Index; p. [516] blank; p. 517–600, Passages cited; p. 601–612, Hebrew and Aramaic words; p. 612, Piyyutim.)

See 1909, v. 1, for binding.

"The plan and purpose of the *Legends of the Jews* has been thoroughly expounded by Prof. Ginzberg in his introductions to vols. I and V. Suffice it to say that this work represents the greatest single contribution to the study of the Agada within a century. Its significance lies not only in its unsurpassed collection of materials from all out of the way sources, but also in the fact that it paves the way for numerous monographs in the various fields of theology, folklore, superstition, customs and legends." — Boaz Cohen's preface, p. ix.

5706–1946 reprint, with seal 3b. "4,500 copies — 2nd printing." — *AJYB*, 5708, p. 813.

Selected Works of Israel Zangwill

SELECTED WORKS | of | ISRAEL | ZANGWILL | Children of the Ghetto | Ghetto Comedies | Ghetto Tragedies | A Golden Jubilee | Volume | [*seal 3c*] | The Jewish Publication Society | of America | Philadelphia MCMXXXVIII |

[Note: The foregoing appears within a black double rule box and an ornamental border in red. Author's name and seal also in red.]

COLLATION: 8°. xix, 553 p., 4 l., 485, viii, 486 p.

Issued in light green cloth; top edges green; front cover: title and author in gilt on black, within rule box and ornamental border in gilt; back: titles, author, publisher, on black, with ornamental designs on green, all in gilt.

Reproduces the text of:

Children of the Ghetto. New York, The Macmillan Company, 1895. See also 1892.

Ghetto Comedies. New York, The Macmillan Company, 1907.

"They that Walk in Darkness" [i. e. Ghetto Tragedies]. Philadelphia, The Jewish Publication Society of America, 1899.

Translations into French: of *Ghetto Comedies*:

Comédies du Ghetto; traduit de l'anglais par Mme. Marcel Girette. Paris: Rieder, 1928. CONTENTS: "Hamlet" en yiddish. Le trinité juive. Anglicisation. Sous le faix. Le "Luftmensch." La question du Sabbat à Sudminster.

Nouvelles comédies du Ghetto, traduit de l'anglais par Mme. Marcel Girette. Paris: Rieder, 1930. CONTENTS: Lutte amoureuse. Les convertis. Pieux hyménée. Le gobelet d'Élie. Les salariés. Samooborona.

The American Jewish Year Book
5699

The American Jewish | Year Book | 5699 | September 26, 1938 to September 13, 1939 | Volume 40 | Edited by | Harry Schneiderman | for | The American Jewish Committee | [*seal 3b*] | A Golden Jubilee Volume | Philadelphia | The Jewish Publication Society of America | 1938 |

COLLATION: 12°. xxvii, 771 p. (p. [i] Title; p. [ii] Copyright, All rights reserved; p. iii–iv, Preface; p. v, Contents; p. [vi] blank; p. [vii]–xxvii, Index to Volumes 1–40 of the American Jewish Year Book; p. [1]–574, Text; p. [575]–638, The American Jewish Committee 31st annual report 1938; p. [639]–744, Report of the 50th year of The Jewish Publication Society of America 1937–1938; p. 745–771, Catalogue.)

Bound uniformly with 5697 (1936–1937).

"The recurrent features remain essentially the same as they have been for several years. Owing to limitation of space, it was not possible to present the directory of national Jewish organizations in two lists — one alphabetical and one classified — as we did in the preceding volume. This, as well as all the other lists and tables, have been brought up to date. Special attention is called to the Index to the entire series of the American Jewish Year Book, now grown to forty volumes." — Preface, p. iii, iv.

SPECIAL ARTICLES: Felix M. Warburg, by Cyrus Adler, pp. 23–40. — Henry Pereira Mendes, by David de Sola Pool, pp. 41–60. — Statistics of Jews and Jewish organizations in the United States. An historical review of ten censuses, 1850–1937, by H. S. Linfield, pp. 61–84.

Solomon Schechter

Solomon Schechter | A Biography | By | Norman Bentwich | [*seal 3b*] | A Golden Jubilee Volume | Philadelphia | The Jewish Publication Society of America | MCMXXXVIII |

COLLATION: 8°. xvi, 373 p. (p. [i] Half-title; p. [ii] Other books by the same author . . .; p. [iii] Title; p. [iv] Copyright, All rights reserved; p. [v] Dedication*; p. [vii] Contents; p. [ix] List of Illustrations; p. [vi, viii, x] blank; p. xi–xvi, Preface; 1 l. and p. 1–349, Text; p. 351–352, Bibliography of the principal writings of Solomon Schechter; p. [353]–366, Notes; p. 367, Glossary of Hebrew words; p. [350, 368] blank; p. 369–373, Index.) ports. (including front.), plate, facsim.

Issued in dark blue cloth; top edges blue; back: rule, title, rule, author, rule, seal 3c, publisher all in gilt.

*"To Alexander Marx | librarian and professor | of the Jewish Theological Seminary | of America | colleague and friend | of Solomon Schechter | ."

"I have endeavored to give an account not only of his life but of his thought, and I have used to this end both the published essays and addresses and a number of unpublished papers. The present generation knew not Solomon Schechter; and it seemed desirable to give extracts from writings which, better than any paraphrase, expound his outlook ... I have been anxious not to inflate the currency of praise, but to describe Schechter as he was, with his idiosyncrasies and human weaknesses, which made him not the less lovable." — Author's preface, p. xiv, xv.

"The Cambridge University Press of London purchased a printing of this title for English distribution." — *AJYB*, 5700, p. 674.

5708–1948 edition: as above. Verso of title-page: "Second Impression, 1940; Third Impression, 1948."

The Pharisees

... | THE PHARISEES | The sociological background | of their faith | By | Louis Finkelstein | Provost and Solomon Schechter Professor of Theology | at the Jewish Theological Seminary of America | [*seal 3b*] | Volume I [and II] | A Golden Jubilee Volume | Philadelphia | The Jewish Publication Society of America | 1938 |

At head of title: The Morris Loeb Series.

COLLATION: 8°. 2 v. (paged continuously). v. 1: xxviii, 442 p. (p. [i] Half-title; p. [ii] (Note)*; p. [iii] Title; p. [iv] Copyright, All rights reserved; p. [v] Dedication**; p. [vi] Other books by the same author ...; p. vii–viii, Table of Contents; p. ix–xxviii, Foreword; p. 1–442, Text.); v. 2: vi, 443–793 p. (p. [i] Half-title; p. [iii] Title; p. [iv] Copyright, All rights reserved; p. v, Table of Contents; p. [ii, vi] blank; p. 443–626, Text; p. 627–645, Appendix A–C; p. [647]–710, Notes; p. 711–751, Bibliography; p. [646, 752] blank; p. [753]–793, Indices.) diagrams.

Issued in dark blue cloth; top edges blue; back: rules, title, rule, author, rules, volume, seal 3b, publisher all in gilt.

1. at end of v. 2: "The text of this book was set in the composing rooms of the Press of the Jewish Publication Society of America on the monotype in Caslon Old Style. The original letter on which this type is based was cut by William Caslon about 1720."

*Note on the Morris Loeb Series. See Malter, *Saadia Gaon*, 1921. "The present work is the second issued under this Fund."

**"To | Sol M. Stroock | who, like the ancient teachers, combines | in himself profound love of man with the | scholar's reverence for law and truth. | "

"The thesis presented in this work was first proposed, in a simpler form, in an article published through the courtesy of Professors G. F. Moore and James Ropes in *Harvard Theological Review*, XXII (1929), pp. 185–261." — Foreword, p. xxvii.

5706–1946 edition: as above. Verso of title-page: "Second edition, Revised, January, 1940; Third Impression, 1946." vol. 1 has Foreword to the Second Edition, p. xxix–xxxiv; Chronological Table, p. xxxv–xxxvii.

In Polish Woods

IN POLISH WOODS | by Joseph Opatoshu [pseud. of Joseph Opatovsky] | Translated from the Yiddish | by Isaac Goldberg | [*seal 3b*] | A Golden Jubilee Volume | Philadelphia | The Jewish Publication Society of America | · 1938 |

COLLATION: 8°. 2 p. l., 392 p. (l. 1, Half-title, verso blank; l. 2, Title, verso Copyright, All rights reserved; p. [1]–392, Text.)

Issued in green cloth; front cover: title; back: title, author, and rules (on maroon), publisher all in gilt.

Verso of l. at end: "The text of this book was set in the composing rooms of the Press of the Jewish Publication Society of America on the monotype in Caslon Old Style. The original letter on which this type is based was cut by William Caslon about 1720."

5704–1943 edition: as above. Verso of title-page: "Second Impression, 1943."

1939

Numbers

... | NUMBERS | with commentary | By | Julius H. Greenstone, Ph.D., L.H.D. | [*seal 3b*] | A Golden Jubilee Volume | Philadelphia | The Jewish Publication Society of America | 5699–1939 |

At head of title: The Holy Scriptures | [rule] | .

COLLATION: 8°. xxxviii p., 1 l., 373 p. (p. [i] Half-title; p. [iii] Title; p. [iv] Copyright, All rights reserved; p. [v] Foreword; p. vii–viii, Preface; p. ix, Table of Contents; p. [ii, vi, x] blank; p. xi–xxxviii, Introduction; 1 l., and p. [1]–364, Text and Commentary; p. 365–373, Index.) 2 maps at end.

Issued in dark blue cloth; back: rules, series title, rule, title, rule, commentator, publisher and rules in gilt.

Verso of p. 373: "The text of this book was set in the composing rooms of the Press of the Jewish Publication Society of America on the monotype in Binny Old Style. The basis of this useful letter was a type cut in Scotland, and it was first put on the Monotype Machine in 1908."

See Margolis, *Micah*, 1908, for note on Series. This volume is the third in the Series.

"The present commentary on the Book of Numbers . . . has the avowed purpose of furnishing a clear and concise interpretation of the book 'for the teacher, the interested pupil and the general reader.' . . . Since the book is intended primarily for Jewish readers, the Jewish point of view and the Jewish attitude toward the ideas, laws and legends were given special emphasis and illumination." — Preface, p. vii, viii.

1948: "2,000 copies reprinted." — *JPSA* [61st annual report] 1948, p. 3.

Regensburg and Augsburg

... | REGENSBURG | and | AUGSBURG | by Raphael Straus |
Translated from the German | by Felix N. Gerson | [*seal 3b*] |
Philadelphia | The Jewish Publication Society of America |
1939–5699 |

At head of title: Jewish Communities Series.

COLLATION: 16°. 1 p. l., x, 261 p. (1 l., Half-title, verso blank;
p. [i] (Note)*; p. [ii] (Frontispiece); p. [iii] Title; p. [iv] Copyright,
All rights reserved; p. v, Contents; p. [vii] List of Illustrations;
[p. vi, viii] blank; p. ix–x, Foreword; 1 l. and p. 1–236, Text;
p. [237]–248, Notes; p. 249–261, Index.) plates, map.

Bound uniformly with Aron Freimann, *Frankfort*, 1929.

*See Max Grunwald, *Vienna*, 1936.

"The work presented in the following pages is based in large
measures upon unpublished sources found by the author in various
German and Austrian archives." — Foreword, p. ix.

The Ship of Hope

THE SHIP OF HOPE | by Ruben Rothgiesser | Translated from
the German | by Felix N. Gerson | [*seal 3b*] | Philadelphia |
The Jewish Publication Society of America | 1939–5699 |

COLLATION: 12°. x, 144 p. (p. [i] Half-title; p. [ii] blank; p. [iii]
Title; p. [iv] Copyright, All rights reserved; p. [v] "Dedicated to
Erich Gompertz in gratitude and friendship;" p. [vi] blank; p. [vii]–
x, A Foreword; p. [1]–144 Text.)

Issued in gray cloth; front cover: ornamental design; back:
title, author, translator and publisher all in gilt; title on blue with
ornamental design in gilt.

At end: "The text of this book was set in the composing
rooms of the Press of the Jewish Publication Society of America on

the monotype in Caslon Old Style. The original letter on which this type is based was cut by William Caslon about 1720."

"A book about young people which offered a ray of hope to those of our faith who saw nothing but darkness ahead." — *AJYB*, 5701, p. 684.

5704–1944 edition: as above. Verso of title-page: "Second Impression, 1944."

The Jew in the Literature of England

THE JEW | IN THE LITERATURE | OF ENGLAND | To the end of the 19th century | by | Montagu Frank Modder | [*seal 3b*] | Philadelphia | The Jewish Publication Society of America | 1939–5700 |

COLLATION: 8°. xvi p. 1 l., 435 p. (p. [i] Half-title; p. [ii]*; p. [iii] Title; p. [iv] Copyright, All rights reserved; p. [v] Dedication: "To | Mary, Anne, Lucy |;" p. vii–ix, Preface; p. [xi] Contents; p. [vi, x, xii] blank; p. xiii–xvi, Introduction by Howard Mumford Jones; 1 l. and p. 1–364, Text; p. [365]–380 Notes; p. 381–426, Bibliography; p. 427–435, Index.)

Issued in green cloth; top edges green; front cover: title; back: rules, title, rules, author, rules, seal 3c, publisher all in gilt.

Verso of p. 435: "The text of this book was set in the composing rooms of the Press of the Jewish Publication Society of America on the monotype in Caslon Old Style. The original letter on which this type is based was cut by William Caslon about 1720."

*"In memory of | Henry and Diana L. Gitterman | ."

"The object of this introductory study is to tell the story of the Jew as a character in the literature of England, and to make available to the general reader a selection of the considerable amount of material not easily accessible in the average library." — Preface, p. vii.

"Dr. Modder, a non-Jew, made a very intensive study of his subject and this book has been hailed by the press and by critics as a real contribution on the part of the Society. Reviews in both the Jewish and non-Jewish press have been, with few exceptions, excellent." — *AJYB*, 5701, p. 684.

5705–1944 edition: as above. Verso of title-page: "Second Printing, 1944."

The American Jewish Year Book
5700

The American Jewish | Year Book | 5700 | September 14, 1939 to October 2, 1940 | Volume 41 | Edited by | Harry Schneiderman | for | The American Jewish Committee | [*seal 3b*] | Philadelphia | The Jewish Publication Society of America | 1939–5700 |

COLLATION: 12°. xxix, 790 p. (p. [i] Title; p. [ii] Copyright, All rights reserved; p. iii–v, Preface; p. vii, Contents; p. [vi, viii] blank; p. [ix]–xxix, Index to Volumes 1–40 of the American Jewish Year Book; p. [1]–614, Text; p. [615]–664, The American Jewish Committee 32nd annual report 1939; p. [665]–790, Report of the 51st year of The Jewish Publication Society of America 1938–1939; at end: 1939 Catalogue, 25 p., with separate title-page.) ports.

Bound uniformly with 5697 (1936–1937).

"Professor Solomon Zeitlin, who contributed a biography of Moses Maimonides on the occasion of the eight-hundredth anniversary of the birth of that great sage, has written for this volume an interesting and enlightening article on another great figure in the history of the development of Judaism, namely, Rabbi Shelomo Izhaki of Troyes, France, known to millions of Jews throughout the world as Rashi, the ninth-hundredth anniversary of whose birth will be celebrated during the coming year." — Preface, p. iv.

SPECIAL ARTICLES: Benjamin Nathan Cardozo, by Edgar J. Nathan, Jr., pp. 25–34. — Israel Davidson, by Louis Finkelstein,

pp. 35–56. — Isaac Husik, by Julius H. Greenstone, pp. 57–65. —
William N. Lewis, by David J. Galter, pp. 67–73. — A. Leo Weil,
by Samuel H. Goldenson, pp. 75–78. — Baruch Charney Vladeck,
by John Herling, pp. 79–93. — Samuel William Jacobs, by Herman
Abramowitz, pp. 95–110. — Rashi, by Solomon Zeitlin, pp. 111–
140. — Twenty-five years of American aid to Jews overseas: A
record of the Joint Distribution Committee, by Joseph C. Hyman,
pp. 141–179. — The Jews of the United States, number and distribution. Preliminary figures for 1937, by H. S. Linfield, pp. 181–186.

1939 Catalogue

1939 CATALOGUE | "Jewish Books in Every Jewish Home" |
[*seal 3b*] | The Jewish Publication Society of America | 225
South Fifteenth Street | Philadelphia, Penna. |

[Note: The foregoing appears within a double rule box, in
black.]

COLLATION: 12°. 25 p.

Originally issued with American Jewish Year Book, 5700
(1939–1940).

Cold Pogrom

COLD POGROM | by Max L. Berges | Translated from the
German | by Benjamin R. Epstein | [*seal 3b*] | Philadelphia |
The Jewish Publication Society of America | 1939–5700 |

[Note: The foregoing appears within a black double rule box.]

COLLATION: 8°. 4 p. l., 280 p. (l. 1, Half-title; l. 2, Title, verso
Copyright . . . All rights reserved; l. 3, Excerpt from "Gerechtig-
keit" (Vienna, March 25, 1937); l. 4, Foreword; verso l. 1, 3, 4,
blank; p. [1]–280, Text.)

Issued in rose-beige cloth; top edges rose-beige; front cover:
title; back: decoration, title, author, decoration, seal, publisher,
all in gilt.

"A section from this book has been reprinted in pamphlet form by the Anti-Defamation League of B'nai B'rith and widely distributed." — *AJYB*, 5701, p. 684–685.

Aftergrowth

... | AFTERGROWTH | and other stories | [*rule*] | Translated from the Hebrew | by I. M. Lask | [*triangular block*] | [*seal 3b*] | Philadelphia | The Jewish Publication Society of America | 1939–5700 |

At head of title: Hayyim Nahman Bialik | [rule].

COLLATION: 8°. v, 216 p. (p. [i] Half-title; p. [ii] blank; p. [iii] Title; p. [iv] Copyright, All rights reserved; p. v, Table of Contents; p. [1]–216, Text.) front. (port.)

Issued in blue cloth; top edges blue; front cover: design, title, design; back: design, author, design, title, design, seal 3c, publisher all in gilt.

Verso of l. at end: "The text of this book was set in the composing rooms of the Press of the Jewish Publication Society of America on the monotype in Caslon Old Style. The original letter on which this type is based was cut by William Caslon about 1720."

CONTENTS: I. Hayyim Nahman Bialik — An interpretation [by I. M. Lask]. II. Aftergrowth. III. The shamed trumpet. IV. The short Friday.

5705–1944 edition: as above. Verso of title-page: "Reprinted, 1944."

1940

Cologne

... | COLOGNE | by Adolf Kober | Translated from the German | by Solomon Grayzel | [*seal 3b*] Philadelphia | The Jewish Publication Society of America | 1940–5700 |

208

At head of title: Jewish Communities Series.

[Note: The foregoing appears within a black single rule box.]

COLLATION: 16°. xiii, 412 p. (p. [i] Half-title, p. [ii] (Note)*; p. [iii] Title; p. [iv] Copyright, All rights reserved; p. [v] Dedication**; p. vii–viii, Contents; p. [ix] List of Illustrations; p. [vi, x,] blank; p. xi–xiii, Introduction; p. 1–316, Text; p. 317–347, Appendices; p. [349]–386, Notes; p. 387–393, Bibliography; p. [348, 394] blank; p. 395–412, Index.) plates (including front.), ports., map, plan, facsim.

Bound uniformly with Aron Freimann, *Frankfort*, 1929.

*See Max Grunwald, *Vienna*, 1936.

**"To my dear wife, Hanna, *née* Samoje."

"This book tells the story of one of the oldest Jewish communities in Europe — the oldest in Germany if one considers the age of the documents in which mention of it is made. The history of this community reflects every phase of the history of all German Jewry." — Introduction, p. xi.

Candles in the Night

CANDLES IN THE NIGHT | Jewish tales by Gentile authors | Edited by | Joseph L. Baron | With a preface by | Carl Van Doren | [*seal 3b*] | Philadelphia | The Jewish Publication Society of America | 1940–5700 |

COLLATION: 8°. xxv, 391 p. (p. [i] Half-title; p. [iii] Title; p. [iv] Copyright, All rights reserved; p. [v] Dedication: "To | Bernice Judith |;" p. vii–xix, Introduction by Joseph L. Baron; p. xxi–xxiii, Preface: A note on Anti-Semitism; p. [ii, vi, xx, xxiv] blank; p. xxv, Contents; 1 l. and p. [1]–391, Text.)

Issued in gray cloth; top edges gray; front cover: title; back: design, rules, title, rule, editor, rules, design, publisher, all in gilt.

Verso of p. 391: "The text of this book was set in the composing rooms of The Press of the Jewish Publication Society of

America on the monotype in Caslon Old Style. The original letter on which this type is based was cut by William Caslon about 1720."

CONTENTS: 1. Giovanni Boccaccio. A tale of three rings. — 2. Carl Ewald. My little boy. — 3. Maurus Jokai. How I became a friend of the Jews. — 4. Anton Chekhov. Rothschild's fiddle. — 5. Maxim Gorky. The little boy. — 6. Ricarda Huch. The Jew's grave. — 7. Anatole France. An Anti-Semite in the country. — 8. Thomas Nelson Page. The Jew and the Christian. — 9. Johan August Strindberg. Peter the hermit. — 10. Per Hallström. Arsareth. — 11. Villiers de l'Isle Adam. The torture of hope.— 12. I. L. Cargiale. The Easter torch. — 13. Karl Klostermann. The Jew of S. — 14. Adam Szymanski. Srul — from Lubartów. — 15. Hamlen Hunt. The saluting doll. — 16. Eliza Orzeszko. "Give me a flower!" — 17. Leopold von Sacher-Masoch. Galeb Jekarim.— 18. Ernests Birznieks-Upīts. Seskinš. — 19. Stephen Vincent Benét. Jacob and the Indians. — 20. Myra Kelly. Morris and the Honorable Tim. — 21. Ben Ames Williams. Sheener. — 22. Sinclair Lewis. The life and death of a god. — 23. Coningsby Dawson, The unknown soldier.

"The history of Israel, so replete with examples of anti-Jewish persecution and propaganda, records many such gleams in the dark from non-Jewish hearts. In critical moments, Gentile friends have often rendered aid and comfort to communities and to individual members of the martyred people. At times, they carried the torch in the struggle for equal rights, and espoused valiantly the cause of liberty and justice, for the Jew.

"The arrangement of the stories follows three central motives: the plea for toleration (Nos. 1–8), the description of Jewish martyrdom (Nos. 9–15), and the portrayal of Jewish life and character (Nos. 16–23). While there is naturally overlapping in this organization of the material, and some of the stories may be transposed, there is this merit to the order: the volume begins and ends with the lighter and more positive aspect, while the middle section presents the more somber and tragic side, of the Jewish question." — Introduction, p. vii, xvii.

210

Trade edition: New York, Farrar & Rinehart, 1940.

1944: "2,000 copies — 2nd printing." — *AJYB*, 5706, p. 741.

5706–1945 edition: as above. Verso of title-page: "Third Impression, 1945."

The American Jewish Year Book
5701

The American Jewish | Year Book | 5701 | October 3, 1940 to September 21, 1941 | Volume 42 | Edited by | Harry Schneiderman | for | The American Jewish Committee | [*seal 3b*] | Philadelphia | The Jewish Publication Society of America | 1940–5701 |

COLLATION: 12°. xxxii, 815 p. (p. [i] Half-title; p. [iii] Title; p. [iv] Copyright, All rights reserved; p. v–vii, Preface; p. ix, Contents; p. [ii, viii, x] blank; p. [xi]–xxxii, Index to Volumes 1–41 of the American Jewish Year Book; p. [1]–632, Text; p. [633]–674, The American Jewish Committee 33rd annual report 1940; p. [675]–815, Report of the 52nd year of The Jewish Publication Society of America 1939–1940.) front. (port. of Cyrus Adler)

Bound uniformly with 5697 (1936–1937).

"At a time when a great human cataclysm is convulsing the world and is vitally affecting the lives of fully two-thirds of the Jewish people, a contemporary description of events of interest to Jews is extremely difficult, especially in view of the many obstacles to obtaining reliable information. The Review of the Year presented in this volume is based upon a careful and judicious selection of such information as was available, and is believed to be a fairly accurate account . . . It is believed that, although the task has been a difficult one, the writers of the Review have measurably succeeded in giving at least a partial idea of the indescribable tragedy which has befallen so large a section of our people, — a tragedy which is, alas, part of the disaster from which the entire world is suffering and will continue to suffer for many years to come." — Preface, p. vi, vii.

SPECIAL ARTICLES: Cyrus Adler, A biographical sketch, by Abraham A. Neuman, pp. 23–144. — Abraham H. Friedland, by Emanuel Gamoran, pp. 145–152. — Alexander Harkavy, by Bernard G. Richards, pp. 153–164. — Harold Hirsch, by David Marx, pp. 165–172. — Isador Sobel, by Max C. Currick, pp. 173–177. — The Central Conference of American Rabbis: 1889–1939, by David Philipson, pp. 179–214. — Jewish communities of the United States: Number and distribution of Jews of the United States in urban places and in rural territory, by H. S. Linfield, pp. 215–266.

Pilgrims to Palestine

PILGRIMS | TO PALESTINE | And Other Stories | By | Elma Ehrlich Levinger | [*seal 3b*] | Philadelphia | The Jewish Publication Society of America | 1940–5700 |

[Note: The foregoing appears within a black double rule box.]

COLLATION: 12°. x, 274 p. (p. [i] Half-title; p. [ii] Other books by the same author . . .; p. [iii] Title; p. [iv] Copyright, All rights reserved; p. [v] Dedication*; p. [vii] (Acknowledgment); p. [vi, viii] blank; p. ix–x, Table of Contents; p. [1]–274, Text.) Illus.

Issued in blue cloth; front cover: decoration in silver; back: title in blue on silver ornamental back; title, seal 3c, and publisher in silver.

Verso of l. at end: "The text of this book was set in the composing rooms of the Press of the Jewish Publication Society of America on the Monotype in Scotch Roman. This popular transitional letter has in it some of the characteristics of old Scotch and English types of a century ago."

*"To | Dr. Abraham Levinson | in gratitude for a long friendship | ."

212

CONTENTS: I. America the beautiful: Sarah conquers Plainsville: 1. The corner booth. 2. The spring house. 3. A Portia come to judgment. 4. Ancestors. 5. Hands across the sea. — Emil makes a speech. — Temptation. — When David went to "State:" 1. Grades. 2. Daniel in the lion's den. 3. The sign at the door. — II. Pilgrims to Palestine: The poet who came from afar. — The pigeon ruby. — The traveler's treasure. — III. Back to the homeland: Winter and spring (verse). — Back to the homeland. — ". . . not to leave thee". — Under the olive trees. — IV. Jews in far-off lands: The dark continent. — In old Salonika. — The scroll that Ezra wrote. — The feast of the ancestors. — A girl in Tripoli. — After many years.

Illustrations by Mathilda Keller.

1944: "2,000 copies — 2nd printing." — *AJYB*, 5706, p. 741.

5708–1948 edition: as above. Verso of title-page: "Third Impression, 1948."

Theodore Herzl

Theodore Herzl | A Biography | by | Alex Bein | Translated from the German | by | Maurice Samuel | [*seal 3b*] | Philadelphia | The Jewish Publication Society of America | 1940–5701 |

COLLATION: 8°. 4 p. l., 545 p. (l. 1, Half-title; l. 2, Title, verso Copyright 1941, All rights reserved; l. 3, Contents; l. 4, List of Illustrations; verso of l. 1, 3–4, blank; p. [1]–520, Text; p. 521, A note by the author; p. [522] blank; p. 523–530, Bibliography; p. 531–545, Index.) plate, ports. (including front.)

Issued in dark blue cloth; back: rules, title, rule, author, rules, seal 3c, publisher all in gilt.

Verso of p. 545: "The text of this book was set in the composing rooms of The Press of the Jewish Publication Society of America on the monotype in Caslon Old Style. The original letter on which this type is based was cut by William Caslon about 1720."

"In the present work, which reproduces in somewhat condensed form the Hebrew and German versions of the same subject, I have sought to create as clear and objective a picture as is possible on the basis of existing records, of Theodore Herzl, the man, the writer and the creator of the modern Zionist movement, covering his development, his ideas and his effective influence." — Author's note, p. 521.

5708–1948 edition: as above. Verso of title-page: "Second Impression, 1942; Third Impression, 1943; Fourth Impression, 1945; Fifth Impression, 1948."

Adolphe Crémieux

ADOLPHE CRÉMIEUX | A Biography | by | S. Posener | Translated from the French | by | Eugene Golob | [*seal 3b*] | Philadelphia | The Jewish Publication Society of America | 1940–5701 |

COLLATION: 8°. x, 283 p. (p. [i] Half-title; p. [iii] Title; p. [iv] Copyright 1941, All rights reserved; p. [v] Dedication: "To my wife;" p. [vii] Contents; p. [ii, vi, viii] blank; p. ix–x, Preface; p. [1]–232, Text; p. [233]–246, Notes; p. 247–275, Bibliography; p. [276] blank; p. 277–283, Index.) front. (port.)

Issued in blue cloth, top edges blue; back: rules, title, rule, author, rules, seal 3c and publisher in gilt.

Verso of p. 283: "The text of this book was set in the composing rooms of The Press of the Jewish Publication Society of America on the monotype in Caslon Old Style. The original letter on which this type is based was cut by William Caslon about 1720."

"Adolphe Crémieux was the most brilliant representative of the first generation of Jews born in France after their emancipation, the prototype and promoter of Jewish progress in France. The history of Crémieux's life is, on the one hand, that of French political life during three quarters of the nineteenth century and, on the other hand, that of French Jewry." — Preface, p. ix–x.

214

Rome

... | ROME | by Hermann Vogelstein | Translated from the German | by Moses Hadas | [*seal 3b*] | Philadelphia | The Jewish Publication Society of America | 1940–5701 |

At head of title: Jewish Communities Series.

[Note: The foregoing appears within a black single rule box.]

COLLATION: 16°. xiii, 421 p. (p. [i] Half-title; p. [ii] (Note)*; p. [iii] Title; p. [iv] Copyright 1941, All rights reserved; p. [v] Dedication**; p. vii–viii, Contents; p. [ix] List of Illustrations; p. [vi, x] blank; p. xi–xiii, Preface; 1 l., and p. 1–379, Text; p. 381–392, Appendix; p. [393]–399, Notes; p. 401–407, Selected Bibliography; p. [380, 400, 408] blank; p. 409–421, Index.) 15 plates (including front.).

Bound uniformly with Aron Freimann, *Frankfort*, 1929.

*See Max Grunwald, *Vienna*, 1936.

**"To the memory of | Paul Rieger | 1870–1939 | ."

"Rome is not only the world embracing Imperium of antiquity, but possesses peculiar significance as a city. It is the oldest large Jewish community, and it has continued without interruption for two thousand years . . . . It is this which gives the history of the Jews in Rome its peculiar character." — Introduction, p. 3.

1941

The Fire Eater

THE FIRE EATER | by | Henry J. Berkowitz | [*seal 3b*] | Philadelphia | The Jewish Publication Society of America | 1941–5701 |

[Note: The foregoing appears within an ornamental border and a square rule box, both in black.]

COLLATION: 12°. vii, 394 p. (p. [i] Half-title; p. [iii] Title; p. [iv] Copyright, All rights reserved; p. [v] Dedication*; p. [ii, vi] blank; p. vii, Table of Contents; p. [1]–394, Text.) plates.

Issued in brown cloth; top edges brown; front cover: design; back: design, title, design, author, seal 3c, publisher, all in black.

Verso of l. at end: "The text of this book was set in the composing rooms of the Press of the Jewish Publication Society of America on the Monotype in Scotch Roman. This popular transitional letter has in it some of the characteristics of old Scotch and English types of a century ago."

*"To | Flora, Leon and Victoria | ."

Illustrations by Mathilda Keller.

1943: "1,000 copies reprinted."— *AJYB*, 5705, p. 606.

5706–1945 edition: as above. Verso of title-page: "Third Impression, 1945.

5708–1948 edition: as above. Verso of title-page: "Fourth Impression, 1948."

I Have Considered the Days

I HAVE CONSIDERED | THE DAYS | By | Cyrus Adler | [*seal 3 b*] | Philadelphia | The Jewish Publication Society of America | 1941–5701 |

COLLATION: 8°. xiv, 447 p. (p. [i] Half-title; p. [iii] Title; p. [iv] Copyright, All rights reserved; p. [v] [Hebrew text and English translation from] Psalms, 77.6; p. [vii] Table of Contents; p. [ix] List of Illustrations; p. [ii, vi, viii, x] blank; p. xi–xiii, Foreword [by A. S. W. Rosenbach]; p. [xiv] Acknowledgments; p. [1]–429, Text; p. [430] blank; p. 431–447, Index.) plates, ports. (including front.)

Issued in dark blue; top edges blue; back: title, rule, author and publisher in gilt.

Verso of p. 447: "The text of this book was set in the composing rooms of The Press of the Jewish Publication Society of

America on the monotype in Caslon Old Style. The original letter on which this type is based was cut by William Caslon about 1720."

1945–5706 edition: as above. Verso of title-page: "Reprinted, 1945."

The American Jewish Year Book 5702

The American Jewish | Year Book | 5702 | September 22, 1941 to September 11, 1942 | Volume 43 | Edited by | Harry Schneiderman | for | The American Jewish Committee | [*seal 3b*] | Philadelphia | The Jewish Publication Society of America | 1941–5702 |

COLLATION: 12°. xli, 884 p. (p. [iii] Half-title; p. [v] Title; p. [vi] Copyright, All rights reserved; p. vii–ix, Preface; p. xi–xiii, Contributors; p. [iv, x, xiv] blank; p. xv–xvi, Contents; p. [xvii]–xli, Index to Volumes 1–42; p. [1]–698, Text; p. [699]–762, The American Jewish Committee 34th annual report 1941; p. [763]–884, Report of the 53rd year of The Jewish Publication Society of America 1940.) front. (plate: "Zion's Elegy" Jehudah Halevi mourning over the ruins of the Temple, from a photograph of a statue by Jules L. Butensky), ports.

Bound uniformly with 5697 (1936–1937).

"This year's Review is the cooperative work of a number of collaborators, some the editor's co-workers on the staff of the American Jewish Committee, others his colleagues in various fields of Jewish communal endeavor.

"An added feature of this volume of the Year Book is an annotated bibliography of books of Jewish interest in English published in the United States, compiled by Mr. Harry J. Alderman, Librarian of the American Jewish Committee. The period covered is from January, 1940 to June, 1941. Since a summary for the year would be incomplete without indicating the cultural activity for the period, this bibliography has been included as a part of the Review of the

Year. It is hoped to make this a regular feature in succeeding volumes.

"The necrology has been expanded; instead of a mere list, as it formerly was, it now gives in most cases brief biographical notes indicating more fully than formerly the achievements of the deceased persons.

"Three special articles are presented in this volume. Two of them are occasioned by the incidence of anniversaries in the lives of men who lived in widely separated periods of history but each of whom has left an indelible impression upon Jewish culture. During the past year occurred the 800th anniversary of the traditional date of the death of Jehuda Halevi, one of the foremost Spanish Jewish poets and philosophers of his day. The other anniversary article is published in honor of Professor Heinrich Graetz, the author of the standard 'History of the Jews,' whose death occurred fifty years ago.

"The third special article is a bibliography of works of Jewish fiction in English which appeared during the first four decades of the present century. These decades constitute in a sense a special era in modern Jewish history.

"It has been deemed advisable, instead of presenting the usual lists of Jews in the Congress of the United States, in the diplomatic service and as governors of states, to present a more inclusive list of Jews who have occupied or are occupying positions of distinction in the Government of the United States. This list is intended to serve as a sort of 'roll of honor' of Jews who have given notable service."
— Preface, p. vii, viii.

SPECIAL ARTICLES: American Jewish bibliography January 1940–June 1941: An annotated list of books of Jewish interest in English published in the United States, compiled by Harry J. Alderman, pp. 59–71. — David Werner Amram, by Louis E. Levinthal, pp. 375–380. — Charles E. Bloch, by Stephen S. Wise, pp. 381–384. — Hart Blumenthal, A biographical sketch, by Joseph H. Hagedorn, pp. 385–390. — Zevi Diesendruck, by Abraham Heschel, pp. 391–398. — Henry Horner 1878–1940, by Herbert M. Lautmann, pp. 399–406. — Jacob Mann 1888–1940, by Victor E. Reichert, pp. 407–414. — Bernard Revel, by Leo Jung, pp. 415–424. — Theodore Rosen, A biographical appreciation, by David J.

Galter, pp. 425–430. — Alice L. Seligsberg, by Rose G. Jacobs, pp. 431–436. — Siegmund Bacharach Sonneborn, by William Rosenau, pp. 437–440.—Joseph Stolz, by Tobias Schanfarber, pp. 441–444. — Jehuda Halevi, by Samuel S. Cohon, pp. 447–488. — Heinrich Graetz, the historian of the Jews, by Ismar Elbogen, pp. 489–498. — Jewish fiction in English 1900–1940. A list of selected titles, by Fanny Goldstein, pp. 499–518.

Let Laughter Ring

[*rule* | LET LAUGHTER | RING | [*rule* | compiled and retold | by | S. Felix Mendelsohn | [*triangular block*] | [*seal 3b*] | Philadelphia | The Jewish Publication Society of America | 1941–5702 |

COLLATION: 8°. x, 239 p. (p. [i] Half-title; p. [iii] Title; p. [iv] Copyright, All rights reserved; p. [v] Dedication: "To Herzl and Judith;" p. [vii] Contents; p. [ii, vi, viii]blank; p. IX–X, Preface; 1 l. and p. [1]–236, Text; p. 237–239, Glossary.)

Issued in yellow cloth; top edges yellow; front cover: title between serrated lines; back: title and author between serrated lines, publisher all in black.

Verso of p. 239: "The text of this book was set in the composing rooms of The Press of the Jewish Publication Society of America on the monotype in Caslon Old Style. The original letter on which this type is based was cut by William Caslon about 1720."

CONTENTS: I. Wit and genius. — II. Helpmates. — III. The nations. — IV. Sages. — V. Seed of Abraham. — VI. Wiseacres and heretics. — VII. Third Reich. — VIII. The promised land. — IX. Business. — X. East Side. — XI. In the land of Columbus. — XII. The transplanted faith.

"The stories come from a variety of sources. Many were actually told by American Jews and Gentiles. Others were culled from the humor column of the Yiddish and Anglo-Jewish press. The remainder were sent in by numerous friends in response to an appeal issued through the Chicago *Jewish Sentinel.*" — Preface p. ix.

1944: "2,000 copies — 3rd printing." — *AJYB*, 5706, p. 741.

1945: "1,000 copies — 4th printing."— *AJYB*, 5707, p. 649.

5706–1946 edition: as above. Verso of title-page: "Fifth Impression, 1946."

Reprints: September 1, 1952 — 1,500 copies. Information from Lesser Zussman, Executive Secretary, January, 1953.

1942

What the Moon Brought

What the Moon Brought | By | Sadie R. Weilerstein | [*illustration*] Illustrated by Mathilda Keller | Philadelphia | The Jewish Publication Society of America | 5702–1942 |

COLLATION: 4°. 5 p. l., 159 p. (l. 1, Half-title, verso Books by the same author . . .; l. 2, Title, verso Copyright, All rights reserved; l. 3, Dedication*; l. 4, Acknowledgment; l. 5, Table of Contents; verso of l. 3–5, blank; 1 l. and p. 1–159, Text.) colored front., illus. Illustrated lining papers.

Issued in tan and orange cloth; front cover: title, illustration, author in orange and black on tan; back: author, title, and publisher in black.

*"To | Baruch Reuben | Ps. 4.8 |. "

CONTENTS: Introducing Ruth and Debby. — Happy Birthday, World! (Rosh Hashanah). — For a good and sweet year (Rosh Hashanah). — I'm sorry (Yom Kippur). — A streetful of friends (Succot). — Seven times round (Simhat Torah). — Come, O Queen (Sabbath). — The Sabbath taste (Sabbath). — Farewell, O Queen (Sabbath). — The dolls' Hanukkah. — A tree for George Washington (Hamisha 'Asar B'Shebat). — Eight days' fun all in one (Purim). — Open your eyes! Surprise, surprise! — Helping for Pesah (Passover). — The adventure of the Pesah dishes (Passover). Lag Ba'Omer eggs. — How Ruthie was Ruth-in-the-Bible (Shabuot).

5707–1947 edition: as above. Verso of title-page: "First Impression, June 1942; Second Impression, October 1942; Third Impression, July 1944; Fourth Impression, February 1946; Fifth Impression, February, 1947."

The Jews in Spain

... | THE JEWS IN SPAIN | Their social, political and cultural life | during the Middle Ages | By | Abraham A. Neuman | President, The Dropsie College for Hebrew | and Cognate Learning | Volume I | A Political-Economic Study | [and Volume II | A Social-Cultural Study] [*seal 3b*] | Philadelphia | The Jewish Publication Society of America | 1942–5702 |

At head of title: The Morris Loeb Series.

COLLATION: 8°. 2 v. v. 1: xxxi, 286 p. (p. [i] Half-title; p. [ii] (Note)*; p. [iii] Title; p. [iv] Copyright, All rights reserved; p. [v] Dedication**; p. vii–ix, Preface; p. [vi; x] blank; p. xi–xx, Table of Contents; p. xxi–xxii, List of Illustrations; p. xxiii–xxxi, Introduction; p. [1]–226, Text; p. [227]–286, Notes); v. 2: xi, 399 p. (p. [i] Half-title; p. [iii] Title; p. [iv] Copyright, All rights reserved; p. v–ix, Table of Contents; p. [ii, x] blank; p. xi, List of Illustrations; p. [1]–274, Text; p. [275]–344, Notes; p. 345–350, Glossary; p. [351]–370, Bibliography; p. [371]–399, Index.) fronts., plates, maps, facsims. Maps on lining paper.

Issued in dark blue cloth; top edges blue; back: rules, title, rule, author, rules, volume, seal 3b, publisher all in gilt.

*Note on the Morris Loeb Series. See Malter, *Saadia Gaon*, 1921. "The present work is the third issued under this Fund."

**"To the memory of | Solomon Schechter | 1850–1915 | Joseph Jacobs | 1854–1916 | Cyrus Adler | 1863–1940 | teachers and friends | who profoundly affected my life | ."

1944: "1,000 copies each, 2nd printing." — *AJYB*, 5706, p. 741.

1948: "2 Volume set, 2,000 copies reprinted." — *JPSA* [61st annual report] 1948, p. 3.

Renegade

RENEGADE | by | Ludwig Lewisohn | [*seal 3b*] | The Jewish Publication | Society of America | 1942–5702 |

[Note: The foregoing appears within a triple and a single rule box, all in black.]

COLLATION: 3 p. l., 333 p. (l. 1, Half-title, verso The fiction works of Ludwig Lewisohn . . .; l. 2, Title, verso Copyright 1942 by Ludwig Lewisohn, Designed by Peter Döblin; l. 3, Contents, verso blank; p. [1]–333, Text.)

Issued in orange cloth; top edges orange; front cover: title; back: designs, title, author, rules, seal 3c, publisher, all in gilt.

Trade edition: "The Dial Press | New York 1942 | ."

The American Jewish Year Book 5703

The American Jewish | Year Book | 5703 | September 12, 1942 to September 29, 1943 | Volume 44 | Edited for | The American Jewish Committee | by Harry Schneiderman, Editor | Morris T. Fine, Assistant Editor | [*seal 3b*] | Philadelphia | The Jewish Publication Society of America | 1942–5703 |

COLLATION: 12°. xxix, 522 p. (p. [i] Half-title; p. [iii] Title; p. [iv] Copyright, All rights reserved; p. v–vii, Preface by Harry Schneiderman; p. [ii, viii] blank; p. ix–x, Contributors; p. xi–xii, Contents; p. [xiii]–xxix, Index to special articles and features in Volumes 1–43; p. [1]–450, Text; p. [451]–499, The American Jewish Committee 35th annual report 1942; p. [500] blank; p. [501]–522, Report of the 54th year of The Jewish Publication Society of America 1941.) ports. (including front. of Louis Dembitz Brandeis)

Bound uniformly with 5697 (1936–1937).

"Appearing at a time when our country is at war, this volume has had to be considerably reduced in size as compared with those of recent years, because of the rise in printing costs and the necessity of economizing in materials.

"The section containing the monthly calendars regularly appearing at the beginning of the volume is this year expanded to include brief descriptions of the Jewish Holy Days, Festivals and Fasts as well as tables of abridged calendars for fifty years. For these additional features, as well as for the monthly calendars prepared annually, the Editor is indebted to Dr. Julius H. Greenstone, whose valuable contribution will, we trust, make this section more useful and meaningful to those who consult the Year Book for information on the Jewish calendar.

"A timely innovation worth noting is the lists of American Jewish men who have been cited for bravery or have lost their lives in the service. These lists were compiled for the Year Book by the Jewish Welfare Board." — Preface, p. v, vi.

SPECIAL ARTICLES: Louis Dembitz Brandeis, by Louis E. Levinthal, pp. 37–52. — Sol M. Strook, by James N. Rosenberg, pp. 53–60. — Rabbi Saadia Gaon, by Robert Gordis, pp. 61–72. — Alexander Kohut 1842–1942, by Ismar Elbogen, pp. 73–80. — Nachman Krochmal: The philosopher of Israel's eternity, by Max Nussbaum, pp. 81–92. — American Jewish bibliography July 1941– June 1942. Books of Jewish interest in English published in the United States, compiled by Harry J. Alderman, pp. 303–318.

Cyrus Adler

CYRUS ADLER | A Biographical Sketch | By | Abraham A. Neuman | [*seal 3b*] | Philadelphia | The Jewish Publication Society of America | 1942–5703 |

COLLATION: 12°. ix, 233 p. (p. [i] Half-title; p. [iii] Title; p. [iv] Copyright, All rights reserved; p. [v] Dedication: "To my mother;" p. [ii, vi] blank; p. vii–viii, Preface; p. [ix] List of Illustrations; p. [1]–228, Text; p. 229–233, Index.) plates, ports. (including front.), facsims.

Issued in red cloth; front cover: title, rule, author; back: title, rule, author, seal 3c, publisher all in gilt.

223

"This biography was originally written for publication in the *American Jewish Year Book*, where it appeared in Volume 42 (1940–41). It is here reprinted in its entirety with a few additions." — Preface, p. vii.

Special edition: New York, The American Jewish Committee, 1942.

The Jewish Community

. . . | THE JEWISH COMMUNITY | Its history and structure to | the American Revolution | By | Salo Wittmayer Baron | Jur.D., Ph.D., Pol.Sc.D., Rabbi | Professor of Jewish History, Literature and Institutions | on the Miller Foundation, Columbia University | [*seal 3b*] | Volume[s] One [Two and Three] | Philadelphia | The Jewish Publication Society of America | 1942–5702 |

At head of title: The Morris Loeb Series.

COLLATION: 8°. 3 v. v. 1: xiii, 374 p. (p. [1] Half-title; p. [ii] (Note)*; p. [iii] Title; p. [iv] Copyright, All rights reserved; p. [v] Dedication**; p. vii–ix, Preface; p. [vi, x] blank; p. xi–xii, Contents; p. [xiii] Notes, Bibliography, and Index to this work will be found in Volume Three; p. [1]–374, Text); v. 2: vi, 366 p. (p. [i–iv] same as v. 1; p. [v] Contents; p. [vi] same as v. 1, p. [xiii]; p. [1]–366, Text); v. 3: ix, 572 p. (p. [i–iv] same as v. 1; p. v–vi, Preface; p. [vii] Contents; p. [viii] blank; p. [ix] Abbreviations; p. [1]–221, Notes; p. [223]–335, Bibliography; p. [222, 336] blank; p. [337]–572, Index.)

Issued in dark blue cloth; top edges blue; back: rules, title, rule, author, volume, seal 3b, publisher all in gilt.

*Note on the Morris Loeb Series. See Malter, *Saadia Gaon*, 1921. "The present work is the fourth issued under this Fund."

**"To | my parents | on the completion of more than half a | century of tireless communal endeavor | ."

"The focus of this entire work is centered on the European community of the Middle Ages and early modern times, both because of the great richness and variety of its historic accomplishments and, genetically, because of its intimate linkage to Jewish community life throughout the world today. At the same time its deep moorings in the ancient and contemporaneous eastern communities have come to the fore ever more insistently. In fact, while trying to detect the hidden springs of this phenomenally tenacious evolution, the writer found himself delving deeper and deeper not only into the obscure realms of the First Exile and the Persian and Hellenistic dispersion, but also into the early manifestations of ancient Palestinian municipal life." — Preface, p. viii.

5708–1948 edition: as above. Verso of title-page: "Second Printing, 1945; Third Printing, 1948."

Jewish Pioneers and Patriots

Jewish | Pioneers and Patriots | Lee M. Friedman | with a Preface by | A. S. W. Rosenbach | [*seal 3b*] | Philadelphia | The Jewish Publication Society of America | 5703–1942 |

COLLATION: 8°. xvii, 430 p. (p. [i] blank; p. [ii]*; p. [iii] Half-title; p. [iv] Other books by Lee M. Friedman . . . ; p. [v] Title; p. [vi] Copyright, All rights reserved; p. [vii] [Quotation from] Franklin D. Roosevelt, Address to the Jewish War Veterans, August 26, 1938; p. [ix] Dedication**; p. [viii, x] blank; p. xi–xii, Table of Contents; p. xiii–xiv, List of Illustrations; p. xv–xvii, Preface; p. [1]–374, Text; p. [375]–409, Notes and Bibliography; p. [410] blank; p. [411]–430, Index.) colored front. (coat of arms), plates, port., facsim. (including music.)

Issued in red cloth; top edges red; back: title (on black), author and publisher in gilt.

*"The publication of this volume has been made possible through the generosity of the late Abraham Erlanger who died October 1, 1929, and who left a bequest to the Jewish Publication Society of America."

**"To | Elsie T. Friedman | Sophie M. Friedman | sisters and companions on our | happy life's journey | ."

Trade edition: New York, The Macmillan Company, 1943.

5708–1948 edition: as above. Verso of title-page: "Second Impression, 1943; Third Impression; 1945, Fourth Impression, 1948."

1943

Stars and Sand

STARS AND SAND | Jewish Notes By Non-Jewish Notables | Selected and Edited by | Joseph L. Baron | [Quotation from] Genesis 22.15 ff. | [*seal 3b*] | Philadelphia | The Jewish Publication Society of America | 5703–1943 |

COLLATION: 8°. xvii, 555 p. (p. [i] Half-title; p. [ii] Books by the same author . . .; p. [iii] Title; p. [iv] Copyright, All rights reserved; p. [v] Dedication: "To the memory of my parents"; p. [vii] Table of Contents; p. [ix]–xiii, List of Illustrations; p. [vi, viii, xiv] blank; p. xv–xvii, Preface; p. [1]–32, Introduction; p. 33–528, Text; p. 529–532, Bibliography; p. [533]–543, Index of Authors; p. 544–555, Index of Subjects.) ports., plates, (including front.)

Issued in light blue cloth; top edges blue; front cover: title; back: designs, rules, title, author and publisher all in gilt.

A companion volume to the editor's *Candles in the night*, Jewish tales by Gentile authors, 1940. Cf. Preface, p. xv.

5708–1948 edition: as above. Verso of title-page: "Second Impression, 1944; Third Impression, 1945; Fourth Impression, 1948."

Memoirs of my People

MEMOIRS OF | MY PEOPLE | Through | A Thousand Years | Selected and edited by | Leo W. Schwarz | [*seal 3b*] | Philadelphia | The Jewish Publication Society | of America | 5703–1943 |

[Note: The foregoing appears within a single and a double rule box, all in black.]

COLLATION: 8°. xxvi, 597 p. (p. [i] Half-title; p. [ii] Books by Leo W. Schwarz . . .; p. [iii] Title; p. [iv] Copyright by Leo W. Schwarz, All rights reserved; p. v–viii, Contents; p. ix–xi, Foreword; p. [xii] blank; p. xiii–xxvi, Introduction; p. [1]–567, Text; p. 568–589, Sources and Literature; p. [590] blank; p. 591–597, Index.)

Issued in light blue cloth; top edges blue; front cover: title, design; back: title, design, editor, publisher all in gilt.

"The fifty-nine selections chosen for this collection are mostly rendered from foreign tongues (the bulk from Hebrew, Yiddish and German; the remainder from Latin, Italian, French, Danish, and English), and several are printed from manuscript for the first time . . . I have noted the relevant literature in appendices which chart the original sources." — Foreword, p. ix.

CONTENTS: Book One: Flood tide of remembrance. — Family album, Ahimaaz ben Paltiel. — Logbook of a physician, Moses Maimonides. — Every man his own Messiah, Abraham Aboulafia. — By the waters of the Tagus, Judah Asheri. — Castilian vignette, Menahem ben Zerah. — Adventure in the Holy Land, Meshullam ben Menahem. — Twilight of Spanish glory, Don Isaac Abravanel. — The road to Rome, David Reubeni. — Pope, emperor and the Inquisition, Solomon Molko. — The story of my imprisonment, Yomtob Lipmann Heller. — Life in Lombardy, Leone da Modena. — My double life and excommunication, Uriel da Costa. — Trouble in the Siena Ghetto, Joseph da Modena. — Memories of an unhappy childhood, Anonymous. — My joys and sorrows, Glückel of Hameln. — Defeat of Satan, Jacob Emden. — I was a slave, Abraham Hertz. — King for a night, Pinhas Katzenellenbogen. — Daybook of an adventurer, Simon von Geldern. — Victory for justice, Ber Birkenthal. — Pioneer in Sweden, Aron Isak. — A Kabbalist in Paris, Hayyim David Azulai. — A trip with Israel Baalshem, Meir Margolis. — My struggle with Amazons, Solomon Maimon. — Wedded to the muse, Mendele Mocher Seforim. — How I wrote my songs, Eliakum Zunser. — Love found a way, Ezekiel Kotick. — Life of a humorist, Sholem Aleichem. — Memories of childhood, Ahad Ha'am. — Before thirty, Hayyim Nahman Bialik. — Childhood in Lithuania, Rebecca Himber Berg. — Book Two: Tangled destinies. — When the British captured Savannah, Mordecai Sheftall. — I protected Old Glory, Mordecai Manuel Noah. — Mendoza, the famous pugilist, Daniel Mendoza. — A salonist remembers, Henriette Herz. — Schooldays, Leopold Zunz. — The stamp of my being, Heinrich Heine. — Rothschild of artists, Moritz Oppenheim. — Vanities of youth, Ferdinand Lassalle. — My mother's magic, Berthold Auerbach. — Musical recollections, Heymann Steinthal. — Torah in America, Isaac Mayer Wise. — My soul's true native land, George Brandes.— Wellsprings of my faith, Luigi Luzzatti. — A festival reverie, Israel Abrahams. — Preface to skepticism, Fritz Mauthner. — The death and birth of an artist, Boris Schatz. — From Russian Pale to Argentinian Pampas, Marcos Alperson. — Birth pangs in Zion, Moses Smilanski. — Birth of a Zionist, Theodor Herzl. — The prophet's language — and the people's, Eliezer ben Yehuda. — My life in San Francisco, Rebekah Kohut. — The anarchist ideal, Abraham Frumkin. — My road to Hasidism, Martin Buber. — In the wake of the Russian Revolution, Jacob Masé. — The world is my fatherland, Ernst Toller. — On the Mount of Olives, Jessie E. Sampter. — Israel, lost and regained, Edmond Fleg.

Trade edition: New York, Farrar & Rinehart, incorporated [1943].

5705–1945 reprint.

1948: "2,085 copies reprinted." — *JPSA* [61st annual report] 1948, p. 3.

In the Steps of Moses

IN THE STEPS | OF MOSES | By | Louis Golding | [*seal 3b*] | Philadelphia | The Jewish Publication Society of America | 5703–1943 |

[Note: The foregoing appears within a black double rule box.]

COLLATION: 8°. 3 p. l., 556 p. (l. 1, Half-title, verso Books by Louis Golding . . .; l. 2, Title, verso Copyright, All rights reserved; l. 3, List of illustrations, verso blank; p. [1]–551, Text; p. [552]

blank; p. 553-556, Bibliography.) 16 plates. Maps on lining-papers.

Issued in blue cloth; top edges blue; back: title, decoration, author and publisher in gilt.

First published in two volumes under the titles: *In the steps of Moses the lawgiver* (New York, Macmillan Co., 1938) and *In the steps of Moses the conqueror* (London, Rich & Cowan Ltd., 1938).

5704-1944 edition: as above. Verso of title-page: "Second Impression, 1944."

The American Jewish Year Book
5704

The American Jewish | Year Book | 5704 | September 30, 1943 to September 17, 1944 | Volume 45 | Edited for | The American Jewish Committee | by | Harry Schneiderman, Editor | Morris T. Fine, Assistant Editor | [*seal 3b*] | Philadelphia | The Jewish Publication Society of America | 1943–5704 |

COLLATION: 12°. xxix, 704 p. (p. [i] Half-title; p. [iii] Title; p. [iv] Copyright, 1943, All rights reserved; p. v–vii, Preface by Harry Schneiderman; p. [ii, viii] blank; p. ix–x, Contributors; p. xi–xii, Contents; p. [xiii]–xxix, Index to special articles and features in Volumes 1–44; p. [1]–600, Text; p. [601]–677, The American Jewish Committee 36th annual report 1943; p. [678] blank; p. [679]–704, Report of the 55th year of The Jewish Publication Society of America 1942) ports. (including front. of Louis Edward Kirstein).

Bound uniformly with 5660 (1899–1900), without seal but in green. On front cover: titles of special articles in gilt.

"We publish in this volume a Directory of Federations, Welfare Funds and Community Councils, prepared especially for the Year Book by the Council of Jewish Federations and Welfare Funds. This is a directory which is not published every year. In its present form this directory last appeared in volume 40. We believe that it is a highly interesting and useful feature, listing as it does not only local organizations affiliated with, or supported by, federations and welfare funds, but also independent local social service agencies. Thus, it constitutes a virtually complete list of local Jewish philanthropic institutions throughout the United States and Canada." — Preface, p. vi.

SPECIAL ARTICLES: Louis Edward Kirstein 1867–1942, by Benjamin M. Selekman, pp. 35–46. — American Jewish scholarship: A survey, in honor of the centenary of Kaufmann Kohler, by Ismar Elbogen, pp. 47–65. — Jewish book collections in the United States. In commemoration of the centenary of Mayer Sulzberger, by Adolph S. Oko, pp. 67–96. — B'nai B'rith: A century of service, by Bernard Postal, pp. 97–116. — New York Federation — After twenty-five years, by George Z. Medalie, pp. 117–134. — American Jewish war service, from December 7, 1941 to June 30, 1943, pp. 406–422. — American Jewish bibliography, July 1942–June 1943, compiled by Iva Cohen, pp. 431–446.

Vilna

... | VILNA | By | Israel Cohen | [*seal 3b*] | Philadelphia | The Jewish Publication Society of America | 5704–1943 |

At head of title: Jewish Communities Series.

[Note: The foregoing appears within a serrated box and a single rule box, both in black.]

COLLATION: 16°. xxiii, 531 p. (p. [i] Half-title; p. [iii] Title; p. [iv] Copyright, All rights reserved; p. [v] Dedication*; p. vii–xv, Contents; p. [xvii] List of Illustrations; p. [ii, vi, xvi, xviii] blank; p. xix–xxiii, Preface; 1 l. and p. 1–480, Text; p. 481–515, Supplementary Notes; p. 517–519, Bibliography; p. [516, 520] blank; p. 521–531, Index.) plates, ports., map, plan, facsim.

Bound uniformly with Aron Freimann, *Frankfort*, 1929.

*"To the memory | of the | tens of thousands | of | Jews of Vilna | who were martyred | by Nazi barbarity | 1941–1943 | ."

1944

Sabbath

SABBATH | The Day of Delight | by | Abraham E. Millgram |
[seal 3b] | Philadelphia | The Jewish Publication Society of
America | 5705–1944 |

COLLATION: 8°. xxx, 495 p. (p. [i] Half-title; p. [ii] Also by
Abraham E. Millgram . . .; p. [iii] Title; p. [iv] Copyright, All
rights reserved; p. [v] Dedication*; p. vii–xvii, Contents; p. [vi,
xviii] blank; p. xix–xxii, List of Illustrations; p. xxiii–xxvi, Preface;
p. xxvii–xxx, Acknowledgments; 1 l. and p. 1–473, Text; p. 474–478,
Glossary; p. 479–486, Bibliography; p. 487–495, Notes.) plates.,
includes songs with Hebrew and Yiddish words (transliterated) with
music.

Issued in light blue cloth; top edges blue; front cover: title,
rule, author, all within square rule box; back: design, rule, author,
rule, title, rule, publisher, designs, all in gilt.

*"To my wife | אישה חיה | ."

"The present volume . . . is meant to serve a purpose. Its aim
is to reaffirm the historic truth that the Sabbath is 'the cornerstone of
Judaism.' In planning this volume the compiler constantly bore in
mind, the needs of the American Jewish community. It was his
purpose not only to make American Jewry more aware of the central
importance of the Sabbath as an institution in the pattern of Jewish
life, but also to provide the observant American Jew with a practical
guide and handbook for Sabbath observance." — Preface, p. xxiii.

CONTENTS: Book I. The Sabbath in practice. — Book II. The
Sabbath in literature, art and music. — Book III. The Sabbath in
history. — Music Supplement.

5706–1946 edition: as above. Verso of title-page: "Second
Impression, 1945."

5707–1947 edition: as above. Verso of title-page: "Third
Impression, 1947."

Reprints: March 14, 1952 — 2,000 copies. Information from Lesser Zussman, Executive Secretary, January, 1953.

A Century of Jewish Life

A CENTURY OF | JEWISH LIFE | by | Ismar Elbogen | [*seal 3b*] | Philadelphia | The Jewish Publication Society of America | 5704–1944 |

[Note: The foregoing appears within a black triple rule box.]

COLLATION: 8°. xliii, 814 p. (p. [i] Half-title; p. [iii] Title; p. [iv] Copyright, All rights reserved; p. [v] Dedication*; p. vii–ix, Preface by Solomon Grayzel, editor . . .; p. [ii, vi, x] blank; p. xi–xx, "Ismar Elbogen: An Appreciation" by Alexander Marx; p. xxi–xxiv, Contents; p. xxv–xliii, Introduction; p. [1]–682, Text; p. [683]–769, Notes; p. [770] blank; p. 771–786, Bibliography; p. [787]–814, Index.) Maps on lining papers.

Issued in red cloth; top edges red; back: rules, title, rules on black; author, rules, seal 3c, rules, publisher, rules all in gilt.

*"Dedicated to | The Dropsie College | for Hebrew and Cognate Learning | The Hebrew Union College | The Jewish Institute of Religion | The Jewish Theological Seminary of America | ."

"Meant as a supplement to the master-work of Graetz, it shows the same warmth of tone, though it is much more objective." — A. Marx, p. xx.

1945: "3,000 copies. — 2nd printing."— *AJYB*, 5707, p. 649.

5707–1946 edition: as above. Verso of title-page: "Third Impression, 1946."

Hebrew translation:

פרופ׳ יצחק משה (איתמר) אלבוגן. דברי ימי ישראל במאת השנים האחרונות. עברית: ברוך קרופניק. תל־אביב, הוצאת ספרים יזרעאל בע״מ [Tel Aviv, 1947].

232

Harvest in the Desert

HARVEST in the DESERT | Maurice Samuel | [*seal 3b*] |
Philadelphia | The Jewish Publication Society of America |
5704–1944 |

[Note: The foregoing appears within an ornamental border
and a single rule box, both in black.]

COLLATION: 8°. 2 p. l., 316 p. (l. 1, Title, verso Copyright, All
rights reserved; l. 2, Contents, verso Also by Maurice Samuel . . .;
p. [1] Half-title, p. [2] (Note)*; p. [3]–316, Text.)

Issued in gray cloth; front cover: title, author; back: title,
author, publisher all in red.

*"The Jewish Publication Society of America has for its aim
the dissemination of Jewish knowledge. Every Jewish work of
literary value, offering positive constructive help in understanding
Jewish life and culture, comes within its scope. To discharge its
obligation, The Society, without necessarily endorsing the opinions
of this or any author, publishes books of diversified subject-matter
and points of view.

"Because of the curtailment of Jewish publication activity in
other parts of the world, The Society deems it its duty to increase,
as far as possible, the number and variety of books it publishes. To
this end, The Jewish Publication Society of America invites the
cooperation and support of the entire Jewish community and of all
who are interested in the advancement of Jewish culture."

"It is the initial volume in a new arrangement made with the
B'nai B'rith Hillel Foundations whereby they propose to initiate
new manuscripts and to agree to purchase a substantial number of
copies if, as and when published by us under our imprint." — *AJYB*,
5705, p. 608.

Trade edition: New York, Alfred A. Knopf, Inc., 1944.

5708–1948 edition: as above. Verso of title-page: "Published
June 26, 1944; Second Printing, November 1944; Third Printing,

August 1947; Fourth Printing, September 1947; Fifth Printing, January 1948."

Germany's Stepchildren

GERMANY'S | STEPCHILDREN | by | Solomon Liptzin | College of the City of New York | [*seal 3b*] | Philadelphia | The Jewish Publication Society of America | 5704–1944 |

[Note: The foregoing appears within an ornamental border and a triple rule box, all in black.]

COLLATION: 8°. xii, 298 p. (p. [i] Half-title; p. [ii] Also by Solomon Liptzin . . .; p. [iii] Title; p. [iv] Copyright, All rights reserved; p. [v] Dedication: "To | my parents | ;" p. [vii]–viii, Contents; p. [ix] List of illustrations; p. [vi, x] blank; p. [xi] Half-title; p. [xii]*; p. 1–298, Text.) ports.

Issued in orange cloth; top edges green; back: title, rule, author and publisher in green.

*See Note *Maurice Samuel, *Harvest in the desert, 1944.*

CONTENTS: Introduction. — Part I: From emancipation to baptism. I. Rahel Varnhagen. — II. Ludwig Börne. — III. Jewish Christians. — Part II: From assimilation to nationalism. IV. Heinrich Heine. — V. Berthold Auerbach. — VI. Moses Hess. — Part III: The turn of the century. VII. Theodor Herzl. — VIII. Arthur Schnitzler. — IX. Walter Rathenau. — X. Theodor Lessing. — Part IV: The end of emancipation. XI. Jakob Wassermann. — XII. Jewish Aryans. — XIII. Marginal Jews. — XIV. Stefan Zweig. — Part V: The renaissance of a people. XV. Gustav Landauer. — XVI. Richard Beer-Hofmann. — XVII. Martin Buber. — XVIII. Pan-Humanists. — Bibliographic Notes. — Index.

5708–1948 edition: as above. Verso of title-page: "Second Impression, 1948."

234

The Lionhearted

THE | LIONHEARTED | A story about the Jews in | medieval England | by | Charles Reznikoff | [*seal 3 b*] | Philadelphia | The Jewish Publication Society of America | 5704–1944 |

[Note: The foregoing appears within an ornamental border and a single rule box, both in black.]

COLLATION: 8°. 3 p. l., 243 p. (l. 1, Half-title, verso Also by Charles Reznikoff . . .; l. 2, Title, verso Copyright, All rights reserved; l. 3, Dedication*; verso Acknowledgment; p. [1]–243, Text.)

Issued in green cloth, top edges red; front cover: title, author; back: author, title, publisher all in red.

*"To | Harry and Rose Luber | ."

The American Jewish Year Book
5705

The American Jewish | Year Book | 5705 | September 18, 1944 to September 7, 1945 | Volume 46 | Edited for | The American Jewish Committee | by | Harry Schneiderman, Editor | [*seal 3 b*] | Philadelphia | The Jewish Publication Society of America | 5705–1944 |

COLLATION: 12°. xxx, 620 p. (p. [i] Half-title; p. [iii] Title; p. [iv] Copyright, All rights reserved; p. v–vii, Preface; p. [ii, viii] blank; p. ix–x, Contributors; p. xi–xii, Contents; p. [xiii]–xxx, Index to special articles and features in Volumes 1–45; p. [1]–519, Text; p. [521]–595, The American Jewish Committee 37th annual report 1944; p. [520, 596] blank; p. [597]–620, Report of the 56th year of The Jewish Publication Society of America 1943.) ports.

Bound uniformly with 5704 (1943–1944).

"In the present volume, we present articles commemorating the fiftieth anniversary of the establishment of the National Council of Jewish Women and of the Educational Alliance of New York City ... Besides these two contributions, we present two biographical sketches: one of the late Julian W. Mack, who was in his lifetime an outstanding leader in the Jewish community as well as a distinguished jurist and public worker; the other of the late Herbert Friedenwald, who was editor of five issues of the American Jewish Year Book." — Preface, p. v.

SPECIAL ARTICLES: Julian William Mack, 1866–1943, by Horace M. Kallen, pp. 35–46. — Herbert Friedenwald, Editor of American Jewish Year Book 1908–1912, by Harry Schneiderman, pp. 47–54. — The National Council of Jewish Women, by Mildred G. Welt, pp. 55–72. — A half century of community service: The story of the New York Educational Alliance, by S. P. Rudens, pp. 73–86. — American Jewish war service, from July 1, 1943 to June 30, 1944, pp. 354–391. — American Jewish bibliography July 1943–June 1944, compiled by Iva Cohen, pp. 401–415.

Poems

POEMS | by | A. M. Klein | [*seal 3 b*] | Philadelphia | The Jewish Publication Society of America | 5705–1944 |

[Note: The foregoing appears within a black double rule box.]

COLLATION: 8°. 5 p. l., 82 p. (l. 1, Sub-title, verso Also by A. M. Klein . . .; l. 2, Title, verso Copyright, All rights reserved; l. 3, Dedication*; verso Acknowledgements; l. 4, Contents, verso blank; l. 5, Sub-title, verso blank; p. 1–82, Text.)

Issued in gray and dark blue cloth; front cover: title, author, vertical rule all in gilt on gray; back: author, title, publisher all in gilt on blue.

*"Dedicated to | The Memory of My Father | ."

CONTENTS: The Psalter of Avram Haktani. — A voice was heard in Ramah. — Yehuda Halevi, his pilgrimage.

236

1945

The Rise of the Jewish Community of New York

The Rise of | The Jewish Community | of New York | 1654–1860 | by | Hyman B. Grinstein | [*seal 3b*] | Philadelphia | The Jewish Publication Society of America | 5705–1945 |

[Note: The foregoing appears within an ornamental border and a triple rule box, all in black.]

COLLATION: 8°. xiii, 645 p. (p. [i] Half-title; p. [iii] Title; p. [iv] Copyright, All rights reserved; p. [v] Dedication*; p. vii–ix, Preface; p. [ii, vi, x] blank; p. xi–xii, Table of Contents; p. xiii, List of Illustrations and Maps; p. [1]–465, Text; p. [467]–524, Appendices; p. [525]–595, Notes; p. 597–607, Bibliography; p. [466, 596, 608] blank; p. [609]–645, Index.) plates, ports. (including front.) Maps on lining papers.

Issued in green cloth; top edges green; front cover: title; back: rules, title, author, and rules (on red), seal 3c, publisher, all in gilt.

*"Dedicated to | the memory of my dear parents | The Rev. Henry and Rebecca (Saxia) | Grinstein | who guided many in the path of | a living Judaism | ת׳ נ׳ צ׳ ב׳ ה׳ | ."

"The historical study presented herewith is primarily concerned with the inner life of the Jews of New York City — their institutions, their religion and their culture — and with the social, philanthropic and other activities which grew out of their living together in a Jewish community." — Preface, p. vii.

Special edition: Title page reads: . . . "by | Hyman Bogomolny Grinstein | Submitted in partial fulfillment of the | requirements for the Degree of Doctor | of Philosophy in the Faculty of Political | Science, Columbia University. | " . . .

5707–1947 edition: as above. Verso of title-page: "Second Impression, 1947."

For the Sake of Heaven

FOR THE SAKE | OF HEAVEN | By | Martin Buber | Translated by | Ludwig Lewisohn | [*seal 3 b*] | Philadelphia | The Jewish Publication Society of America | 5705–1945 |

[Note: The foregoing appears within an ornamental border and a single rule box, both in black.]

COLLATION: 8°. viii, 316 p. (p. [i] Half-title; p. [iii] Title; p. [iv] Copyright, All rights reserved; p. [v] Dedication*; p. [ii, vi] blank; p. vii–viii, Contents; p. [1]–314, Text; p. 315–316, Glossary.)

Issued in light gray cloth; top edges red; front cover: title, author; back: author, rule, title, publisher all in red.

*"To my wife | Paula Judith | ."

5706–1946 edition: as above. Verso of title-page: "Second Impression, 1946."

The Nightingale's Song

THE | NIGHTINGALE'S | SONG | By | Dorothy Alofsin | [*seal 3 b*] | Philadelphia | The Jewish Publication Society of America | 5705–1945 |

[Note: The foregoing appears within a black triple rule box on the top and bottom of which is inserted a black floret.]

COLLATION: 12°. 5 p. l., 306 p. (l. 1, Half-title, verso By the same author . . .; l. 2, Title, verso Copyright, All rights reserved; l. 3, Dedication*; l. 4, Contents; l. 5, Half-title; verso of l. 3–5, blank; p. 1–306, Text.) Illustrated lining papers.

Issued in green and gray cloth; top edges green; front cover: title and author; back: title, author and publisher all in black.

*"To my Sisters and Brothers | . . . | this story is affectionately dedicated | ."

1948: "2,000 copies reprinted." — *JPSA* [61st annual report] 1948, p. 3.

The American Jewish Year Book 5706

The American Jewish | Year Book 5706 | 1945–46 | Volume 47 | Prepared by the Staff of | The American Jewish Committee | Under the direction of | Harry Schneiderman and Julius B. Maller | Editors | [*seal 3b*] | Philadelphia | The Jewish Publication Society of America | 5706–1945 |

COLLATION: 12°. xxx, 760 p. (p. [i] Half-title; p. [ii] blank; p. [iii] Title; p. [iv] Copyright, All rights reserved; p. v–viii, Preface; p. ix–x, Contributors; p. xi–xii, Contents; p. [xiii]–xxx, Index to special articles and features in Volumes 1–46; p. [1]–658, Text; p. [659]–731, The American Jewish Committee 38th annual report 1945; p. [732] blank; p. [733]–760, Report of the 57th year of The Jewish Publication Society of America 1944.) front. (port. of Henrietta Szold)

Bound uniformly with 5704 (1943–1944). On front cover also title and date.

"What the editors hope will be the first of a series of articles on the experiences of the various Jewish communities of Europe during Nazi occupation is the highly interesting article on the Jews of France written by Acting Grand Rabbi Jacob Kaplan of Paris . . . Rabbi Kaplan's original article presents a vivid picture of the situation of the Jews of France on the eve of the Nazi invasion, a detailed account of the Jewish experience during the occupation, the steps being taken by the French authorities to restore pre-war status to the surviving Jews, and the progress of the latter, with the active assistance of the American Jewish Joint Distribution Committee, in their efforts to rehabilitate themselves economically and to reconstitute their community life." — Preface, p. v, vi.

SPECIAL ARTICLES: Franklin D. Roosevelt and the Jewish crises 1933–1945, by Edward N. Saveth, pp. 37–50. — Henrietta Szold

December 21, 1860–February 13, 1945, by Lotta Levensohn, pp. 51–70. — French Jewry under the occupation, by Jacob Kaplan, pp. 71–118. — Jewish community life in Latin America, by Louis H. Sobel, pp. 119–140. — The B'nai B'rith Hillel Foundations in American universities, by Abram L. Sachar, pp. 141–152. — Jewish war records of World War II, by S. C. Kohs, pp. 153–172. — Jewish chaplains in World War II, by Philip Bernstein, pp. 173–200. — Simon Miller, by Edwin H. Schloss, pp. 201–206. — American Jewish bibliography July 1944–June 1945, compiled by Iva Cohen, pp. 545–556.

1946

The Son of the Lost Son

The | SON of the | LOST SON | by | Soma Morgenstern | [*rule*] | Translated by | Joseph Leftwich and Peter Gross | [*rule*] | [*seal 3b*] | Philadelphia | The Jewish Publication Society of America | 5706–1946 |

COLLATION: 4 p. l., 269 p. (l 1, Half-title; l. 2, Title, verso Copyright, All rights reserved; l. 3, Contents; verso of l. 1, 3, blank; l. 4 and p. [1]–269, Text.)

Issued in tan cloth; top edges brown; back: rules, title (in tan on brown), rules, author and publisher in brown.

Trade edition: New York, Rinehart & Company, Inc., 1946.

The History of the Jews of Italy

The | History of the Jews | of Italy | [*floral design*] | [*rule*] | by | Cecil Roth | [*rule*] | [*floral design*] | [*seal 3b*] | Philadelphia | The Jewish Publication Society of America | 5706–1946 |

COLLATION: 8°. xiv, 575 p. (p. [i] Half-title; p. [ii] Some other books by the same author . . .; p. [iii] Title; p. [iv] Copyright, All rights reserved; p. v–viii, Preface; p. ix, Bibliographical Note; p. x, Note on Currency; p. xi–xii, Contents; p. xiii–xiv, List of Illustrations; 1 l. and p. 1–553, Text; p. [554] blank; p. 555–575, Index.) plates, ports. Map on lining papers.

Issued in dark blue cloth; top edges blue; front cover: title; back: rules, title, author and rules on green, seal 3c, publisher all in gilt.

". . . This is the first history of the Jews in Italy to be written in any language . . ." — Preface, p. v.

Pathways through the Bible

Pathways | Through | The | Bible | By | Mortimer J. Cohen | Illustrations by | Arthur Szyk | [*seal 3b*] | Philadelphia | The Jewish Publication Society of America | 5706–1946 |

COLLATION: 8°. xxv, 548 p., 1 l. (p. [ii] (Note)*; p. [iii] Half-title and [Quotation in Hebrew and English from] Proverbs 3.17; p. [v] Title; p. [vi] Copyright, All rights reserved; p. [vii] [Author's] Dedication**; p. [viii] [Illustrator's] Dedication***; p. ix–xii, Foreword; p. xiii–xix, Table of Contents; p. [i, iv, xx] blank; p. [xxi] List of Illustrations; p. [xxii] Maps; p. xxiii–xxv, "Your Bible;" 1 l., and p. [1]–548, Text; 1 l., Acknowledgments.) illustrations, maps, plates (including colored front.)

Issued in green cloth; top edges green; front cover: title; back: designs, title, author, designs, publisher all in gilt.

*"The publication of this book was made possible through a gift by Sidney Neumann, of Philadelphia, in memory of his parents, Abraham and Emma Neumann."

**"Dedicated | to the memory of | my mother, Rachel, | who was as gentle as her biblical namesake, | and | my father, Joseph, | who in his way was also a man of dreams. | "

***"Dedication | In March 1943 my beloved seventy-year-old mother, Eugenia Szyk, was taken from the ghetto of Lodz to the

241

Nazi furnaces of Maidanek. With her, voluntarily went her faithful servant, the good Christian, Josefa, a Polish peasant. Together, hand in hand, they were burned alive. In memory of the two noble martyrs I dedicate my pictures of the Bible as an eternal Kaddish for these great souls. | Arthur Szyk | New Canaan, Conn. | "

5708–1947 edition: as above. Verso of title-page: "Second Impression, 1946; Third Impression, 1947, 33,000 copies."

1950: "Reprinted 7,000 copies . . . making a total of 44,000 copies." — *AJYB*, 1952, p. 574.

Reprints: March 29, 1951 — 6,400 copies; January 20, 1952 — 7,500 copies; November 28, 1952 — 7,100 copies. Information from Lesser Zussman, Executive Secretary, January, 1953.

Rembrandt, the Jews and the Bible

REMBRANDT, | The Jews and the Bible | by | Franz Landsberger | translated by | Felix N. Gerson | [*seal 3b*] | Philadelphia | The Jewish Publication Society of America | 5706–1946 |

COLLATION: 4°. xviii, 189 p. (p. [i] Half-title; p. [ii] By the same author . . .; p. [iv] Front.; p. [v] Title; p. [vi] Copyright, All rights reserved; p. [vii] Dedication*; p. ix–x, Foreword; p. [xi] Acknowledgments; p. xiii, Table of Contents; p. [iii, viii, xii, xiv] blank; p. xv–xviii, List of Illustrations; p. [1]–175, Text; p. [176] blank; p. 177–182, Notes; p. 183–186, Bibliography; p. 187–189, Index.) 66 illustrations, including front.

Issued in red cloth; top edges red; front cover: title; back: author, title, publisher all in gilt.

*"To | Lady Mary | and Professor Gilbert Murray | true lovers of mankind | ."

5707–1946 reprint. Verso of title-page: "Second Impression, 1946."

242

The Aleph-Bet Story Book

THE | ALEPH-BET | STORY BOOK | By Deborah Pessin | [*illustration*] | Drawings by Howard Simon | Philadelphia | The Jewish Publication Society of America | 5706–1946 |

COLLATION: 4°. 6 p. l., 176 p. (l. 1, Half-title; l. 2, Title, verso Copyright, All rights reserved; l. 3, Dedication: "To | David | ;" l. 4, Acknowledgments; l. 5, Table of Contents; verso of l. 1, 3–5, blank; l. 6 and p. 1–176, Text.) illus. Illustrated lining papers.

Issued in gray cloth; front cover: title, illustration, author; back: author, title, publisher all in blue.

5707–1947 edition: as above. Verso of title-page: "Second Impression, 1947."

The Spirit Returneth . . .

The | Spirit Returneth . . . | A Novel | By | Selma Stern | Translated from the German manuscript by | Ludwig Lewisohn | [*seal 3 b*] | Philadelphia | The Jewish Publication Society of America | 5706–1946 |

COLLATION: 8°. 3 p. l., 265 p. (l.1, Half-title, [Quotation from] The Liturgy; l. 2, Title, verso Copyright, All rights reserved; l. 3, Dedication*; verso of l. 1, 3, blank; p. 1–265, Text.)

Issued in dark green cloth; top edges red; front cover: rule, title, author, and rule (on red); back: rule, title, rule, author, and rule (on red), and publisher, all in gilt.

*"I dedicate this book | to | the martyrs | of my people | ."

The River Jordan

The River | JORDAN | Being an Illustrated Account of | Earth's Most Storied River | By Nelson Glueck | Director, American School of Oriental Research, Jerusalem | Field Director, American School of Oriental Research, Baghdad | Professor of Bible and Biblical Archaeology, | Hebrew Union College, Cincinnati | [*seal 3 b*] | Philadelphia | The Jewish Publication Society of America | 5706–1946 |

COLLATION: 8°. xvi, 268 p. including front., illus. (incl. ports., map). (p. [i] Half-title; p. [iv] Frontispiece.; p. [v] Title; p. [vi] Copyright by the Westminster Press, International copyright secured, All rights reserved; p. [vii] Dedication*; p. [viii] (Note)**; p. [ix]–x, Foreword; p. [xi] Contents; p. [ii–iii, xii] blank; p. [xiii]–xvi, Illustrations; p. [1] blank; p. [2] Map; p. 3–252, Text; p. [253]–268, Indices: Text; Biblical Citations.) Map on lining papers.

Issued in rust cloth; front cover: title, author; back: title, author, publisher all in gilt.

*"To my wife | Helen | at whose request this book | was written | ."

** . . . "The volume, *The River Jordan*, by one of the foremost archaeologists, was accepted for publication by The Westminster Press. The Jewish Publication Society, considering it a valuable contribution to the understanding of the Hebrew Scriptures, although it includes other material as well, joined in its distribution, without thereby subscribing to statements and judgments for which the author, and not The Jewish Publication Society, must be held responsible."

Trade edition: Philadelphia, The Westminster Press [1946]

Hebrew translations:

נלסון גליק | עבר-הירדן המזרחי | בלוית כ״ח תמונות, ט״ו לוחות ומפה |
[תורגם מאנגלית; פרקים א׳, ב׳, ד׳, ח׳, ו׳ — בידי א. יערי, פרק ג׳ —
בידי ש. ייבין] מוסד ביאליק של הסוכנות היהודית לארץ ישראל. ירושלים,
תש״ו.

נלסון גליק | הירדן | בלוית שמונים וחמש תמונות ומפה | [תירגם מכתבי־יד
א. ד. זינגר] ירושלים תש"ו | מוסד ביאליק של הסוכנות היהודית לארץ־ישראל.

The American Jewish Year Book
5707

The American Jewish | Year Book | 5707 (1946–47) | Volume
48 | Prepared by the Staff of | The American Jewish Commit-
tee | Under the direction of | Harry Schneiderman and Julius
B. Maller | Editors | Morris Fine, Associate Editor | [*seal 3 b*] |
Philadelphia | The Jewish Publication Society of America |
5707–1946 |

COLLATION: 12°. xii, 691 p. (p. [i] Half-title; p. [ii] blank;
p. [iii] Title; p. [iv] Copyright, All rights reserved; p. v–viii, Preface
by Harry Schneiderman and Julius B. Maller; p. ix–x, Contributors;
p. xi–xii, Contents; p. [1]–618, Text; p. [619]–633, The American
Jewish Committee 39th annual report 1946; p. [634] blank; p. [635]–
691, Report of the 58th year of The Jewish Publication Society of
America 1945.) ports.

Bound uniformly with 5704 (1943–1944). On front cover:
title, date, compiler in gilt.

"The period with which the present volume deals, the first
year following six years of world war, was so replete with events
and activities of vital moment to Jews, especially those of the European continent and Palestine, that the Editors found it necessary
to devote more space than in any preceding volume to the Review of
the Year. It was necessary, also, to include special sections. One
of these deals with the problems presented to the world by the most
unfortunate surviving victims of Nazi fury — the so-called displaced
Jews. Another special section deals with the efforts of Great
Britain and the United States, at the suggestion of President Harry
S. Truman, to find solutions for these problems, chiefly the transfer
of 100.000 victims to Palestine.

"Because of the pressure on the limited space, it was necessary in this volume to omit the greater part of the calendar material and the Index to preceding volumes heretofore published regularly. It was decided, also, to publish directories of National Jewish Organizations and of Jewish Periodicals in the United States and Canada in alternate issues of the Year Book, making room for the publication of the Directory of Jewish Federations, Welfare Funds, and Community Councils in the present and in every other issue to follow." — Preface, p. v, vii.

SPECIAL ARTICLES: The Jewish population of Canada. A statistical summary from 1850–1943, by Louis Rosenberg, pp. 19–50. — British and Palestinian Jews in World War II, by Israel Brodie, pp. 51–72. — Yeshiva University. Growth of Rabbi Isaac Elchanan Theological Seminary, by Jacob I. Hartstein, pp. 73–84. — Irving Lehman, 1876–1945, by Harry Schneiderman, pp. 85–92. — George Zerdin Medalie, 1883–1946, by Joseph Willen, pp. 93–100. — Harry A. Hollzer, 1880–1946, by Edgar F. Magnin, pp. 101–106. — Felix N. Gerson, 1862–1945, by David J. Galter, pp. 107–112. — American Jewish bibliography July 1945–May 1946, compiled by Iva Cohen, pp. 511–526.

Jacob's Dream

JACOB'S DREAM | A Prologue | by | Richard Beer-Hofmann | translated from the German by | Ida Bension Wynn | [seal 3 b] | Philadelphia | The Jewish Publication Society of America | 5707–1946 |

COLLATION: 8°. 4 p. l., 188 p. (l. 1, Half-title, verso The Important works of Richard Beer-Hofmann . . .; l. 2, Title, verso "Jacob's Dream, Copyright 1945, by Richard Beer-Hofmann; Foreword, by Solomon Liptzin, Copyright 1946 by The Jewish Publication Society of America, All rights reserved;" l. 3, Contents, verso blank; l. 4 and p. 1–26, "Richard Beer-Hofmann, A Biographical Essay" by Solomon Liptzin; p. [27]–173, Text; p. [174] blank; p. [175]–188, Passages from the Bible.)

Issued in dark gray cloth; top edges red; back: author title and publisher in gilt.

Trade edition, title-page reset: Johannespresse, New York, 1946. Also contains "Introduction" by Thornton Wilder, p. [ix]–xviii.

The Life of Judah Touro

The Life | of | JUDAH TOURO | (1775–1854) | By | Leon Huhner | [seal 3b | Philadelphia | The Jewish Publication Society of America | 5707–1946 |

COLLATION: 12°. xv, 192 p. (p. [i] Half-title; p. [ii] (Note)*; p. [iii] Title; p. [iv] Copyright, All rights reserved; p. [v] Dedication**; p. vii, Table of Contents; p. ix, List of Illustrations; p. [vi, viii, x] blank; p. xi–xv, Introduction; 1 l. and p. 1–128, Text; p. 129–142, Appendices; p. 143–183, Notes; p. [184] blank; p. 185–186, Glossary; p. 187–192, Index.) plates, ports. (including front.), facsim.

Issued in light blue cloth; top edges red; back: author, title and publisher in red.

*The publication of this book was made possible through the Charles and Bertha Eisenman Fund."

**"To the memory of my parents | Edward and Minna Huhner | this book is affectionately dedicated. | "

1947

A History of the Jews

A HISTORY of | THE JEWS | From the Babylonian Exile | to the end of World War II | by | Solomon Grayzel | [seal 3b] | Philadelphia | The Jewish Publication Society of America | 5707–1947 |

COLLATION: 8°. xxv, 835 p. (p. [i] Half-title; p. [iii] Title; p. [iv] Copyright, All rights reserved; p. [v] Dedication*; p. vii–ix, Preface; p. xi–xiii, Contents; p. [ii, vi, x, xiv] blank; p. xv–xxiv, List of Illustrations; p. xxv, List of Maps; 1 l., and p. 1–805, Text; p. [806] blank; p. 807–812, Bibliography; p. 813–835, Index.) illus., maps.

Issued in tan cloth; top edges blue; front cover: title and author in tan on blue, all within a quadruple rule box; back: red rules, title in tan on blue, red rules, title, seal 3c and publisher in blue, red rules.

*"To | Rabbi Elias L. Solomon | bearer of the Jewish tradition | in affection and admiration | ."

"I believe in Judaism, and I have faith in the Jewish people. One of my reasons for writing *A History of the Jews* has been my desire to fortify the spirit and strengthen the determination of my fellow Jews to persevere in the path of our ancestors, and patiently and hopefully to labor for the welfare of mankind. The struggle against injustice, oppression and tyranny, the cooperative effort to expand the human spirit and the hope of achieving a better world for all humanity have been, to my mind, the historic tasks of the Jews. In such conflicts and strivings, they were bound to get hurt. But their misfortunes have been honorable wounds of battle, to be borne with dignity. I do not consider, and have not described, the numerous tragedies of Jewish history except as gauges of the evils that had to be overcome and as tests of the vitality of the Jewish religion." — Preface, p. vii.

5708–1948 edition: as above. Verso of title-page: "Second Impression, 1947; Third Impression, 1948."

1950: Title-page reset, with new sub-title: From the Babylonian Exile to the establishment of Israel. "Reprinted 4,000 copies . . . bringing total to 25,750 copies in print."— *AJYB*, 1952, p. 574.

Reprints: August 15, 1952 — 4,000 copies. Information from Lesser Zussman, Executive Secretary, January, 1953.

248

Little New Angel

LITTLE | NEW ANGEL | by | Sadie Rose Weilerstein | [*illustration*] | Illustrated by Mathilda Keller | Philadelphia | The Jewish Publication Society of America | 5707–1947 |

COLLATION: 4°. 6 p. l., 139 p. (l. 1, Half-title, verso Other books by the same author . . .; l. 2, Title, verso Copyright, All rights reserved; l. 3, Dedication*; l. 4, Acknowledgments; l. 5, Table of Contents; l. 3–5, blank; l. 6 and p. 1–139, Text.) colored front., illus. Illustrated lining papers.

Issued in tan and light blue cloth; front cover: title, illustration, author in blue and black on tan; back: author, title, and publisher in black.

*"In loving remembrance of | "Bobeh" Weilerstein | (Feige bat Yehoshua Zelig) | ל״ז | ."

CONTENTS: Before we begin. — Little new angel. — What happened to Debby. — A tree for Michael. — A little piece of Succoth. — The story of a Sefer Torah. — The Sefer Torah is finished. — A big mistake. — Hear, O Israel. — A Seder on Lincoln's birthday. — The thank-you box. — Tsiggeleh Miggeleh. — A baby in school. — Family reunion.

Blessed is the Match

. . . | BLESSED | is the | MATCH | The Story of Jewish Resistance | by | Marie Syrkin | [*seal 3 b*] | Philadelphia | The Jewish Publication Society of America | 5707–1947 |

At head of title: A Hillel Library Book.

[Note: The foregoing appears within a black double rule box.]

COLLATION: 8°. 4 p. l., 361 p. (l. 1, [Poem]*, verso Note**; l. 2, Title, verso Copyright, All rights reserved; l. 3, Contents; l. 4, Half-title, verso Note***; p. [1]–361, Text.)

Issued in tan cloth; top edges red; front cover: title, within a double rule box; back: title, author, publisher all in red.

> *"Blessed is the Match
>   'Blessed is the match that is consumed
>   in kindling flame.
>   Blessed is the flame that burns
>   in the secret fastness of the heart.
>   Blessed is the heart with strength to stop
>   its beating for honor's sake.
>   Blessed is the match that is consumed
>   in kindling flame.'
>
>   From the Hebrew of Hanna Senesch."

**"This volume is one of a series in the publication of which the Jewish Publication Society cooperates with the B'nai B'rith Hillel Foundations in American Universities. The works published under these joint auspices, while providing informative and inspiring reading material for all, are intended to serve also as stimulating resource material for the college student."

***See Note *Maurice Samuel, *Harvest in the Desert*, 1944.

Trade edition: New York, Alfred A. Knopf, 1947.

"Has a first printing of 8,000 copies for The Society, 3,500 copies for the Hillel Foundations, and 4,500 copies, in two printings, for the trade publisher, Alfred A. Knopf." — *AJYB*, 5709, p. 850.

1948: "1,450 copies reprinted." — *JPSA* [61st annual report] 1948, p. 3.

American Overture

AMERICAN OVERTURE | Jewish Rights in Colonial Times | by | Abram Vossen Goodman | [*seal 3b*] | Philadelphia | The Jewish Publication Society of America | 5707–1947 |

COLLATION: 8°. xiv, 265 p. (p. [i] Half-title, p. [iii] Title; p. [iv] Copyright, All rights reserved; p. [v] Dedication*; p. vii–ix, Preface; p. xi, Table of Contents; p. [ii, vi, x, xii] blank; p. xiii–xiv, List of Illustrations; 1 l., and p. 1–203, Text; p. 205–227, Notes; p. 229–251, Bibliography; p. [204, 228, 252] blank; p. 253–265, Index.) plates, ports. (including front.), map.

Issued in light blue cloth; front cover: title, author within square rule box; back: author, title, publisher all in red.

*"To | my wife | whose encouragement | made this book possible | ."

"My main consideration has been the interaction of Jewish forces with the early American scene as manifested in the expanding rights of the Jewish minority and in the growing recognition that Jews were men who might aspire to full civic equality. This theme has tremendous meaning in the unfolding of Jewish history and in the upbuilding of the democratic principle as we know it today. It serves fittingly as an American overture." — Preface, p. vii.

Essays in Jewish Biography

ESSAYS IN JEWISH | BIOGRAPHY | by | Alexander Marx | [*seal 3b*] | Philadelphia | The Jewish Publication Society of America | 5708–1947 |

[Note: The foregoing appears within a black single rule box, top and bottom also have four rules.]

251

COLLATION: 8°. xi, 298 p. (p. [i] Half-title; p. [ii] (Note)*;
p. [iii] Title; p. [iv] Copyright, 1948, All rights reserved; p. [v]
Dedication**; p. [vi] blank; p. vii–x, Preface; p. [xi] Table of
Contents; p. [1]–289, Text; p. [290] blank; p. [291]–298, Bibliography.)

Issued in brown cloth; back: rules, title, rules, author and
publisher in gilt.

*"The publication of this book was made possible in part
by a gift of the Solis-Cohen Family Fund in honor of Solomon Solis-
Cohen, poet, scientist, physician, one of the founders of The Jewish
Publication Society and a friend of the author of this volume."

**"To the memory of my parents | George and Gertrud Marx | ."

"The twelve biographies included in this volume were not
written according to a plan. Most of them were called forth by
anniversaries of great men; others were intended as memorials to
departed scholars whose names and achievements deserve to be
retained in the minds of our own and future generations ... Five
of them were included in my *Studies in Jewish History and Booklore*,
New York, 1944; but since that book was meant for a smaller circle
of readers and its edition of 650 copies is entirely out of print, they
are repeated here." — Preface, p. vii, x.

CONTENTS: 1. Rab Saadia Gaon. 2. Rabbenu Gershom, light
of the exile. 3. Rashi. 4. Maimonides. 5. Moritz Steinschneider.
6. David Hoffmann. 7. Mayer Sulzberger. 8. Solomon Schechter.
9. The Jewish scholarship of Joseph Jacobs. 10. Henry Malter.
11. Max Leopold Margolis. 12. Israel Friedlaender the scholar.

The House of Nasi
Doña Gracia

THE HOUSE OF NASI | DOÑA GRACIA | by | Cecil Roth | [*seal 3 b*] |
Philadelphia | The Jewish Publication Society of America |
5708–1947 |

[Note: The foregoing appears within a single rule box, with scalloped lines at top and bottom. Title underscored with double lines, all in black.]

COLLATION: 8°. xiii, 208 p. (p. [i] Half-title; p. [ii] Some other books by the same author . . .; p. [iii] Title; p. [iv] Copyright, 1948, All rights reserved; p. [v] Dedication*; p. [vii] Table of Contents; p. [vi, viii] blank; p. ix–x, List of Illustrations; p. xi–xiii, Preface; p. [1]–184, Text; p. 185, Chronological Table; p. [186] blank; p. [187]–192, Bibliography; p. [193]–208, Notes.) plates (including front.: Gracia Mendes, the Younger about 1553, medal made by Pastorius de' Pastorini in Ferrara). Map on lining papers.

Issued in black cloth; back: designs, title, author, and designs in black (on gilt), publisher in gilt.

*" To the memory of | Henrietta Szold | ."

Hebrew translation:

בצלאל רות | בית נשיא | עברית שלמה סימונסון | תל־אביב, מ. ניומן,
תשי"ג.

In my Father's Pastures

In | MY FATHER'S | PASTURES | by | Soma Morgenstern | [*rule*] | Translated from the German manuscript by | Ludwig Lewisohn | [*rule*] | [*seal 3b*] | Philadelphia | The Jewish Publication Society of America | 5707–1947 |

COLLATION: 8°. 4 p. l., 369 p. (l. 1, Half-title; l. 2, Title, verso Copyright, All rights reserved; l. 3, Contents; verso of l. 1, 3 blank; l. 4 and p. [1]–369, Text.)

Issued in tan cloth; top edges brown; back: rules, title (in tan on brown), rules, author and publisher in brown.

A sequel to his *The Son of the Lost Son* published by The Jewish Publication Society of America in 1946, but its plot does not depend upon that of its predecessor . . . Some of the same characters, however, appear in both novels.

American Jewish Year Book
5708

American Jewish | YEAR BOOK | Volume 49 (5708) 1947–
1948 | Prepared by | The American Jewish Committee |
Harry Schneiderman and Morris Fine | Editors | Maurice
Spector | Maurice Basseches | Assistant Editors | [*seal 3b*] |
The Jewish Publication Society of America | Philadelphia,
Pennsylvania |

COLLATION: 12°. xiv, 844 p. (p. [i] Half-title; p. [iii] Title;
p. [iv] Copyright, All rights reserved; p. v–viii, Preface by Harry
Schneiderman; p. ix–xi, Contributors; p. [ii, xii] blank; p. xiii–xiv,
Contents; 1 l., and p. 1–774, Text; p. [775]–844, Annual reports:
p. [777]–795, The American Jewish Committee 40th annual report
1947; p. [797]–844, Report of the 59th year of The Jewish Publication Society of America 1946.) ports.

Bound uniformly with 5707 (1946–47).

"Church-state relations, particularly in the field of public education, were widely discussed in Jewish as well as non-Jewish circles
and were a subject of study by Jewish national and local communal
agencies during the past year. In recognition of the lively interest
in this subject, the editors believed it timely to present, in this volume,
an examination of this question in the light of American history and
legal precedent down to the contemporary period. The editors were
fortunate in securing for this assignment the services of Dr. Nathan
Schachner, author of several historical works, including biographies
of Aaron Burr and Alexander Hamilton.

"The calendars, prepared by Dr. Julius H. Greenstone, are this
year placed in the back of the volume with the other reference
features." — Preface, p. v, vii.

SPECIAL ARTICLES: Church, state and education, by Nathan
Schachner, pp. 1–48. — Morris R. Cohen: 1880–1947, by Milton
R. Konvitz, pp. 49–66. — Sidney Hillman: 1887–1946, by A. H.
Raskin, pp. 67–80. — Emanuel Libman: 1872–1946, by George
Baehr, pp. 81–84. — Henry Monsky: 1890–1947, by Henry W.

Levy, pp. 85–90. — Jewish Institute of Religion, by I. Edward Kiev and John J. Tepfer, pp. 91–100. — The year in retrospect, by Salo W. Baron, pp. 103–122.

The number of directories and lists has been increased and information on organizations and periodicals in Latin American countries is included for the first time.

1948: "2,200 copies reprinted." — *JPSA* [61st annual report] 1948, p. 2.

1948

Mr. Benjamin's Sword

. . . | MR. BENJAMIN'S | SWORD | Illustrated by Herschel Levit | [*seal 3b*] | The Jewish Publication Society of America | 5708 Philadelphia 1948 |

At head of title: Robert D. Abrahams | [rule] | .

[Note: The foregoing appears within a double rule box and a single rule box, all in black.]

COLLATION: 12°. 4 p. l., 183 p. (l. 1, Half-title, verso blank; l. 2, Title, verso Copyright, All rights reserved; l. 3, Dedication*, verso [Author's] Note; l. 4 and p. 1–183, Text.)

Issued in maroon cloth; front cover: title; back: author, title, publisher all in gilt.

*"To the western states, | where brothers learned to be | friends again | ."

The Book of Books

. . . | THE BOOK OF BOOKS: | An Introduction | By | Solomon Goldman | [*seal 3b*] | Philadelphia | The Jewish Publication Society of America | 5708–1948 |

At head of title: The Book of Human Destiny: 1.

255

[Note: The foregoing appears within a black double rule box.]

COLLATION: 8°. xiii, 459 p. (p. [i] Half-title; p. [ii] By the same author . . .; p. [iii] Title; p. [iv] Copyright by Solomon Goldman, All rights . . . reserved . . . For information address Harper & Brothers; p. [v] Dedication*; p. [vii] Contents, Illustrations; p. [vi, viii] blank; p. ix–xiii, Preface; 1 l. and p. 1–355, Text; p. 357–403, Notes; p. [356, 404] blank; p. [405]–436, General Bibliography; p. [437]–459, Index.) plate, 2 facsims. (including front.)

Issued in rust cloth; front cover: series title, rules, title, rules, author; back: series title, rules, title, rules, author, rules, publisher, all in gilt.

*"To | Professor Alexander Marx | on the occasion of | His Seventieth Birthday | Gratefully and Respectfully | ."

"The present volume contains six chapters, Echoes and Allusions, Notes, Bibliographies, and an Index. The first chapter ventures to pry into the mystery of the amazing virility of the Hebrew language and Biblical idiom, their resilience, freshness, energy, and youthfulness, and the ease with which their effect is transferred and preserved in almost any language. The second, after stressing the presence of an art sense among the Jews and demonstrating their appreciation of the beautiful, deals sketchily with the Biblical or Jewish attitude toward the plastic arts, the relation of art to religion and morals, the limitation of form as a statement of truth, and the wealth and power of the Biblical metaphor. The third reviews briefly the history of the Hebrew Canon, the adventures of the Masoretic text, and the origin and labors of the Scribes and their successors. The fourth proceeds from an inquiry into the extent to which the Rabbis and Jewish scholars of the Middle Ages had apprehended the numerous perplexities in the Bible and had set out to solve them, to a resumé of modern Biblical Criticism, and concludes with an analysis of the work of those neo-critics who, while recognizing the invaluable contribution the proponents of the Documentary hypothesis and their followers have made to every phase of the Bible study, question some of their methods and reject many of their conclusions. The fifth concerns itself with both the impact of archaeological discoveries on the Bible and Biblical Criticism and the authenticity of background the resurrected civilizations of the Near East provide for early Jewish history. Unfortunately, the prejudices of men being what they are, much of its space had to be used up in an attempt to account for the charge of plagiarism leveled against the Jews by not a few Assyriologists, Egyptologists and others, and to investigate the evidence which they submit in support of their allegations. The sixth and last chapter pursues, in a certain sense, the theme of the first, contemplating further the effectiveness and influence of the Bible and the magnetism that has drawn to it, throughout endless generations, both the common man and the independent thinker.

"In Echoes and Allusions the author has brought together several hundred quotations from as many men of letters, scientists, philosophers, artists, economists, statesmen, and others, illustrating the use and misuse to which the Bible has been put and directing attention to the part it has had in stimulating everywhere thought and action and forming in the Occidental world the very art of expression. The notes he has employed, for the most part, to indicate the sources to which he is under obligation and here and there to expatiate on a point which in the body of the book was, for obvious reasons, disposed of casually and cursorily. In the Bibliography to Echoes and Allusions the author has assembled into a fairly comprehensive list widely scattered books, dissertations, and articles in journals and magazines which, treating of the Bible as a treasure of literary beauty and excellence, trace out its deep imprint either on the literature of a people, considered as a whole, or on the work of an individual author, and which have been overlooked in the usual introductions to Scriptures. In like manner he has included in the General Bibliography Jewish authorities of medieval and modern times who have been neglected by the various schools of Biblical Criticism ... The Index, aside from being quite complete, offers in addition outlines of the discussion to be found in the text on the more important entries." — Preface, p. xi, xii.

CONTENTS: I. The achievement and the instrument — The Hebrew Bible. — II. Graven images. — III. The Hebrew canon. — IV. Biblical criticism. — V. "The dawn of conscience." — VI. An eternally effective book. — Echoes and allusions.

Trade edition: New York, Harper & Brothers, 1948.

The House of Nasi
The Duke of Naxos

THE HOUSE OF NASI | [*rule*] | THE DUKE OF NAXOS | [*rule* | by | Cecil Roth | [*seal 3b*] | Philadelphia | The Jewish Publication Society of America | 5708–1948 |

[Note: The foregoing appears within a black single rule box, top and bottom lines ornamental.]

COLLATION: 8°. xvi, 250 p. (p. [i] The Gitelson Library seal; p. [ii] (Note)*; p. [iii] Half-title; p. [iv] Other works by the same author . . .; p. [v] Title; p. [vi] Copyright, All rights reserved; p. [vii] Dedication**; p. [ix] Table of Contents; p. xi–xii, List of Illustrations; p. xiii, Preface; p. [viii, x, xiv] blank; p. xv–xvi, Foreword; p. [1]–221, Text; p. 223, Chronological Table; p. [225]–229, Bibliography; p. [222, 224, 230] blank; p. [231]–250, Notes.) facsims., maps, plates (including front.: Gracia Mendes the Younger, later Duchess of Naxos, medal made by Pastorius de' Pastorini in Ferrara). Map on lining papers.

Issued in black cloth; front cover: monogram GL, in gilt, in right hand corner; back: designs, title, author and designs in black (on gilt), publisher in gilt.

A companion volume to his *The House of Nasi Doña Gracia*, 1947.

*"The publication of this volume by The Jewish Publication Society of America was made possible by the Nehemiah Gitelson Fund, established in loving memory of Nehemiah Gitelson (1853–1932) scholar, rabbi, Talmudic teacher, and merchant. The present volume is the first issued under this Fund."

**"To | Chaim Weizmann | ."

Among the Nations

AMONG THE NATIONS | Three Tales and a Play about Jews | By | W. Somerset Maugham | Jacques De Lacretelle | John Galsworthy | Thomas Mann | Edited with an Introduction by

Ludwig Lewisohn | [*seal 3b*] | 5708.Philadelphia.1948 | The Jewish Publication Society of America |

COLLATION: 8°. xviii, 270 p. (p. [i] Half-title; p. [iii] Title; p. [iv] Copyright 1948 by Farrar, Straus and Co. . . .; p. [v] Dedication: "For Louise;" p. [ii, vi] blank; p. [vii] (Contents); p. [viii] [Quotation from] Lamentations of Jeremiah I,3.; p. ix–xviii, Introduction; p. [1]–270, Text.)

Issued in green cloth; back: title, editor, rule and publisher in gilt.

CONTENTS: The alien corn by W. Somerset Maugham. — Silbermann by Jacques de Lacretelle. — Loyalties by John Galsworthy. — Tamar by Thomas Mann.

Trade edition: New York, Farrar and Straus, 1948.

Prince of the Ghetto

PRINCE | of the | Ghetto | by | Maurice Samuel | [*seal 3b*] | Philadelphia | The Jewish Publication Society of America | 5708–1948 |

[Note: The foregoing appears within a black double rule box.]

COLLATION: 8°. 2 l., vi, 294 p. (l. 1, recto blank, verso Also by Maurice Samuel . . .; 2, Half-title, verso blank; p. [i] The Gitelson Library seal; p. [ii] (Note) *; p. [iii] Title; p. [iv] Copyright, 1948 by Maurice Samuel, All rights reserved; p. v–vi, Contents; p. [1]–292, Text; p. 293–294, Biographical Note [on Isaac Loeb Perez].)

Issued in gray cloth; front cover: title and author, with monogram GL in right hand corner; back: title, author and publisher all in red.

At end: "A note on the type used in this book. The text of this book has been set on the Linotype in a type-face called 'Baskerville' . . ."

*Note on the Nehemiah Gitelson Fund. See Roth, *The House of Nasi; The Duke of Naxos*, 1948. "The present volume is the second issued under this Fund."

Another edition with B'nai B'rith Hillel Foundations seal.

Trade edition: New York, Alfred A. Knopf, 1948.

Pilgrims in a New Land

Pilgrims in a New Land | [*four rules*] | Lee M. Friedman | [*seal 3b*] | Philadelphia | The Jewish Publication Society of America | 5708–1948 |

COLLATION: 8°. xii, 471 p. (p. [i] The Gitelson Library seal; p. [ii] (Note) *; p. [iii] Half-title; p. [iv] Frontispiece [A scene in Vermont from a wood engraving by Asa Cheffetz]; p. [v] Title; p. [vi] Copyright, All rights reserved; p. [vii] Statements by L. M. F., Joseph Goldmark and Woodrow Wilson on the Pilgrims; p. [viii] Other books by Lee M. Friedman . . .; p. ix–x, Table of Contents; p. xi–xii, List of Illustrations; p. [1]–383, Text; p. [384] blank; p. [385]–471, Index.) facsims., illus., maps, plates, ports.

Issued in red cloth; top edges red; front cover: monogram GL, in right hand corner; back: title (on black), author and publisher all in gilt.

*Note on the Nehemiah Gitelson Fund. See Roth, *The House of Nasi; the Duke of Naxos*, 1948. "The present volume is the third issued under this Fund."

Trade edition: New York, Farrar and Straus, 1948.

Boot Camp

. . . | BOOT | CAMP | [*seal 3b*] | 5708. Philadelphia. 1948 | The Jewish Publication Society of America |

At head of title: Henry J. Berkowitz.

COLLATION: 12°. 5 p. l., 384 p. (l. 1, Half-title; l. 2, Title, verso Copyright, All rights reserved; l. 3, Dedication*; l. 5, Author's note; verso of l. 1, 3–4, blank; l. 5 and p. 1–384, Text.)

Issued in navy blue cloth; front cover: title across a wreath; back: author, title, publisher, all in white.

*"To | Flora | my shipmate | who also went | through 'Boots' | ."

American Jewish Year Book
5709

American Jewish | YEAR BOOK | Volume 50 (5709) 1948–1949 | Prepared by | The American Jewish Committee | Harry Schneiderman and Morris Fine | Editors | Jacob Sloan | Assitant Editor | [*seal 3b*] | The Jewish Publication Society of America | Philadelphia | Pennsylvania |

COLLATION: 12°. xv, 876 p. (p. [i] Half-title; p. [iii] Title; p. [iv] Copyright, 1949, All rights reserved; p. v–ix, Preface by Morris Fine, dated November 20, 1948; p. [ii, x] blank; p. xi–xii, Contributors; p. xiii–xv, Contents; 1 l., and p. 1–806, Text; p. [807]–864, Annual reports: p. [811]–837, The American Jewish Committee, 41st annual report 1948; p. [838] blank; p. [839]–864, Report of the 60th year of The Jewish Publication Society of America 1947; p. [865]–876, Index to special articles, directories, lists and statistics in Volumes 1–50.) ports.

Bound uniformly with 5707 (1946–47).

"With this volume the *American Jewish Year Book* completes fifty years of regular publication.

"On the occasion of the *Year Book's* fiftieth anniversary it was deemed appropriate and not immodest to publish a special article reviewing the contents of the entire series.

"The *Year Book* anniversary suggested the appropriateness of a feature article on some phase of American Jewish history, one more comprehensive than an institutional survey. The subject chosen was Jewish immigration . . . The emphasis of this article, 'A Century of Jewish Immigration to the United States,' by Oscar and Mary F. Handlin, is not on the contributions of individuals to America . . .

261

but rather on the adjustment and acculturation processes of the Jewish ethno-cultural group, and the influence of the American environment on the immigrants' institutions.

"The study on Jewish migration during the past year, by Sidney Liskofsky, is an attempt to assemble comprehensive data on the exceedingly complex topic of world Jewish migrations, where definitive data, is often impossible to find."— Preface, p. v–vii.

This volume was the last to be edited by Harry Schneiderman.

Report of the Sixty-first Year

[Report of the sixty-first annual meeting of the Jewish Publication Society of America]

COLLATION: 12°. 16 p.

Paper-covers; front cover: seal 3b; back cover: Printed in the United States of America, Press of the Jewish Publication Society Philadelphia, Penna.

CONTENTS: Annual report of the President for the year 1948. Treasurer's report. By-Laws.

To Dwell in Safety

TO DWELL IN SAFETY | The Story of Jewish Migration | Since 1800 | By | Mark Wischnitzer | [*seal 3 b*] | The Jewish Publication Society of America | 5709. Philadelphia. 1948 |

COLLATION: 8°. xxv, 368 p. (p. [i] Half-title; p. [iii] Title; p. [iv] Copyright, 1949, All rights reserved; p. [v] Dedication*; p. vii–viii, Preface by James G. McDonald; p. ix–xiii, Foreword; p. xv, Acknowledgments; p. [ii, vi, xiv, xvi] blank; p. xvii–xx, Contents; p. xxi–xxiv, List of Illustrations; p. xxv, List of Maps; p. [1]–287, Text; p. 288–307, Appendices I–IV; p. [308] blank; p. [309]–352, Notes; p. 353–368, Index.) front., plates, ports., maps, facsim.

Issued in red cloth: back: title, author, publisher in gilt.

*"To | Rachel and Leonard | ."

"Here is a comprehensive and scholarly but never dull survey of one of the most important social phenomena of the nineteenth and twentieth centuries — the migration of millions of Jewish folk from central, eastern and southeastern Europe to the far corners of the world. Nowhere else, in any other single volume or group of volumes, can one find the facts so clearly portrayed or the causes and results of this modern exodus so searchingly analyzed." — Preface by James G. McDonald, p. vii.

1949

The Purim Anthology

THE | PURIM | ANTHOLOGY | By | Philip Goodman | [*seal 3 b*] | 5709. Philadelphia. 1949 | The Jewish Publication Society of America |

COLLATION: 8°. xxxi, 525 p. (p. [i] Half-title; p. [iii] Title; p. [iv] Copyright, All rights reserved; p. [v] Dedication*; p. vii–xvi, Contents; p. xvii–xxi, List of Illustrations; p. [ii, vi, xxii] blank; p. xxiii–xxvi, Preface; p. xxvii–xxxi, Acknowledgments; 1 l. and p. [1]–440, Text; p. [441]–489, Music supplement compiled by A. W. Binder; p. 491–493, Glossary of Purim terms; p. [490, 494] blank; p. 495–512, Bibliography; p. 513–525, Notes.) facsim., illus., plates, music.

Issued in light blue cloth; front cover: title, rule and compiler within single rule box; back: rule, design, rule, compiler, rule, title, rule, publisher, rule, design, rules all in gilt.

*"To My Wife | חנה |

"אשת חיל מי ימצא ורחוק מפנינים מכרה | משלי ל"א, י' | .

CONTENTS: Book 1. The Story of Purim. — Book 2. Purim in literature, art and music. — Book 3. Purim for young people. — Book 4. Purim joy. — Book 5. Commemoration of Purim. — Music supplement.

"It is in the hope of presenting vividly the character and message of this festival and the manner of its observance that this book has been prepared. If it succeeds in conveying to its readers a feeling of optimism concerning the Jewish future, the editor will consider that his efforts have more than realized his hopes." — Preface, p. xxiii–xxiv.

Reprints: January 1, 1952 — 2,500 copies. Information from Lesser Zussman, Executive Secretary, January, 1953.

Trial and Error

TRIAL AND ERROR | The Autobiography | of | Chaim Weizmann | In Two Volumes | Volume[s] I [and II] | [*seal 3b*] | Philadelphia | The Jewish Publication Society of America | 5709–1949 |

[Note: Title and seal in red.]

COLLATION: 8°. 2 v. (paged continuously). (v. 1: viii, 264 p. (p. [i] Half-title; p. [ii] blank; p. [iii] Title; p. [iv] Copyright by The Weizmann Foundation, All rights . . . reserved . . . For information address Harper & Brothers; p. [v] Dedication*; p. vi, Acknowledgment; p. vii–viii, Table of Contents; p. [1]–264, Text); v. 2: v, 265–493 p. (p. [i–iv] same as v. 1; p. v, Table of Contents; p. 265–482, Text; p. 483–493, Index.) front. (port.), map.

Issued in green cloth; top edges green; back: title, author, rule, volume number indicated by * and **, publisher all in gilt.

*"For | My Wife | — my comrade and life companion | ."

Trade edition: New York, Harper & Brothers [cop. 1949] 1 v. (viii, 493 p.)

In the Beginning

. . . | IN THE BEGINNING | By | Solomon Goldman | [*seal 3b*] | Philadelphia | The Jewish Publication Society of America | 5710–1949 |

At head of title: The Book of Human Destiny: 2.

[Note: The foregoing appears within a black double rule box.]

COLLATION: 8°. xiv, 892 p. (p. [i] Half-title; p. [ii] By the same author ...; p. [iii] Title; p. iv, Copyright by The Solomon Goldman Publications Foundation; All rights ... reserved ... For information address Harper & Brothers; p. iv–v, (Acknowledgments); p. [vii] Dedication*; p. [vi, viii] blank; p. [ix]–x, Contents, Illustrations; p. xi–xiv, Preface; 1 l. and p. 1–728, Text; p. 729–730, Abbreviations; p. 731–828, Commentary; p. 829–841, Notes; p. [842] blank; p. [843]–862, General Bibliography; p. [863]–892, Index.) map, plates, facsims. (including front.)

Bound uniformly with his: *The Book of Books*, 1948.

*"To | Professor Mordecai M. Kaplan | Determined and undaunted | wrestler with God and men | ."

Trade edition: New York, Harper & Brothers, 1949.

As A Mighty Stream

AS A | MIGHTY STREAM | [*design*] | The Progress of Judaism | Through History | By | Julian Morgenstern | President Emeritus | Hebrew Union College | [*seal 3b*] | Philadelphia | The Jewish Publication Society of America | 5710–1949 |

[Note: The foregoing appears within a black double rule box, with scalloped line at top and bottom.]

COLLATION: 8°. xi, 442 p. (p. [i] Half-title; p. [iii] Title; p. [iv] Copyright, All rights reserved; p. [v] Dedication*; p. [ii, vi] blank; p. vii–x, Preface; p. [xi] Table of Contents; p. [1]–442, Text.)

Issued in light blue cloth; back: title, design, author, publisher all in gilt.

*"To the memory of my beloved parents | Samuel and Hannah Morgenstern | whose Love, Devotion and Faith made possible | my service to God, Israel and Fellowmen | ."

CONTENTS: The Foundations of Israel's history. — "Behind closed doors." — World-Empire and World-Brotherhood. — The Achievements of Reform Judaism. — Our fathers, ourselves and our children. — Judaism and the modern world. — At the crossroads. — The Reform process in Jewish history. — "Melting-pot," "Cultural pluralism," or What? — Judaism's contribution to post-war religion. — Nation, people, religion — what are we? — Unity in American Judaism. — how and when? — A program for Judaism and the Jewish people. — With history as our guide.

"The primary responsibility for the publication of this volume rests with the Board of Governors of the Hebrew Union College. When I retired from the Presidency of the College, on July 1, 1947, the Board of Governors graciously invited me to prepare a volume of addresses and papers which I had delivered or read during the course of my then forty years of official connection with the College . . . It is a pleasure to be thus associated with the Board of Governors in the responsibility for this volume, which, in a very real way, rounds out my service as President of the College, just as it has been a pleasure to be a partner with it in many other far weightier projects during all the years of my Presidency." — Preface, p. vii.

The Jews

THE JEWS | Their History, | Culture, and Religion | [*double rule*] | Edited by | Louis Finkelstein | President | The Jewish Theological Seminary of America | [*double rule*] | Volume[s] I [II, III and IV] | [*seal 3b*] | Philadelphia | The Jewish Publication Society of America | 5710–1949 |

COLLATION: 8°. 4 v. (paged continuously). (v. 1: xxxiii, 453 p. (p. [i] Half-title, The Gitelson Library seal; p. [ii] (Note)*; p. [iii] Title; p. [iv] Dedication**, (Note)***, Copyright by Louis Finkelstein, All rights . . . reserved . . . For information address Harper & Brothers; p. v–vi, Contributors and Members of the Planning Committee; p. vii–x, Contents; p. xi, Illustrations; p. xii, List of Maps; p. xiii–xviii, Prefatory Letter; p. xix–xx, Intro-

266

ductory Note; p. xxi–xxxiii, Foreword; p. [1]–453, Text); v. 2: v, [455]–744 p. (p. [i–iv] same as v. 1; p. v, Contents; p. [455]–744, Text); v. 3: vi, 745–1148 p. (p. [i–iv] same as v. 1; p. v–vi, Contents; 1 l. and p. 745–1148, Text); v. 4: v, [1149]–1431 p. (p. [i–iv] same as v. 1; p. v, Contents; p. [1149]–1389, Text; p. 1391–1397, Appendix; p. 1399–1403, List of Abbreviations; p. [1390, 1398, 1404] blank; p. 1405–1431, Index.) illus., ports., maps (including 3 colored on folded leaves).

Issued in black cloth; front cover: monogram GL in right hand corner; back: volume numbers, rules, design, rules, title, rule, editor, rules, design, rules (on maroon); publisher all in silver.

*Note on the Nehemiah Gitelson Fund. See Roth, *The House of Nasi; The Duke of Naxos, 1948.* "The present work is the fourth issued under this Fund . . ."

**"To | IRVING LEHMAN | (1876–1945) | Who in life and precept | integrated the ancient tradition | of the Hebrew prophets with the | spirit of American democracy | ."

***"The preparation of this book was made possible by funds generously made available by the American Jewish Committee."

"The purpose of the book is to bring into focus the vast number and wide variety of data concerning Judaism and the Jews, so that they can be seen in relation to one another and to the general phenomena of human culture." — Foreword, p. xxi.

CONTENTS: I. The History of Judaism and the Jews: The Biblical period, William Foxwell Albright. — The Historical foundations of postbiblical Judaism, Elias J. Bickerman. — The Period of the Talmud, Judah Goldin. — The European age in Jewish history, Cecil Roth. — The Jews of Western Europe, Cecil Roth. — The Problem of European Jewry (1939–1945), Arieh Tartakower. — The American Jewish Chronicle, Anita Libman Lebeson. — Jewish religious life and institutions in America, Moshe Davis. — II. The Role of Judaism in civilization: The Bible as a cultural monument, Robert Gordis. — The Influence of Jewish law on the development of the Common Law, Jacob J. Rabinowitz. — On medieval Jewish poetry, Shalom Spiegel. — The Modern renaissance of Hebrew literature, Hillel Bavli. — The Mystical element in Judaism, Abraham J. Heschel. — Judaism and world philosophy, Alexander Altmann. — The Contribution of Judaism to world ethics, Mordecai M. Kaplan. — Judaism and social welfare, Israel S. Chipkin. — Hellenistic Jewish literature, Ralph Marcus. — Judeo-Arabic literature, Abraham S. Halkin. — Israel in Iran, Walter J. Fischel. — Yiddish literature, Yudel Mark. — The Role of education in Jewish history, Julius B. Maller. — Jewish educational institutions, Simon Greenberg. — The Jewish contribution to music, Eric Werner. — Judaism and art, Rachel Wischnitzer. — The Contribution of the Jews to medicine, Arturo Castiglioni. — Science and Judaism, Charles Singer. — Judaism and the democratic ideal, Milton R. Konvitz. — The Influence of the Bible on English literature, David Daiches. — The Influence of the Bible on European literature, Frederick Lehner. — III. The Sociology and demography of the Jews: Who are the Jews?, Melville J. Herskovits. — Sources of Jewish statistics, Uriah Zevi Engelman. — Jewish migrations, 1840–1946, Jacob Lestschinsky. — The Economic structure of modern Jewry, Nathan Reich. — The Jewish community, Samuel C. Kohs. — IV. The Jewish religion: The Jewish religion: Its beliefs and practices, Louis Finkelstein. — Appendix: "What questions should be answered in the book on Judaism and the Jews?"

Trade edition: New York, Harper & Brothers, 1949. 2 v. (744 p.; 745–1431 p.)

Reprints: February 8, 1952 — 1,010 copies. Information from Lesser Zussman, Executive Secretary, January, 1953.

1950

American Jewish Year Book

American | Jewish | Year Book | [*ornamental line*] | Volume 51 | [*rule*] | 1950 | Prepared by | The American Jewish Committee | Morris Fine, Editor | Jacob Sloan, Assistant Editor | Irving Kaplan, Editorial Assistant | The American

Jewish Committee | New York | The Jewish Publication Society of America | Philadelphia |

COLLATION: 8°. xvii, 599 p. (p. [i] Half-title; p. [iii] Title; p. [iv] Copyright 1950 by The American Jewish Committee and The Jewish Publication Society of America, All rights reserved, Printed by Knickerbocker Printing Corporation; p. v–vii, Preface by Morris Fine; p. [ii, viii] blank; p. ix–x, Contributors; p. xi–xiv, Table of Contents; p. xv–xvii, Tables and Graphs; p. [1]–526, Text; p. [527]–546, Calendars; p. [547]–578, Annual Reports: p. 549–562, [42nd of the] American Jewish Committee; p. 563–578, [61st of the] Jewish Publication Society of America; p. [579]–599, Index.)

Issued in dark blue cloth; back: rules, title, rules, year and volume, rules, publishers, rules all in gilt.

"For the past fifty years the American Jewish Year Book has been a publication of the Jewish Publication Society — printed at its press and distributed by the Society. With the present volume, however, as the result of a special agreement between the Society and the American Jewish Committee, the latter, in addition to continuing to serve as editor, joins the Society as co-publisher of the Year Book and will also be responsible for the printing of the volume and the distribution of all copies not reserved for the Society's membership." — Preface, p. vi.

The Court Jew

THE COURT JEW | A Contribution to the History | of the Period of Absolutism in | Central Europe. | by Selma Stern | American Jewish Archives | Translated from the German manuscript | by | Ralph Weiman | [*seal 3b*] | Philadelphia | The Jewish Publication Society of America | 5710–1950 |

[Note: The foregoing appears within a black double rule box.]

Collation: 8°. xvii, 312 p. (p. [i] Half-title; p. [iii] Title; p. [iv] Copyright, All rights reserved; p. [v] Dedication*; p. [ii, vi] blank; p. vii–x, Contents; p. xi–xvii, Preface; 1 l. and p. 1–267, Text; p. [268] blank; p. 269–296, Notes and Bibliography; p. 297–312, Index.)

Issued in black cloth; back: designs, title, author and designs in black (on gilt), *seal 3c* and publisher in gilt.

*"To | Jacob Rader Marcus | in friendship | ."

"This work is based principally on studies made during the years 1920–1938 in the archives of almost everyone of the German *Staats-* and *Stadtarchiven*, in Ansbach, Berlin, Breslau, Danzig, Darmstadt, Duesseldorf, Frankfort on the Main and Frankfort on the Oder, Halberstadt, Heidelberg, Karlsruhe, Koblenz, Koenigsberg, Magdeburg, Muenster, Nuernberg, Stettin, Stuttgart, Tuebingen, Wolfenbuettel and Wuerzburg." — Preface, p. xv–xvi.

Testament of the Lost Son

The | testament of | the lost son | by | Soma Morgenstern | [*rule*] | Translated from the German manuscript by | Jacob Sloan | In collaboration with | Maurice Samuel | [*rule*] | [*seal 3b*] | Philadelphia | The Jewish Publication Society of America | 5710–1950 |

Collation: 8°. 4 p. l., 359 p. (l. 1, Half-title; l. 2, Title, verso Copyright, All rights reserved; l. 3, Contents; verso of l. 1, 3 blank; l. 4 and p. [1]–359, Text.)

Issued in tan cloth; top edges brown; back: rules, title (in tan on brown), rules, author and publisher in brown.

The Jews of Charleston

the jews | of charleston | A History | of an American Jewish | Community | By Charles Reznikoff | With the Collaboration of | Uriah Z. Engelman | [*seal 3b*] | Phila-

270

delphia | The Jewish Publication Society of America | 5711–1950 |

[Note: The foregoing appears within a black double rule box, with ornamental design and rule at top.]

COLLATION: 8°. xii, 343 p. (1 l., Half-title, verso blank; p. [i] Title; p. [ii] Copyright, All rights reserved; p. iii–iv, Foreword by Salo W. Baron; p. v, Contents; p. [vi] blank; p. vii–viii, List of Illustrations; p. ix–xii, Preface by C[harles] R[eznikoff]; p. [1]–242, Text; p. [243]–325, Appendix and Notes; p. [326] blank; p. 327–343, Index.) facsim., ports., plates (including front.). Illustrated lining papers.

Issued in turquoise cloth; top edges turquoise; back: rules, title, rules, authors, publisher all in gilt.

"This history was undertaken, as part of a bicentennial celebration in the autumn of 1950 of the continuous existence of Charleston's Jewish community, in the belief that there should be a history of the community from the beginning to the present . . .

"The preparation of this book was made possible by funds generously made available by the American Jewish Committee, by the Anti-Defamation League of B'nai B'rith, and by the Jewish community of Charleston," — Preface, p. ix, xii.

Proverbs

. . . | PROVERBS | with commentary | By | Julius H. Greenstone, Ph.D., L.H.D. | [seal 3b] | Philadelphia | The Jewish Publication Society of America | 5711–1950 |

At head of title: The Holy Scriptures | [rule] | .

COLLATION: 8°. xlii, 354 p. (p. [i] Half-title; p. [iii] Title; p. [iv] Copyright, All rights reserved; p. v–vi, Preface; p. [vii] Table of Contents; p. [ii, viii,] blank; p. [ix]–xlii, Introduction; 1 l. and p. [1]–339, Text and Commentary; p. [340] blank; p. 341–354, Topical Index.)

Bound uniformly with *Numbers*, 1939.

This volume is the fourth in The Holy Scriptures series.

"The present commentary, like the other Bible commentaries issued by the Jewish Publication Society, is intended primarily to serve as an aid to the study of the book by the average student and uninitiated layman." — Preface, p. v.

1951
American Jewish Year Book

American | Jewish | Year Book | [*ornamental line*] | Volume 52 | [*rule*] | 1951 | Prepared by | The American Jewish Committee | Morris Fine, Editor | Jacob Sloan, Associate Editor | The American Jewish Committee | New York | The Jewish Publication Society of America | Philadelphia |

COLLATION: 8°. xv, 585 p. (p. [i] Half-title; p. [ii] blank; p. [iii] Title; p. [iv] Copyright, 1951 by The American Jewish Committee and the Jewish Publication Society of America; All rights reserved, Printed by Norwood Press Sales; p. v–vi, Preface by Morris Fine; p. vii–viii, Contributors; p. ix–xii, Table of Contents; p. xiii–xv, Tables; p. [1]–505, Text; p. [507]–522, Calendars; p. [523]–555, Annual Reports: p. 525–537, [43rd of the] American Jewish Committee; p. 538–555, [62nd of the] Jewish Publication Society of America; p. [506, 556] blank; p. [557]–585, Index.)

Bound uniformly with Volume 51 (1950).

"Requirements of space have made necessary the elimination of the directories of organizations and periodicals in foreign countries (except Canada) and the condensation of the obituary notices. The principal features of the Directories section have been retained, however. Also dropped for reasons of space economy is the Calendar for Fifty Years. The Index, however, has been considerably expanded."— Preface, p. v.

Man Is Not Alone

MAN IS NOT | ALONE | Abraham Joshua Heschel | The Jewish Publication Society of America | 5711–1951 | [*seal 3b*] |

COLLATION: 8°. 7 p. l., 305 p. (l. 1, geometric design consisting of six spheres in a hexagon formation, verso . . . Heschel . . . is the author of the following books . . .; l. 2, recto blank, verso Title; l. 3, Sub-title: A philosophy of religion, verso Copyright by Abraham Joshua Heschel, All rights reserved, Manufactured by H. Wolff, New York, Designed by Marshall Lee; l. 4–7, Contents; p. [1]–296, Text; p. [297]–305, Index; verso of p. 305, [Author's Note].)

Issued in yellow cloth; top edges light green; front cover: title in silver; back: publisher in silver, title and author in black.

Trade edition: New York, Farrar, Straus and Young, 1951.

Reprints: February 12, 1952 — 1,000 copies. Information from Lesser Zussman, January, 1953.

Stories and Fantasies

STORIES AND | FANTASIES | From the Jewish past | by | Emil Bernhard Cohn | Translated from the German manuscript | by | Charles Reznikoff | [*seal 3b*] | Philadelphia | The Jewish Publication Society of America | 5711–1951 |

[Note: The foregoing appears within a black double rule box.]

COLLATION: 8°. 3 p. l., 262 p. (l. 1, Half-title; l. 2, Title, verso Copyright; l. 3, Contents; verso l. 1, 3 blank; p. [1]–262, Text.)

Issued in gray cloth; top edges red; back: author, title, publisher in burnt orange.

CONTENTS: The Given years. — Simha of Worms. — Rabbi and emperor. — The Remains of virtue. — The Legend of

Rabbi Akiba. — Honi ha-Meaggel. — The Rebellious tree. — Rabban Gamaliel. — The Waters of Shiloah. — It looks like justice.

American Jewry and the Civil War

AMERICAN JEWRY | AND THE CIVIL WAR | by Bertram Wallace Korn | with an introduction by Allan Nevins | [*seal 3b*] | [*rule*] | The Jewish Publication Society of America | Philadelphia, Pennsylvania . 5711–1951 |

COLLATION: 8°. xii, 331 p. (p. [i] Title; p. [ii] Copyright, All rights reserved; p. [iii] Dedication*; p. [iv] blank; p. v–vi, Table of Contents; p. vii–viii, List of Illustrations; p. ix–x, Introduction; p. xi–xii, Author's Preface; 1 l. and p. 1–219, Text; p. 221–244, Appendix A–D; p. 245, Abbreviations used in Notes; p. 247–305, Chapter Notes; p. 307–313, Bibliography; p. [220, 246, 306, 314] blank; p. 315–316, Acknowledgments; p. 317–331, Index.) facsims., ports.

Issued in dark blue cloth; back: author, rule and title within a single rule box, publisher all in silver.

*"DEDICATED | with love and reverence to my Grandparents. | To Joseph Bergman | whom God has preserved to us these many years. | And to the blessed memory of | Rebecca Bergman (1866–1938) | Ray Folkman Korn (1870–1930) | Charles Korn (1866–1945) | ."

"It does not attempt to offer a full-scale portrait of American Jews — as individuals — in this period, but rather a portrait of American Jewry — as an organized, articulate, self-conscious community of Jews who expressed their sense of togetherness or distinctiveness in a concrete manner: religious, cultural, philanthropic, social or political. Our concern is not with individuals, Americans who happened to be Jews, but with the community *qua* community, with group experience rather than personal experience."— Author's preface, p. xi.

Room for a Son

Room | for | A Son | A novel by | Robert D. Abrahams |
The Jewish Publication Society of America | Philadelphia,
Pa. | 1951–5711 |

[Note: Title and author within a "room."]

COLLATION: 8°. 4 p. l., 164 p. (l. 1, Half-title; l. 2, Title,
verso Copyright; l. 3, (Poem) "Newcomer" by R. D. A.; verso of
l. 1, 3 blank; l. 4 and p. 1–164, Text.)

Issued in light blue cloth; back: author, title, publisher in dark
blue.

"A simple, moving and intensely human story about a Jewish
family in a small American town and the young refugee whom they
adopted . . . The one word that cements Americanism and Judaism
at their best, and which lies at the basis of this delightful story, is
the word which expresses the depth of religious teaching — *Loving-
kindness*."— From book-jacket.

Judaism and Modern Man

JUDAISM AND | MODERN MAN | An interpretation of | Jewish
religion | Will Herberg | The Jewish Publication Society |
of America. Philadelphia |

COLLATION: 8°. xi, 313 p. (p. [i] Half-title; p. [iii] Title;
p. [iv] Copyright 1951 by Will Herberg, All rights reserved,
Designed by Stefan Salter; p. [v] Dedication: "To Anna"; p. vii,
Contents; p. [ii, vi, viii] blank; p. ix–xi, Foreword; p. [1]–310, Text;
p. 311–313, Index.)

Issued in gray cloth; back: title and author (on maroon),
publisher all in white.

Trade edition: New York, Farrar, Straus & Young, 1951.

Reprints: April 25, 1952 — 500 copies; December 19, 1952 — 500 copies. Information from Lesser Zussman, Executive Secretary, January, 1953.

Early American Jewry

Early American Jewry | The Jews of New York | New England and Canada | 1649–1794 | [rule] | Jacob Rader Marcus | Director, American Jewish Archives; | Adolph S. Ochs Professor of Jewish History, Hebrew Union | College— Jewish Institute of Religion, Cincinnati | [seal 3b] | Volume One | [rule] | Philadelphia | The Jewish Publication Society of America | 1951–5712 |

[Note: The foregoing appears within a black double rule box.]

COLLATION: 8°. xxviii, 301 p. (p. [i] Half-title; p. [iii] Title; p. [iv] Copyright, All rights reserved, Printed . . . American Book-Stratford Press, Inc., New York; p. [v] Dedication*; p. vii–xx, Preface; p. xxi–xxv, Contents; p. [ii, vi, xxvi] blank; p. xxvii–xxviii, List of Illustrations; p. [1]–285, Text; p. 287–289, Notes; p. [286, 290] blank; p. 291–301, Index.) plates, ports.

Issued in light green cloth; back: rules, title, rule, author and rules (on black), volume and publisher all in gilt.

*"Many years ago a graduate student at the | University of Berlin dedicated his thesis | To | Pretty Nettie Brody | Today, after twenty-five years of married | life, he dedicates this book to the same woman, | His Wife | ."

1952

A Social and Religious History of the Jews

A SOCIAL | AND RELIGIOUS | HISTORY OF | THE JEWS | by Salo Wittmayer Baron | Professor of Jewish history, literature, and institutions | on the Miller Foundation, Columbia Univer-

276

sity | Second Edition, Revised and Enlarged | Volume[s] I [and II]: Ancient Times, Part[s] I [and II] | [*seal 3b*] | The Jewish Publication Society of America | 5712 Philadelphia 1952 |

COLLATION: 8°. 2 v. (v. 1: xi, 415 p. (p. [i] Half-title; p. [iii] Title; p. [iv], Copyright by Columbia University Press, New York; p. [v] Dedication: "To My Wife;" p. [vii]–ix, Preface; p. [ii, vi, x] blank; p. [xi] Contents; p. [1]–285, Text; p. [286] blank; p. [287]–415, Notes); v. 2: 3 p. l., 493 p. (l. 1–2, Same as v.1, p. [i–iv]; l. 3, Contents, verso blank; p. [1]–321, Text; p. [322] blank; p. [323]–436, Notes; p. [437]–493, Index to Volumes I and II.)

Issued in dark blue cloth; top edges dusty pink; back: design, author, rule, title, rule, volume number, design, publisher all in gilt.

"... a mere revision of the work done fifteen years ago no longer seemed feasible. In the process of rewriting, some of the older views had to be abandoned, but many others had to be amplified and newly documented in such a way as to make the present edition to all intents and purposes a new work ... Not only have many older references been replaced by newer literature but, in view of the increased size, an effort was made to quote more fully the primary sources as well, so as to acquaint the reader with the nature of the available evidence. Not to multiply the number of notes, however, brief references to sources were often given in the text itself, while more extensive source material was frequently combined in longer annotations at the end of the respective paragraphs. As in the first edition more detailed discussions were relegated to the notes, some of which have therefore assumed the character of regular excursuses." — Preface, p. viii.

Trade edition: New York, Columbia University Press, 1952.

Reprints: May 26, 1952 — 500 copies of each volume. Information from Lesser Zussman, Executive Secretary, January, 1953.

American Jewish Year Book

American | Jewish | Year Book | [*ornamental line*] | Volume 53 | [*rule*] | 1952 | Prepared by | The American Jewish Committee | Morris Fine, Editor | Jacob Sloan, Associate Editor | The American Jewish Committee | New York | The Jewish Publication Society of America | Philadelphia |

COLLATION: 8°. xii, 608 p. (p. [i] Half-title; p. [ii] blank; p. [iii] Title; p. [iv] Copyright 1952 by The American Jewish Committee and The Jewish Publication Society of America, All rights reserved, Printed by American Book-Stratford Press, Inc., New York; p. v–vi, Preface by Morris Fine; p. vii–viii, Contributors; p. ix–xii, Table of Contents; p. [1]–529, Text; p. [531]–545, Calendars; p. [530, 546] blank; p. [547]–578, Annual Reports: p. 549–568, [44th of the] American Jewish Committee; p. 569–578, [63rd of the] Jewish Publication Society of America; p. [579]–608, Index.)

Bound uniformly with Volume 51 (1950).

"Of special interest in the present volume, the fifty-third in the series, is the article, 'The Jewish Labor Movement in the United States,' by Will Herberg. Its purpose is to present a popular, yet authoritative summary of the growth and development of the major unions with large Jewish memberships, their influence on the individual immigrant, their role in American Jewish life, and their impact on general American society."— Preface, p. v.

Unambo

UNAMBO | A novel of the war in Israel | By Max Brod | Translated by Ludwig Lewisohn | [*seal 3 b*] | The Jewish Publication Society of America | 5712–1952 |

COLLATION: 8°. 4 p. l., 309 p. (l. 1, Half-title; l. 2, Title, verso Copyright by Farrar, Straus and Young. All rights reserved . . . Printed by H. Wolff, New York, Designed by Stefan Salter; l. 3, Author's Note; l. 4, Contents; verso of l. 1, 3, 4, blank; p. [1]–309, Text.)

278

Issued in brown cloth; back: tan cloth: title and author within rule box, publisher all in blue.

Trade edition: New York, Farrar, Straus, and Young [1952].

"For the factual material used in this narrative I am obliged to those whose accounts complemented my personal experiences, as well as to others who permitted me to cover the battle scenes under expert guidance . . . I have utilized with utmost scrupulousness all the military and political data based on the evidence of accessible delineations and documents. I have permitted myself a single chronological and geographic shift in Chapter Six. The narrative demanded it. But in this instance, too, I have changed no decisive details of the occurrences. Tel Aviv, December 6, 1948."— Author's note, l. 3.

Fallen Angels

Fallen | Angels | Bernard J. Bamberger | The Jewish Publication Society of America | Philadelphia | 5712–1952 |

COLLATION: 8°. xi, 295 p. (p. [i] Half-title; p. [ii] (Illustration of a fallen angel); p. [iii] Title; p. [iv] Copyright, All rights reserved, seal 3b, Printed by American Book-Stratford Press, Inc., New York, Designed by Sidney Feinberg; p. [v] Dedication: "To | EKB | "; p. [vi] blank; p. vii–viii, Acknowledgments; p. ix–xi, Contents; p. [1]–251, Text; p. 252–261, Bibliography; p. 262–290, Notes; p. 291–295, Index.)

Issued in black cloth; top edges and back in burnt orange; front cover: illustration of a fallen angel; back: author, title, publisher all in white.

The Last Revolt

The Last Revolt | The story of Rabbi Akiba | By Joseph Opatoshu | Translated from the Yiddish | By Moshe Spiegel | [seal 3b] | The Jewish Publication Society of America | Philadelphia 5712–1952 |

COLLATION: 8°. 4 p. l., 307 p. (l. 1, Half-title, verso illustration by Marc Chagall; l. 2, Title, verso Copyright, All rights reserved; l. 3, Dedication: "To Adele", verso blank; l. 4, Contents; p. [1]–307, Text.)

Issued in green cloth; back: title, author, publisher in gilt.

Stories of King David

[*Illustration*] | STORIES OF | King David | by Lillian S. Freehof | Illustrated by Seymour R. Kaplan | Philadelphia | The Jewish Publication Society of America |

COLLATION: 4°. 3 p. l., 161 p. (l. 1, Illustration, verso blank; l. 2, Title, verso Copyright 1952; l. 3, Dedication*, verso Acknowledgments; p. [1] Contents; p. [2]–161, Text.) Colored illustrations. Illustrated lining papers.

Issued in tan cloth; top edges blue; front cover: title; back: author, title, publisher all in blue.

*"Dedicated | with Love | to | My Brothers | and | My Sisters | ."

Joel

JOEL | A Novel of Young America | by Nora Benjamin Kubie | [*seal 3b*] | Philadelphia | The Jewish Publication Society of America | 5713–1952 |

COLLATION: 8°. 5 p.l., 207 p. (l. 1, Half-title; l. 2, Title, verso Copyright by Nora Benjamin Kubie, All rights . . . reserved, For information address Harper & Brothers; l. 3, [Quotation from] The Old Testament, Book of Joel [1.2–3]; l. 4, [Author's acknowledgment]; verso, l. 1, 3, 4 blank; l. 5 and p. 1–207, Text.) Maps on lining papers.

Issued in light blue cloth; front cover: title and author; back: author, title and publisher, all in maroon.

Trade edition: New York, Harper & Brothers, 1952.

Appendix and Indexes

APPENDIX

Members of the Directing Boards
OF THE JEWISH PUBLICATION SOCIETY
1888–1952

The following is a list of persons who have served the community through their official connection with the governing boards of the Jewish Publication Society: as officers of the Society, as trustees, or as members of its Publication Committee. A few others are included because they served the Society only through a special committee.

Generally speaking the information stops with the year 1952. Occasionally it was found necessary to carry it into 1953.

The following abbreviations are used:

T   Member of the Board of Trustees.
PC   Member of the Publication Committee.
VP   Vice President of the Society.
HVP   Honorary Vice President of the Society.
Bible Ed. Member of the Board of Editors for the Translation of the Bible.

Although the term "trustee" is used for all those who were members of the governing board of the Society from its inception, attention is called to the fact that from 1888 to 1896 that board went by the name of "Executive Committee."

AARON, MARCUS. Pittsburgh. *T*, 1926–1946.

ADLER, DR. CYRUS. Philadelphia. *T*, 1888–1940. *PC*, 1888–1940, Chairman, 1925–1934. *Bible Ed.*, Chairman, 1908–1916.

ADLER, DR. HERMANN. Chief Rabbi, London. Corresponding member of the Editorial Committee for the Translation of the Bible, 1896.

ALEXANDER, BENJAMIN, Philadelphia. *T*, Secretary, 1913–1919.

AMRAM, DAVID W. Philadelphia. *PC*, 1897–1902.
AMRAM, PHILIP W. Washington. *T*, 1929–.
ANNENBERG, WALTER H. Philadelphia. *T*, 1946–.

BACHARACH, SOLOMON. Philadelphia. *T*, 1923–1927.
BAKER, EDWARD M. Cleveland. *T*, 1927–1946.
BAMBERGER, LOUIS. Newark. *T*, 1927–1928.
BAMBERGER, REV. DR. BERNARD J. New York. *PC*, 1940–.
BARON, DR. SALO W. New York. *PC*, 1941–.
BECKER, JAMES. Chicago. *T*, 1924–1928.
BELKIN, DR. SAMUEL. New York. *PC*, 1941–.
BERENSON, MRS. WYMAN S. Dorchester. *HVP*, 1952–1953.
BERKOWITZ, REV. DR. HENRY. Philadelphia. *T*, 1896–1898. *PC*, 1898–1924.
BERNHEIM, ISAAC W. Louisville. *HVP*, 1900–1945.
BERNHEIMER, DR. CHARLES S. Philadelphia. Assistant Secretary, Board of Trustees, 1890–1906.
BERNHEIMER, MARCUS. St. Louis. *T*, 1892–1896; *VP*, 1894–1896. *HVP*, 1896–1912.
BETTMANN, BERNHARD. Cincinnati. *T*, 1888–1890. *VP*, 1888–1890.
BLAUSTEIN, JACOB. Baltimore. *HVP*, 1949–1953.
BLOCH, DR. JOSHUA. New York. *PC*, 1941–.
BLONDHEIM, DAVID S. Baltimore. *PC*, 1924–1934.
BLUMENTHAL, HART. Philadelphia. *T*, 1913–1940.
BLUMENTHAL, SOLOMON. Philadelphia. *T*, 1892–1908. *VP*, 1892–1896; 1904–1908.
BRONFMAN, SAMUEL. Montreal. *HVP*, 1940–.
BROWDY, BENJAMIN G. New York. *HVP*, 1951–1952.
BROWN, LEO M. Mobile. *T*, 1919–1931.
BUSH, ISIDORE. St. Louis. *T*, 1888–1892.
BUTZEL, FRED M. Detroit. *T*, 1938–1948.

CALISH, REV. DR. EDWARD N. Richmond. *T*, 1892–1893.
COHEN, ALFRED M. Cincinnati. *VP*, 1890–1892.
COHEN, REV. DR. HENRY. Galveston. *T*, 1894–1896. *HVP*, 1896–1952.
COHEN, DR. JOSIAH. Pittsburgh. *T*, 1888–1890, 1925–1931.
COHEN, MISS MARY M. Philadelphia. Corresponding Secretary, 1888–1892.

284

COHEN, REV. DR. MORTIMER J. Philadelphia. *PC*, 1937–.
COWEN, NEWMAN. New York. *T*, 1890.

DANNENBAUM, MORRIS. Philadelphia. Treasurer, 1891–1903.
DAROFF, SAMUEL H. Philadelphia. *T*, 1950–.
DAVIDSON, DR. ISRAEL. New York. Jewish Classics Committee, 1923–1939.
DOBSEVAGE, I. GEORGE. New York. Assistant Secretary, 1906–1925. Secretary, *PC*, 1920–1921.
DUSHKIN, DR. ALEXANDER M. New York. 1946–1949.

EDISON, IRVING. St. Louis. *HVP*, 1951–1952.
EFROS, DR. ISRAEL. New York. *PC*, 1946–.
EICHHOLZ, ADOLPH. Philadelphia. *T*, 1888–1890.
EISENBERG, DR. AZRIEL. New York. *PC*, 1949–.
EISENMAN, CHARLES. Cleveland. *T*, 1911–1919.
EISNER, MARK. New York. *HVP*, 1946–1947.
ELKUS, ABRAM I. New York. *VP*, 1918–1923. *T*, 1923–1926. *HVP*, 1926–1947.
ENELOW, REV. DR. HYMAN G. New York. *PC*, 1914–1934.
ENGEL, MRS. IRVING M. New York. *HVP*, 1949–1953.
EPSTEIN, MRS. MOSES P. New York. *HVP*, 1946–1948.
ETTELSON, REV. DR. HARRY W. Memphis. *PC*, 1924–.
EZEKIEL, HENRY C. Cincinnati. *T*, 1892–1896. *HVP*, 1896–1898.

FASMAN, RABBI OSCAR Z. Chicago. *PC*, 1949–.
FEIBELMAN, REV. DR. JULIAN B. New Orleans. *PC*, 1940–.
FEINSTEIN, MYER. Philadelphia. *T*, 1952–1953. Treasurer, 1953–.
FELDMAN, REV. DR. ABRAHAM J. HARTFORD. *PC*, 1946–.
FELSENTHAL, REV. DR. B. Chicago. *PC*, 1888–1908.
FERNBERGER, HENRY. Philadelphia. Treasurer, 1903–1926. *HVP*, 1926–1929.
FINE, DR. BENJAMIN. New York. *T*, 1949–.
FINEMAN, IRVING. Shaftsbury, Vt. *PC*, 1950–.
FINESHRIBER, REV. DR. WILLIAM H. Philadelphia. *PC*, 1937–1950.
FINKELSTEIN, DR. LOUIS. New York. *PC*, 1939–.
FLEISHER, ALFRED W. Philadelphia. *T*, 1923–1924.
FLEISHER, BENJAMIN W. Philadelphia. *T*, 1897–1901.

FLEISHER, EDWIN A. Philadelphia. *T*, 1901–1913.

FRANK, JULIUS J. New York. *T*, 1891–1896.

FRANKEL, BERNARD L. Philadelphia. *T*, 1931–. *PC*, 1933–.

FREEHOF, REV. DR. SOLOMON B. Pittsburgh. *PC*, 1944–.

FRIEDENWALD, DR. AARON. Baltimore. *T*, 1888–1896. *HVP*, 1896–1902.

FRIEDENWALD, DR. HERBERT. Washington. *PC*, 1900–1927.

FRIEDLAENDER, DR. ISRAEL. New York. *Bible Ed.*, 1908. *PC*, 1909–1920.

FRIEDMAN, HERMAN S. Philadelphia. Treasurer, 1888–1891. *T*, 1896–1898. *VP*, 1898–1904.

FRIEDMAN, LEE M. Boston. *T*, 1946–1949. *HVP*, 1949–.

FRIEDMAN, LIONEL. Philadelphia. *T*, 1923–1949; Treasurer, 1927–1931.

GALTER, DAVID J. Philadelphia. *PC*, 1951–.

GATZERT, J. L. Chicago. *HVP*, 1896–1900.

GERSON, MR. FELIX N. *PC*, 1902–1945.

GINZBERG, DR. LOUIS. New York. Jewish Classics Committee, 1916–1945.

GITELSON, DR. M. LEO. New York. *T*, 1949–.

GLUECK, REV. DR. NELSON. Cincinnati. *PC*, 1948–.

GOLDIN, JUDAH I. New York. *PC*, 1945–.

GOLDMAN, FRANK. Lowell. *HVP*, 1948–1952.

GOLDMAN, REV. DR. SOLOMON. Chicago. *T*, 1938–1949. *PC*, 1949–1953.

GOLDSTEIN, REV. DR. ISRAEL. New York. *HVP*, 1952–1953.

GOODMAN, DR. NATHAN G. Philadelphia. *PC*, 1937–1940.

GORDIS, DR. ROBERT. New York. *HVP*, 1948–1949. *PC*, 1949–.

GOTTHEIL, DR. GUSTAVE. New York. *VP*, 1888–1889.

GRAYZEL, DR. SOLOMON. Philadelphia. *PC*, 1932–1940. Assistant Editor, March 1–April 1, 1939. Editor, 1939–. Secretary, *PC*, 1950–.

GREENEBAUM, HENRY. Chicago. *T*, 1890–1892.

GRODINSKY, DR. JULIUS. Philadelphia. Secretary, 1926–1936. *T*, 1936–1939.

GROSS, PROF. CHARLES. Cambridge, Mass. *T*, 1888–1890. *PC*, 1888–1910.

GUGGENHEIM, DANIEL. New York. *T*, 1890, 1892–1919.
GUTMAN, JACOB C. Philadelphia. *T*, 1950–1953.
GUTMAN, LOUIS K. Baltimore. *HVP*, 1903–1927.

HAAS, JACOB. Atlanta. *HVP*, 1896–1910.
HAGEDORN, JOSEPH. Philadelphia. *T*, 1908–1933.
HALKIN, DR. SIMON. New York. *PC*, 1945–1949.
HALPER, DR. BENZION. Philadelphia. Editor, 1916–1924.
HALPRIN, MRS. SAMUEL. New York. *HVP*, 1948–1951.
HANO, LESTER. Philadelphia. Treasurer, 1946–1949.
HAYS, DANIEL P. New York. *T*, 1893–1909.
HECHT, JACOB. Boston. *T*, 1888.
HECHT, MRS. JACOB H. Boston. *HVP*, 1896–1911.
HELLER, REV. DR. MAX. New Orleans. *HVP*, 1896–1929. *PC*,
    1903–1919.
HESCHEL, DR. ABRAHAM J. New York. *PC*, 1950–.
HEYMAN, ARTHUR. Atlanta. *HVP*, 1911–1912.
HIRSH, JOSEPH. Vicksburg. *HVP*, 1896–1906.
HOCHSTADTER, ALBERT F. New York. *T*, 1892–1896.
HOLLANDER, DR. JACOB H. Baltimore. *PC*, 1902–1924.
HOLLZER, JUDGE HARRY A. Los Angeles. *T*, 1945.
HONOR, DR. LEO L. Philadelphia. *PC*, 1949–.
HURWITZ, HENRY. New York. *PC*, 1940–1944.
HUSIK, DR. ISAAC. Philadelphia. Editor, 1924–1939.
HUTZLER, DAVID. Baltimore. *T*, 1896.

ISAACS, DR. ABRAM S. New York. *PC*, 1888–1895.
ISAACS, MRS. MOSES L. New York. *HVP*, 1950–1952.

JACOBS, MISS ELLA. Philadelphia. Corresponding Secretary, 1892–
    1896. *HVP*, 1896–1917.
JACOBS, JOSEPH. New York. *PC*, 1904–1916. *Bible Ed.*, 1908–
    1916.
JACOBS, DR. MAURICE. Philadelphia. Secretary, 1936–1950. Exec-
    utive Director, 1939–1944. Executive *VP*, 1944–1950. *T*,
    1950–1953.
JACOBS, S. W. Montreal. *HVP*, 1913–1938.
JASTROW, REV. DR. MARCUS. Philadelphia. *PC*, 1888–1904.

Kaplan, Dr. Louis L. Baltimore, *PC*, 1941–.
Kaplan, Dr. Mordecai M. New York. *PC*, 1950–.
Kirstein, Louis E. Boston. *HVP*, 1915–1942.
Klein, Rabbi Max D. Philadelphia. *PC*, 1924–.
Kohler, Rev. Dr. Kaufmann. Cincinnati. *Bible Ed.*, 1908–1916.
Kohn, Rev. Dr. Jacob. New York. *PC*, 1914–1932.
Kohut, Rev. Dr. A. New York. *T*, 1888–1890. *PC*, 1890–1894.
Kopelman, Mrs. Barnett E. New York. *HVP*, 1946–1951.
Korn, Rev. Dr. Bertram W. Philadelphia. *PC*, 1950–.
Krass, Rev. Dr. Nathan. New York. *T*, 1924–1946. *PC*, 1946–1949.
Krauskopf, Rev. Dr. Joseph. Philadelphia. *T*, 1888–1898; Recording Secretary, 1888–1896. *PC*, 1888–1898.
Kurzman, Ferdinand. New York. *T*, 1890.

Lamport, Samuel Charles. New York. *T*, 1915–1941.
Laemmle, Carl. New York. *T*, 1926–1927.
Landsberg, Rev. Dr. Max. Rochester. *HVP*, 1896–1897. *PC*, 1894–1905.
Lauterbach, Dr. Jacob Z. Cincinnati. Jewish Classics Committee, 1916–1942.
Lederer, Ephraim. Philadelphia. Assistant Secretary, 1888–1890. *T*, 1896–1925.
Lelyveld, Rabbi Arthur J. New York. *PC*, 1950–.
Lencher, Judge Benjamin. Pittsburgh. *T*, 1950–.
Lefton, Al Paul. Philadelphia. *T*, 1941–.
Leipziger, Dr. Henry. New York. *T*, 1888–1890. *VP*, 1890–1918. *PC*, 1892–1905.
Levi, Leo N. Galveston. *VP*, 1888–1894.
Levias, Caspar. Cincinnati. Board of Editors for the Translation of the Bible, 1905.
Levin, Judge Theodore. Detroit. *T*, 1950–.
Levinthal, Judge Louis E. Philadelphia. *T*, 1926–. *PC*, 1933–; Chairman, 1939–1949. President, 1949–.
Levy, Rev. Dr. Felix A. Chicago. *PC*, 1939–.
Levy, Felix H. New York. *T*, 1923–1934.
Levy, Howard S. Philadelphia. *T*, 1923–.
Lewis, Hon. William M. Philadelphia. *T*, 1922–1938.

LIEBMAN, REV. DR. JOSHUA LOTH. Boston. *PC*, 1944–1948.

LIPPMAN, A. Pittsburgh. *HVP*, 1906–1910.

LOEB, OSCAR. Philadelphia. *PC*, 1927–1932.

LOOKSTEIN, REV. DR. JOSEPH H. New York. *PC*, 1949–.

LOUCHHEIM, WILLIAM S. Los Angeles. *T*, 1941–1949.

LOWENTHAL, MARVIN. New York. *PC*, 1946–.

LOWN, PHILIP W. Auburn. *T*, 1950–.

MACK, HON. JULIAN W. New York. *HVP*, 1906–1943.

MAGNES, REV. DR. J. L. New York. *PC*, 1905–1924.

MALTER, DR. HENRY. Philadelphia. Jewish Classics Committee, 1916–1925.

MANN, REV. DR. LOUIS L. Chicago. *T*, 1924–1949.

MARCUS, DR. JACOB R. Cincinnati. *PC*, 1939–; Chairman, 1949–.

MARCUS, DR. RALPH. Chicago. *PC*, 1949–.

MARGOLIS, DR. MAX L. Philadelphia. Bible Ed.-in-Chief, 1908–1916. *PC*, 1916–1932.

MARKS, MARCUS M. New York. *T*, 1890–1893.

MARSHALL, JAMES. New York. *HVP*, 1940–.

MARSHALL, LOUIS. New York. *T*, 1890–1892.

MARX, DR. ALEXANDER. New York. *PC*, 1916–.

MENDES, REV. DR. F. DE SOLA. New York. Editorial Committee for the Translation of the Bible, 1892–1901.

MERZ, DANIEL. Philadelphia. *T*, 1898–1902.

MEYER, REV. DR. MARTIN A. San Francisco. *HVP*, 1911–1923.

MEYERHOFF, JOSEPH. Baltimore. *T*, 1951–.

MILLER, ALPHONSE B. Philadelphia. *T*, 1919–1927.

MILLER, RABBI IRVING. New York. *HVP*, 1950–1952.

MILLER, NATHAN J. New York. *T*, 1924–1928.

MILLER, SIMON. Philadelphia. *T*, 1898–1945; *VP*, 1908–1913; President, 1913–1933. *PC*, 1927–1945.

MOISSEIFF, LEON S. New York. *PC*, 1909–1933.

MONSKY, HENRY. Omaha. *HVP*, 1940–1947.

MONTEFIORE, CLAUDE. London, England. Corresponding Member of the Editorial Committee for the translation of the Bible, 1896.

MORDELL, ALBERT. Philadelphia. *PC*, 1939–.

MORGENSTERN, REV. DR. JULIAN. Cincinnati. *PC*, 1924–.

MORRIS, NATHAN. Indianapolis. *HVP*, 1897–1900.

NEUMAN, REV. DR. ABRAHAM A. Philadelphia. *PC*, 1937–.
NEUMANN, SIDNEY. Philadelphia. *T*, 1947–.
NEWBURGER, FRANK L. Philadelphia. *T*, 1947–1950.
NEWBURGER, MORRIS. Philadelphia. *T*, 1888–1918; President, 1888–1903.
NIGER, SH. (S. CHARNEY). New York. *PC*, 1946–.
NORMAN, EDWARD A. New York. *T*, 1940–1950.

OBERDORFER, GENERAL EUGENE. Atlanta. *T*, 1949–1951.
OCHS, ADOLPH S. New York. *T*, 1922–1923. *VP*, 1923–1935.
ORLINSKY, HARRY M. Brooklyn. *PC*, 1949–.

PEISER, DR. KURT. Miami. *T*, 1950–.
PEIXOTTO, BENJAMIN F. New York. *T*, 1888–1890.
PERLMAN, PHILIP B. Baltimore. *T*, 1923–1934.
PFORZHEIMER, CARL H. New York. *T*, 1927–1946.
PHILIPSON, REV. DR. DAVID. Cincinnati. *PC*, 1897–1949. *Bible Ed.*, 1908–1916.
PINSON, DR. KOPPEL S. New York. *PC*, 1949–.
POOL, REV. DR. DAVID DE SOLA. New York. *PC*, 1940–.
PROSKAUER, JOSEPH M. New York. *HVP*, 1946–1948.

RABINOWITZ, DR. ISAAC. Brooklyn. *PC*, 1945–.
RABINOWITZ, LOUIS M. New York. *T*, 1949–.
REIDER, DR. JOSEPH. Philadelphia. *PC*, 1927–.
ROSEN, BEN. New York. *PC*, 1944.
ROSENBACH, DR. A. S. W. Philadelphia. *PC*, 1919–1946. *T*, 1923–1946. *HVP*, 1946–1952.
ROSENBERG, LOUIS JAMES. Detroit. *T*, 1919–1922.
ROSENBLOOM, SOL. Pittsburgh. *T*, 1925–1926.
ROSENBLUM, RABBI WILLIAM F. New York. *HVP*, 1948.
ROSENDALE, HON. SIMON W. Albany. *T*, 1888–1896. *HVP*, 1896–1937.
ROSENSOHN, MRS. SAMUEL J. New York. *HVP*, 1952–1953.
ROSENTHAL, JULIUS. Chicago. *T*, 1888.
ROSENWALD, JULIUS. Chicago. *T*, 1908–1923.
ROSENWALD, LESSING. Philadelphia. *T*, 1923–1927.
ROSETT, MRS. LOUIS A. Cincinnati. *HVP*, 1946–1953.

Rubel, Jacob. Philadelphia. *T*, 1923–1929.
Rubenstein, Frank J. *T*, 1934–.

Sachar, Dr. Abram L. Waltham, Mass. *PC*, 1937–.
Sale, Rev. Dr. Samuel. St. Louis. *PC*, 1898–1903.
Sandmel, Rev. Dr. Samuel. Cincinnati. *PC*, 1950–.
Samfield, Rev. Dr. M. Memphis. *T*, 1890–1892.
Satinsky, Sol. Philadelphia. Treasurer, 1949–1953. *VP*, 1953–.
Schechter, Dr. Frank I. New York. *PC*, 1924–1937. *T*, 1927–
    1937.
Schechter, Dr. Solomon. New York. *PC*, 1904–1915. *Bible Ed.*,
    1908–1915.
Scherman, Harry. New York. *T*, 1936–1942.
Schiff, Jacob H. New York. *VP*, 1888–1890.
Schneiderman, Harry. New York. *PC*, 1940–.
Schoenthal, Joseph. Columbus. *T*, 1927–1930.
Schulman, Rev. Dr. Samuel. New York. *PC*, 1905–. *Bible Ed.*,
    1908–1916.
Seasongood, Alfred. Cincinnati. *HVP*, 1898–1911.
Seasongood, Murray. Cincinnati. *HVP*, 1911–1953.
Shapiro, Judah J. New York. *PC*, 1947–1950.
Silver, Rev. Dr. Abba Hillel. Cleveland. *T*, 1925–1949.
Silver, Louis H. Chicago. *T*, 1949–.
Siner, Mrs. Emanuel. Kew Gardens. *HVP*, 1951–1953.
Slomovitz, Philip. Detroit. *HVP*, 1950–.
Sloss, M. C. San Francisco. *HVP*, 1908–1946.
Solis-Cohen, Jr., J. Philadelphia. *T*, 1929–1933. President, 1933–
    1949. *PC*, 1933–; Acting Chairman, 1933–1939. Honorary
    President, 1949–.
Solis-Cohen, Solomon. Philadelphia. *T*, 1888–1894. *PC*, 1894–
    1948.
Solomon, Mrs. Henry. Chicago. *T*, 1893–1900. *HVP*, 1900–1906.
Sonneborn, Sigmund. Baltimore. *T*, 1908–1922. *HVP*, 1922–
    1931.
Speiser, Dr. Ephraim A. Philadelphia. *PC*, 1939–1942.
Spiegel, Dr. Shalom. New York. *PC*, 1939–.
Starr, Harry. New York. *T*, 1949–.
Stavitsky, Michael A. Newark. *HVP*, 1950–.

Steinbach, Dr. Lewis W. Philadelphia. Secretary, 1898–1913.

Steinberg, Rabbi Milton. New York. *PC*, 1940–1945, 1950.

Steinbrink, Meier. Brooklyn. *T*, 1927–1937.

Stern, Chief Justice Horace. Philadelphia. *T*, 1908–1913. *VP*, 1913–. *PC*, 1921–1926.

Stern, Simon A. Philadelphia. *PC*, 1888–1904.

Stolz, Rev. Dr. Joseph. Chicago. *T*, 1892–1896. *HVP*, 1896–1941.

Stone, Dewey D. Brockton. *T*, 1949–.

Straus, Nathan, Jr. New York. *T*, 1926–1927.

Straus, Oscar S. New York. *PC*, 1895–1926.

Straus, Roger W., Jr. New York. *T*, 1949–.

Strauss, Admiral Lewis. New York. *T*, 1950–1953. *HVP*, 1953–.

Strauss, Samuel. New York. *T*, 1908–1921. *PC*, 1909–1933.

Strauss, Seligman J. Wilkes-Barre. *T*, 1896–1927.

Strouse, Isaac. Baltimore. *HVP*, 1896–1897.

Sulzberger, Cyrus L. New York. *T*, 1904–1932.

Sulzberger, Mayer. Philadelphia. *PC*, Chairman, 1888–1923. *T*, 1888–1923.

Szold, Dr. Benjamin. Baltimore. Sub-Committee on the Revision of the Bible Translation, 1892.

Szold, Miss Henrietta. Jerusalem. *PC*, 1888–1933; Secretary (Editor), 1893–1916. *HVP*, 1940–1945.

Tedesche, Rev. Dr. Sidney. Brooklyn. *PC*, 1932–.

Teller, Benjamin F. Philadelphia. *T*, 1900–1905.

Vogelstein, Ludwig. New York. *T*, 1924–1935.

Voorsanger, Dr. Jacob. San Francisco. *HVP*, 1896–1908.

Warburg, Felix M. New York. *T*, 1909–1910.

Weil, A. Leo. Pittsburgh. *T*, 1908–1938.

Weil, Frank L. New York. *HVP*, 1946–1951.

Weinstock, Harris. Sacramento. *T*, 1890–1919; *VP*, 1890–1896.

Welt, Mrs. Joseph M. New York. *HVP*, 1946–1950.

Weyl, Julius S. Philadelphia. *T*, 1920–1932.

Wilner, Morton H. Washington. *T*, 1950–.

WISE, DR. I. M. Cincinnati. Corresponding member of the Editorial Committee for the translation of the Bible, 1896.

WISE, REV. DR. STEPHEN S. New York. *HVP*, 1946–1949.

WOLF, EDWIN. Philadelphia. *T*, 1902–1934; President, 1903–1913.

WOLF, EDWIN, 2nd. Philadelphia. *T*, 1935–. *PC*, 1937–. *VP*, 1949–.

WOLF, HOWARD A. Philadelphia. *T*, 1931–; Treasurer, 1931–1946.

WOLF, MORRIS. Philadelphia. *T*, 1926–1934.

WOLF, RALPH. New York. *T*, 1928–1937.

WOLF, SIMON. Washington, D. C. *T*, 1888–1890, 1892–1896. *HVP*, 1897–1923.

WOLFENSTEIN, S. Cleveland. *T*, 1908–1909.

WOLFSON, DR. HARRY A. Cambridge. *PC*, 1939–.

ZUSSMAN, LESSER. Philadelphia. Secretary and Executive Secretary, 1950–.

INDEX A

List of Authors, Compilers, Editors, Illustrators
and Translators

A.

ABRAHAMS, ISRAEL, 1858–1925:
The Book of delight, 1912.
By-paths in Hebraic bookland, 1920.
Chapters on Jewish literature, 1899.
Jewish life in the Middle Ages, 1896.
Maimonides, 1903, joint author.
Hebrew ethical wills, 1926, editor.

ABRAHAMS, ROBERT DAVID, 1905–   :
Mr. Benjamin's sword, 1948.
Room for a son, 1951.

ADLER, CYRUS, 1863–1940:
I have considered the days, 1941.
American Jewish Year Book, 1899–1905, 1916, editor.
The Voice of America on Kishineff, 1904, editor.

ADLER, ELKAN NATHAN, 1861–1946:
Jews in many lands, 1905.
London, 1930.

ADLER, LIEBMAN, 1812–1892:
Sabbath hours, 1893.

AGUDATH HA-RABBONIM:
Abridged prayer book, 1917.

AGUILAR, GRACE, 1816–1847:
The Vale of cedars, 1902.

AHAD HA'AM, (pseud. of ASHER GINZBERG), 1856–1927:
Selected essays, 1912.

ALBO, JOSEPH, ca. 1380–1444:
Sefer ha-'Ikkarim, 1929, 1930.

ALOFSIN, DOROTHY:
The Nightingale's song, 1945.

AMERICAN JEWISH COMMITTEE:
Report [1]–[44]. *See* American Jewish Year Book, v. [10]–53,
1908–1948, 1950–52.

ASCH, SHOLOM. *See* ASH, S.
ASH, SHOLOM, 1880–   :
Kiddush ha-Shem, 1926.
Sabbatai Zevi, 1930.

B.

BAMBERGER, BERNARD JACOB, 1904–   :
Fallen angels, 1952.

BARON, JOSEPH LOUIS, 1894–   , editor:
Candles in the night, 1940.
Stars and sand, 1943.

BARON, SALO WITTMAYER, 1895–   :
The Jewish community, 1942.
A Social and religious history of the Jews, 1952.
See The Jews of Charleston, 1950.

BASSECHES, MAURICE, editor:
American Jewish Year Book, 1947.

BEER-HOFMANN, RICHARD, 1866–1945:
Jacob's dream, 1946.

BEIN, ALEX, 1903–   :
Theodore Herzl, 1940.

BENTWICH, NORMAN DE MATTOS, 1883–   :
Hellenism, 1919.
Josephus, 1914.
Philo-Judaeus of Alexandria, 1910.
Solomon Schechter, 1938.

BERGES, MAX LUDWIG:
Cold pogrom, 1939.

BERKOWITZ, HENRY JOSEPH, 1894–1949:
Boot camp, 1948.
The Fire eater, 1941.

BERMAN, HAROLD, 1879–1949, translator:
Worlds that passed, 1928.

BERNSTEIN, HERMAN, 1876–1935, editor:
American Jewish Year Book, 1914.

BIALIK, HAYYIM NACHMAN, 1873–1934:
Aftergrowth, 1939.

BIBLE:
The Book of Psalms, 1903, 1925.
Bridal Bible. *See* The Holy Scriptures, 1917.
Freemasons Bible, 1917.
The Holy Scriptures, 1917, 1919.
The Holy Scriptures, an abridgment, Emily Solis-Cohen, ed.,
    1931.
The Holy Scriptures with commentary:
    Numbers, 1939.
    Deuteronomy, 1937.
    Micah, 1908.
    Proverbs, 1950.
The Pulpit Bible. *See* The Holy Scriptures, 1919.
Readings from the Holy Scriptures for Jewish soldiers and
    sailors, 1918.
See also The Book of Books, 1948.
See also In the beginning, 1949.
See also Pathways through the Bible, 1946.

BINDER, ABRAHAM WOLF, 1895–   :
See The Purim anthology, 1949.

BISNO, BEATRICE:
Tomorrow's bread, 1938.

BLOCH, PHILIPP, 1841–1923:
"Memoir of the author," See History of the Jews, v. 6, 1898.

BLOOMGARDEN, SOLOMON, 1871–1927:
The Feet of the messenger, 1923.

BLUMGARTEN, SOLOMON. See BLOOMGARDEN, S.

BOSNIAK, JACOB, 1887–   :
See Studies in Judaism, Third Series, 1924.

BROD, MAX, 1884–   :
Unambo, 1952.

BRODY, HEINRICH, 1868–1942, editor:
Selected poems of Moses Ibn Ezra, 1934.
Selected poems of Jehudah Halevi, 1924.

BUBER, MARTIN, 1878–   :
For the sake of heaven, 1945.

C.

CANFIELD, WILLIAM WALKER, 1855–1937:
The Sign above the door, 1912.

CENTRAL CONFERENCE OF AMERICAN RABBIS:
Abridged prayer book, 1917.

CHAGALL, MARC, 1887–   , illustrator:
The Last revolt, 1952.

COHEN, BOAZ, 1899–   :
See The Legends of the Jews, v. 7, 1938.

COHEN, HARRIET LIEBÉR, translator:
Jewish literature, 1895.

COHEN, ISABEL E., compiler:
Legends and tales, 1905.
Readings and recitations, 1895.

COHEN, ISRAEL, 1879–   :
Vilna, 1943.

COHEN, KATHERINE MYRTILLA, 1859–1915:
A Jewish child's book, 1913.

COHEN, MORTIMER JOSEPH, 1894–   :
Pathways through the Bible, 1946.

COHN, EMIL BERNHARD, 1881–1948:
Stories and fantasies, 1951.

COOPER, SAMUEL WILLIAMS, 1860–1939:
Think and thank, 1890.

COUNCIL OF YOUNG MEN'S HEBREW AND KINDRED ASSOCIATIONS:
Abridged prayer book, 1917.

D.

DARMESTETER, ARSÈNE, 1846–1888:
The Talmud, 1897.

DAVIDSON, ISRAEL, 1870–1939, editor:
Selected religious poems of Solomon Ibn Gabirol, 1923.

DAVIS, NINA. *See* SALAMAN, NINA RUTH (DAVIS).

DAVITT, MICHAEL, 1846–1906:
Within the pale, 1903.

DEMBITZ, LEWIS NAPHTALI, 1833–1907:
Jewish services in synagogue and home, 1898.

DEUTSCH, EMANUEL OSCAR MENAHEM, 1829–1873:
The Talmud, 1895.

DONIACH, NAKDIMON SHABBATHAI:
Purim, 1933.

DREY, SYLVAN, translator:
Some Jewish women, 1892.

DUBNOW, SIMON MARKOVICH, 1860–1941:
History of the Jews in Russia and Poland, 1916, 1918, 1920.
Jewish history, 1903.

E.

ELBOGEN, ISMAR, 1874–1943:
A Century of Jewish life, 1944.

ENGELMAN, URIAH ZEVI, joint author:
The Jews of Charleston, 1950.

EPSTEIN, BENJAMIN R., translator:
Cold pogrom, 1939.

F.

FEINBERG, ALFRED, illustrator:
The Breakfast of the birds, 1917.
David the giant killer, 1908.
The Game of Doeg, 1914.
The Power of Purim, 1915.
Step by step, 1910.

FINE, MORRIS T., editor:
American Jewish Year Book, 1942–43, 1947–48, 1950–52.

FINKELSTEIN, LOUIS, 1895–   :
The Pharisees, 1938.
The Jews, editor, 1949.

FRANK, HELENA, 1872–   , translator:
Stories and pictures, 1906.
Yiddish tales, 1912.

FRANK, ULRICH (pseud. of ULLA WOLFF), 1848–1924:
Simon Eichelkatz, 1907.

FREEHOF, LILLIAN (SIMON), 1906–   :
Stories of King David, 1952.

FREIMANN, ARON, 1871–1948, joint author:
Frankfort, 1929.

FRIEDENBERG, ALBERT MARX, 1881–1942:
The Sunday laws of the United States, 1908.

FRIEDENWALD, HERBERT, 1870–1944, editor:
American Jewish Year Book, 1908–13.

FRIEDLAENDER, ISRAEL, 1867–1920:
History of the Jews in Russia and Poland, 1916, 1918, 1920, translator.
See Jewish history, 1903.

FRIEDLÄNDER, MICHAEL, 1833–1910:
See Outlines of Jewish history, 1890, 1929.

FRIEDMAN, HARRY GEORGE, 1881–   , editor:
American Jewish Year Book, 1913.

FRIEDMAN, LEE MAX, 1871–   :
Jewish pioneers and patriots, 1942.
Pilgrims in a new land, 1948.

G.

GABIROL, SOLOMON IBN, 1021–1069:
Selected religious poems, 1923.

GALSWORTHY, JOHN, 1867–1933:
Loyalties. *See* Among the nations, 1948.

GASTER, MOSES, 1856–1939, translator:
Ma'aseh book, 1934.

GELLER, TODROS, 1889–1949, illustrator:
Wonder tales, 1929.

GERSON, FELIX NAPOLEON, 1862–1945, translator:
Regensburg and Augsburg, 1939.
Rembrandt, the Jews and the Bible, 1946.
The ship of hope, 1939.

GINZBERG, ASHER. *See* AHAD HA'AM, pseud.

GINZBERG, LOUIS, 1873–1953:
The Legends of the Jews, 1909, 1910, 1911, 1913, 1925, 1928, 1938.
Students, scholars and saints, 1928.

GLUECK, NELSON, 1900–   :
The River Jordan, 1946.

GOLDBERG, ISAAC, 1887–1938:
Major Noah, 1936.
The Feet of the messenger, 1923, translator.
In Polish woods, 1938, translator.

GOLDBERG, ISRAEL, 1887–   :
Kasriel the watchman, 1925.
Kiddush ha-Shem, 1926, translator.

GOLDING, LOUIS, 1895–   :
In the steps of Moses, 1943.

GOLDMAN, SOLOMON, 1893–1953:
The Book of Books: an introduction, 1948.
In the beginning, 1949.

GOLDSMITH, MILTON, 1861–1953:
Rabbi and priest, 1891.

GOLOB, EUGENE OWEN, 1915–   , translator:
Adolphe Crémieux, 1940.

302

GOODMAN, ABRAM VOSSEN, 1903–   :
  American overture, 1947.

GOODMAN, PAUL, 1875–1949:
  Moses Montefiore, 1925.

GOODMAN, PHILIP, 1911–   , editor:
  The Purim anthology, 1949.

GORDON, SAMUEL, 1871–1927:
  Sons of the covenant, 1900.
  Strangers at the gate, 1902.

GOTTHEIL, RICHARD JAMES HORATIO, 1862–1936:
  Zionism, 1914.

GOTTLIEB, MAXIM B., illustrator:
  Brand plucked from the fire, 1937.

GRAETZ, HEINRICH HIRSCH, 1817–1891:
  History of the Jews, 1891, 1893, 1894, 1895, 1898.

GRATZ, REBECCA, 1781–1869:
  Letters, 1929.

GRAYZEL, Solomon, 1896–   :
  A History of the Jews, 1947.
  See Outlines of Jewish history, 1929.
  A century of Jewish life, 1944, editor.
  Cologne, 1940, translator.
  Vienna, 1936, translator.

GREENSTONE, JULIUS HILLEL, 1873–   :
  The Messiah idea in Jewish history, 1906.
  Numbers, 1939.
  Proverbs, 1950.

GRINSTEIN, HYMAN BOGOMOLNY, 1899–   :
  The Rise of the Jewish community of New York, 1945.

GROSS, PETER, translator:
  The Son of the lost son, 1946.

GRUNWALD, MAX, 1871–1953:
Vienna, 1936.

H.

HADAS, MOSES, 1900–   , translator:
Rome, 1940.

HALPER, BENZION, 1884–1924, compiler and editor:
Post-Biblical Hebrew literature, 1921.

HARRIS, ELEANOR E.:
The Game of Doeg, 1914.

HEBREW SUNDAY SCHOOL SOCIETY OF PHILADELPHIA:
See The Holy Scriptures, 1931.

HERBERG, WILL:
Judaism and modern man, 1951.

HESCHEL, ABRAHAM JOSHUA, 1907–   :
Man is not alone, 1951.

HUHNER, LEON, 1871–   :
The Life of Judah Touro, 1946.

HUSIK, ISAAC, 1876–1939:
A History of mediaeval Jewish philosophy, 1916.
Sefer ha-'Ikkarim, 1929, 1930, editor and translator.
See The Legends of the Jews, v. 3, 1911.

I.

IBN EZRA, MOSES, ca. 1070–1139:
Selected poems, 1934.

IBN GABIROL, SOLOMON. *See* GABIROL, SOLOMON IBN.

ILIOWIZI, HENRY, 1850–1911:
In the pale, 1897.

ISAACS, ABRAM SAMUEL, 1852–1920:
School days in home town, 1928.
Step by step, 1910.
Under the Sabbath lamp, 1919.
The Young champion, 1913.

J.

JACOBS, JOSEPH, 1854–1916:
Jewish contributions to civilization, 1919.
American Jewish Year Book, 1915, editor.
The persecution of the Jews in Russia, 1891, editor.

JASTROW, WILHEMINA. *See* WALLERSTEIN, WILHEMINA JASTROW.

JEHUDAH HALEVI, fl. 12th cent.
Selected poems, 1924.

JERROLD, WALTER COPELAND, 1865–1929:
See The Vale of cedars, 1902.

JESHURUN, GEORGE, 1863–1934, translator:
In those days, 1915.

JEWISH CHAUTAUQUA SOCIETY:
Papers, 1902.

JEWISH HISTORICAL SOCIETY OF ENGLAND:
Jewish history, 1903.
Maimonides, 1903.

JEWISH PUBLICATION SOCIETY OF AMERICA:
Abridged prayer book, 1917.
Address of Simon Miller, 1920.
American Jewish Year Book, 1899–1948, 1950–52.
Announcement of a popular commentary on the Holy Scriptures, 1920.
Catalogue, 1939.
Jewish calendar for 100 years, 1917.

305

The Jewish Classics series, general statement, 1920.
Report: Past, present and future, 1917.

Reports:

    1st–4th biennial, 1890, 1892, 1894, 1896.
    9th–11th report, 1897–1899.
    12th–[63rd] report. *See* American Jewish Year Book,
        1900–48, 1950–52.
    Report of the 61st annual meeting, 1948.

The Rise of a new and cultural American Jewry, 1929.
Rules for the Jewish Publication Society Press, 1931.
Thirty-five years of Jewish endeavor, 1924.
Twenty-fifth anniversary, 1913.
What it is and what is has done, 1911, 1918.

Jewish Welfare Board:
    Abridged prayer book, 1917.
    Readings from the Holy Scriptures, 1918.
    Woman in Jewish law and life, 1932.

JEWISH WOMEN'S CONGRESS:
    Papers, 1894.

JOFFE, JUDAH A., 1873–   :
    See Worlds that passed, 1928.

JONES, HOWARD MUMFORD, 1892–   :
    See The Jew in the literature of England, 1939.

JUDAH HA-LEVI. *See* Jehudah Halevi.

K.

KAPLAN, IRVING, editor:
American Jewish Year Book, 1950.

KAPLAN, LOUIS L.:
See A History of the Jewish people, 1927.

KAPLAN, MORDECAI MENAHEM, 1881–   , editor and translator:
Mesillat Yesharim, 1936.

KAPLAN, SEYMOUR R., illustrator:
Stories of King David, 1952.

KARPELES, GUSTAV, 1848–1909:
Jewish literature, 1895.
Jews and Judaism in the nineteenth century, 1905.
A Sketch of Jewish history, 1897.

KELLER, MATHILDA, illustrator:
The Fire eater, 1941.
Little new angel, 1947.
Pilgrims to Palestine, 1940.
What the moon brought, 1942.

KLEIN, ABRAHAM MOSES, 1909–   :
Poems, 1944.

KOBER, ADOLF, 1879–   :
Cologne, 1940.

KOHLER, KAUFMANN, 1843–1926, translator:
The Book of Psalms, 1903.

KOHLER, MAX JAMES, 1871–1934:
Jewish rights at International Congresses, 1917.

KORN, BERTRAM WALLACE, 1916–   :
American Jewry and the Civil War, 1951.

KRACAUER, F., joint author:
Frankfort, 1929.

KRAFT, IRMA:
The Power of Purim, 1915.

KUBIE, NORA (BENJAMIN):
Joel, 1952.

L.

LACRETELLE, JACQUES DE, 1888–   :
Silbermann. *See* Among the nations, 1948.

LANDSBERGER, FRANZ, 1883–   :
Rembrandt, the Jews and the Bible, 1946.

LASK, ISRAEL M., 1905–   , translator:
Aftergrowth, 1939.

LAUTERBACH, JACOB ZALLEL, 1873–1942, editor and translator:
Mekilta de-Rabbi Ishmael, 1933, 1935.

LAZARRE, JACOB, pseud.
Beating sea and changeless bar, 1905.

LAZARUS, MORITZ, 1824–1903:
The Ethics of Judaism, 1900, 1901.

LEAF, REUBEN, 1889–   , illustrator:
Kasriel the watchman, 1925.

LEARSI, RUFUS, pseud. *See* GOLDBERG, ISRAEL.

LEFTWICH, JOSEPH, 1892–   , translator:
The Son of the lost son, 1946.

LEVIN, BERTHA (SZOLD), translator:
Frankfort, 1929.

LEVINGER, ELMA EHRLICH, 1887–   :
Pilgrims to Palestine, 1940.
Playmates in Egypt, 1920.
Wonder tales, 1929.

LEVIT, HERSCHEL, illustrator:
Mr. Benjamin's sword, 1948.

LEWISOHN, LUDWIG, 1882–   :
Renegade, 1942.
Among the nations, 1948, editor.
For the sake of heaven, 1945, translator.

In my father's pastures, 1947, translator.
The Spirit returneth, 1946, translator.
Unambo, 1952, translator.

LIBER, MAURICE, 1884–   :
Rashi, 1906.
Hebrew Scriptures in the Making, 1922.

LIBOWITZ, NEHEMIAH SAMUEL, 1862–1939:
Additament to Peniné ha-Zohar, 1933.

LIPTZIN, SOLOMON, 1901–   :
Germany's stepchildren, 1944.
"Richard Beer-Hofmann, a biographical essay," *see* Jacob's
dream, 1946.

LOEB, LOUIS, 1866–1909, illustrator.
"They that walk in darkness," 1899.

LÖWY, BELLA, 1853–1918, translator and editor:
History of the Jews, 1891, 1893–95, 1898.

LOWENTHAL, MARVIN, 1890–   :
The Jews of Germany, 1936.

LUZZATTO, MOSES HAYYIM, 1707–1747:
Mesillat Yesharim, 1936.

M.

MAGNUS, KATIE (EMANUEL), lady, 1844–1924:
Outlines of Jewish history, 1890, 1929.

MALLER, JULIUS BERNARD, 1901–   , editor:
American Jewish Year Book, 1945–46.

MALTER, HENRY, 1864–1925:
Saadia Gaon, 1921.
The Treatise Ta'anit, 1928, editor and translator.

MANN, THOMAS, 1875–   :
Tamar. *See* Among the nations, 1948.

MARCUS, JACOB RADER, 1896–   :
Early American Jewry, 1951.

MARGOLIS, MAX LEOPOLD, 1866–1932:
The Hebrew Scriptures in the making, 1922.
Micah, 1908.
The New English translation of the Bible, 1917.
The Story of Bible translations, 1917.
A History of the Jewish people, 1927, joint author.
The Holy Scriptures, 1917, editor.
Introduction to the Talmud and Midrash, 1931, translator.

MARX, ALEXANDER, 1878–   :
Essays in Jewish biography, 1947.
"Ismar Elbogen: an appreciation," *See* A Century of Jewish life,
1944.
A History of the Jewish people, 1927, joint author.
Studies in Judaism, Third series, 1924, editor.

MAUGHAM, WILLIAM SOMERSET, 1874–   :
The Alien corn. *See* Among the nations, 1948.

McDONALD, JAMES GROVER, 1886–   :
See To dwell in safety, 1948.

MENDELSOHN, SAMUEL FELIX, 1889–1953:
Let laughter ring, 1941.

MIDRASH:
Mekilta de-Rabbi Ishmael, 1933, 1935.

MILLER, SARA, 1876–   :
Under the eagle's wing, 1899.

MILLER, SIMON, 1862–1945:
Address, 1920.

MILLGRAM, ABRAHAM EZRA, 1901–   :
Sabbath, 1944.

MISCH, MARION L. SIMONS, 1869–1941:
Selections for homes and schools, 1911.

310

MODDER, MONTAGU FRANK:
The Jew in the literature of England, 1939.

MORGENSTERN, JULIAN, 1881–   :
As a mighty stream, 1949.

MORGENSTERN, SOMA, 1896–   :
In my father's pastures, 1947.
The Son of the lost son, 1946.
The Testament of the lost son, 1949

MOSENTHAL, SALOMON HERMANN, RITTER VON, 1821–1877:
Stories of Jewish home life, 1907.

N.

NATIONAL COUNCIL OF JEWISH WOMEN:
Proceedings, 1897.

NATIONAL JEWISH WELFARE BOARD. *See* JEWISH WELFARE BOARD.

NEUMAN, ABRAHAM AARON, 1890–   :
Cyrus Adler, 1942.
The Jews in Spain, 1942.

NEVINS, ALLAN, 1890–   :
See American Jewry and the Civil War, 1951.

NOYES, GEORGE RAPALL, 1873–   , translator:
Sabbatai Zevi, 1930.

O.

OPATOSHU, JOSEPH, 1886–   :
In Polish woods, 1938.
The last revolt, 1952.

OPATOVSKY, JOSEPH. *See* OPATOSHU, J.

OPPENHEIM, SAMSON D., editor:
American Jewish Year Book, 1917–18.

P.

PENDLETON, LOUIS BEAUREGARD, 1861–1939:
In Assyrian tents, 1904.
Lost Prince Almon, 1898.

PEREZ, ISAAC LOEB, 1851–1915:
Stories and pictures, 1906.

PESSIN, DEBORAH:
The Aleph-Bet story book, 1946.

PHILIPSON, DAVID, 1862–1949:
Old European Jewries, 1894.
Letters of Rebecca Gratz, 1929, editor.

POSENER, SOLOMON VLADIMIROVICH, 1876–1946:
Adolphe Crémieux, 1940.

POZNER, SOLOMON V. *See* POSENER, S. V.

R.

RADIN, MAX, 1880–1950:
The Jews among the Greeks and Romans, 1915.
The Life of the people in biblical times, 1929.

RADIN, PAUL, 1883–   , translator:
The Legends of the Jews, v. 3, 1911.

RAISIN, JACOB SALMON, 1877–1946:
The Haskalah movement in Russia, 1913.

RASKIN, PHILIP MAX, 1880–1944:
Songs of a wanderer, 1917.

REIDER, JOSEPH, 1884–   :
Deuteronomy, 1937.
See Hebrew ethical wills, 1926.

REZNIKOFF, CHARLES, 1894–   :
  The Lionhearted, 1944.
  The Jews of Charleston, 1950, joint author.
  Stories and fantasies, 1951, translator.

RHINE, ABRAHAM BENEDICT, 1876–1941:
  Leon Gordon, 1910.

ROBINSON, T. H., illustrator:
  The Vale of cedars, 1902.

ROSENBACH, ABRAHAM SIMON WOLF, 1876–1952:
  See I have considered the days, 1941.
  See Jewish pioneers and patriots, 1942.

ROTH, CECIL, 1899–   :
  The History of the Jews of Italy, 1946.
  A History of the Marranos, 1932.
  The House of Nasi, Doña Gracia, 1947.
  The House of Nasi, The Duke of Naxos, 1948.
  A Life of Menasseh ben Israel, 1934.
  Venice, 1930.

ROTHGIESSER, RUBEN:
  The Ship of hope, 1939.

RUDIN, EDITH, illustrator:
  The Breakfast of the birds, 1917.

RUSKAY, ESTHER JANE:
  Hearth and home essays, 1902.

RUSSO-JEWISH COMMITTEE OF LONDON:
  The Persecution of the Jews in Russia, 1891.

S.

SACHS, ABRAHAM SIMHA, 1879–1931:
  Worlds that passed, 1928.

SALAMAN, NINA RUTH (DAVIS), 1876–1925, translator.
Selected poems of Jehudah Halevi, 1924.
Songs of exile, 1901.

SAMPTER, JESSIE ETHEL, 1883–1938:
Brand plucked from the fire, 1937.

SAMUEL, MAURICE, 1895–   :
Harvest in the desert, 1944.
Prince of the Ghetto, 1948.
The Testament of the lost son, 1950, translator.
Theodore Herzl, 1940, translator.

SCHECHTER, AMY E., translator:
Travels in North Africa, 1927.

SCHECHTER, FRANK ISAAC, 1890–1937, editor:
Studies in Judaism, Third series, 1924.

SCHECHTER, SOLOMON, 1847–1915:
Studies in Judaism, 1896, 1908, 1924.

SCHNABEL, LOUIS, 1829–1897:
Voegele's marriage, 1892.

SCHNEIDERMAN, HARRY, 1885–   , editor:
American Jewish Year Book, 1919–48.

SCHULMAN, SAMUEL, 1865–   :
Rosh ha-Shanah and Yom Kippur, 1920.

SCHWARZ, LEO WALDER, 1906–   , editor:
Memoirs of my people, 1943.

SELTZER, ADELE SZOLD (*Mrs. Thomas*), 1876–   , translator:
Jews and Judaism in the nineteenth century, 1905.
Rashi, 1906.
Simon Eichelkatz, 1907.
Stories of Jewish home life, 1907.

SIMON, HOWARD, 1902–   , illustrator:
The Aleph-Bet story book, 1946.

314

SIMON, LEON, 1881–   , translator:
   Selected essays by Ahad Ha-'Am, 1912.

SLOAN, JACOB:
   American Jewish Year Book, 1948, 1950–52, editor.
   The Testament of the lost son, 1950, translator.

SLOUSCHZ, NAHUM, 1872–   :
   The Renascence of Hebrew literature, 1909.
   The Jews of North Africa. *See his*: Travels in North Africa.
      1927.
   Travels in North Africa, 1927.

SOLIS-COHEN, EMILY:
   David the giant killer, 1908.
   Woman in Jewish law and life, 1932.
   The Breakfast of the birds, 1917, translator.
   Hanukkah, 1937, compiler and editor.
   The Holy Scriptures, an abridgment, 1931, compiler and editor.

SOLIS-COHEN, SOLOMON, 1857–1948, translator:
   Selected poems of Moses Ibn Ezra, 1934.

SPECTOR, MAURICE, editor:
   American Jewish Year Book, 1947.

SPIEGEL, MOSHE, translator:
   The Last revolt, 1952.

STEINBERG, JUDAH, 1863–1908:
   The Breakfast of the birds, 1917.
   In those days, 1915.

STERN, SELMA, 1890–   :
   The Court Jew, 1950.
   The Spirit returneth, 1946.

STRACK, HERMANN LEBERECHT, 1848–1922:
   Introduction to the Talmud and Midrash, 1931.

STRAUS, RAPHAEL, 1887–   :
   Regensburg and Augsburg, 1939.

SULZBERGER, MAYER, 1843–1923:
    See Report of the tenth year, 1898.

SYRKIN, MARIE, 1900–   :
    Blessed is the match, 1947.

SZYK, ARTHUR, 1894–1951, illustrator:
    Pathways through the Bible, 1946.

SZOLD, ADELE. *See* SELTZER, ADELE SZOLD (MRS. THOMAS).

SZOLD, BERTHA. *See* LEVIN, BERTHA (SZOLD).

SZOLD, HENRIETTA, 1860–1945, author, compiler, editor or translator:
    American Jewish Year Book, 1904–07, 1916.
    The Ethics of Judaism, 1900, 1901.
    History of the Jews, v. 6, 1898.
    Jewish history, 1903.
    Jewish literature, 1895.
    Jews and Judaism in the nineteenth century, 1905.
    The Legends of the Jews, 1909, 1910.
    Outlines of Jewish history, 1890.
    The Renascence of Hebrew literature, 1909.
    A Sketch of Jewish history, 1897.
    The Talmud, 1897.

T.

TAGER, ALEXANDER SEMENOVICH, 1888–
    The Decay of Czarism, 1935.

TALMUD, BABYLONIAN.
    The Treatise Ta'anit, 1928.

U.

UNION OF AMERICAN HEBREW CONGREGATIONS:
    Abridged prayer book, 1917.

UNION OF ORTHODOX JEWISH CONGREGATIONS:
Abridged prayer book, 1917.

UNITED SYNAGOGUE OF AMERICA:
Abridged prayer book, 1917.

V.

VAN DOREN, CARL CLINTON, 1885–1950:
See Candles in the night, 1940.

VILNAY, ZEV, 1900–   :
Legends of Palestine, 1932.

VOGELSTEIN, HERMANN, 1870–1942:
Rome, 1940.

W.

WALLERSTEIN, WILHEMINA JASTROW *(Mrs. Alfred)*, translator:
Sabbath hours, 1893.

WEILERSTEIN, SADIE (ROSE):
Little new angel, 1947.
What the moon brought, 1942.

WEIMAN, RALPH, translator:
The Court Jew, 1950.

WEIZMANN, CHAIM, 1874–1952:
Trial and error, 1949.

WHYTE, FLORENCE, translator:
Sabbatai Zevi, 1930.

WILDER, THORNTON NIVEN, 1897–   :
See Jacob's dream, 1946.

WISCHNITZER, MARK, 1882–   :
To dwell in safety, 1948.

WOLFENSTEIN, MARTHA, 1869–1905:
Idyls of the Gass, 1901.
A Renegade, 1905

WOLFF, ULLA. *See* FRANK, ULRICH, pseud.

WOLFSON, HARRY AUSTRYN, 1887–   :
See A History of mediaeval Jewish philosophy, 1916.

WYNN, IDA BENSION, translator:
Jacob's dream, 1946.

Y.

YEHOASH, pseud. *See* BLOOMGARDEN, S.

YELLIN, DAVID, 1864–1941, joint author:
Maimonides, 1903.

Z.

ZANGWILL, ISRAEL, 1864–1926:
Children of the Ghetto, 1892, 1938.
Dreamers of the Ghetto, 1898.
Ghetto comedies, 1938.
Ghetto tragedies, 1938. *See also* "They that walk in darkness,"
1899.
Selected works, 1938.
"They that walk in darkness," 1899, 1938.
Selected religious poems of Solomon Ibn Gabirol, 1923, translator.

ZANGWILL, MARK, illustrator:
Sons of the covenant, 1900.

ZIRNDORF, HENRY, 1829–1893:
Some Jewish women, 1892.

INDEX B

List of Titles

A.

Abridged prayer book for Jews in the Army and Navy, 1917.
Additament to Peniné ha-Zohar, N. S. Libowitz, 1933.
Adolphe Crémieux, S. V. Posener, 1940.
Aftergrowth, H. N. Bialik, 1939.
The Aleph-Bet story book, Deborah Pessin, 1946.
The Alien corn, W. S. Maugham. *See* Among the nations, 1948.
American Jewish Year Book, 1899–1948, 1950–52.
American Jewry and the Civil War, B. W. Korn, 1951.
American overture, A. V. Goodman, 1947.
Among the nations, Ludwig Lewisohn, ed., 1948.
As a mighty stream, Julian Morgenstern, 1949.

B.

Beating sea and changeless bar, Jacob Lazarre, 1905.
Blessed is the match, Marie Syrkin, 1947.
The Book of Books: an introduction, Solomon Goldman, 1948.
The Book of delight, Israel Abrahams, 1912.
The Book of Psalms, 1903, 1925.
Boot camp, H. J. Berkowitz, 1948.
Brand plucked from the fire, Jessie E. Sampter, 1937.
The Breakfast of the birds, Judah Steinberg, 1917.
By-paths in Hebraic bookland, Israel Abrahams, 1920.

C.

Candles in the night, J. L. Baron, ed., 1940.
A Century of Jewish life, Ismar Elbogen, 1944.
Chapters on Jewish literature, Israel Abrahams, 1899.
Children of the Ghetto, Israel Zangwill, 1892, 1938.
Cold pogrom, M. L. Berges, 1939.
Cologne, Adolf Kober, 1940.

The Court Jew, Selma Stern, 1950.
Cyrus Adler, A. A. Neuman, 1942.

D.

David the giant killer, Emily Solis-Cohen, 1908.
The Decay of Czarism, A. S. Tager, 1935.
Deuteronomy, Joseph Reider, 1937.
Dreamers of the Ghetto, Israel Zangwill, 1898.

E.

Early American Jews, J. R. Marcus, 1951.
Essays in Jewish biography, Alexander Marx, 1947.
The Ethics of Judaism, Moritz Lazarus, 1900, 1901.

F.

Fallen angels, B. J. Bamberger, 1952.
The Feet of the messenger, Solomon Bloomgarden, 1923.
The Fire eater, H. J. Berkowitz, 1941.
For the sake of heaven, Martin Buber, 1945.
Frankfort, Aron Freimann and F. Kracauer, 1929.

G.

The Game of Doeg, Eleanor E. Harris, 1914.
Germany's stepchildren, Solomon Liptzin, 1944.
Ghetto comedies, Israel Zangwill, 1938.
Ghetto tragedies, Israel Zangwill, 1938. *See also his* "They that walk in darkness," 1899.

H.

Hanukkah, Emily Solis-Cohen, comp., 1937.
Harvest in the desert, Maurice Samuel, 1944.
The Haskalah movement in Russia, J. S. Raisin, 1913.
Hearth and home essays, Esther J. Ruskay, 1902.

Hebrew ethical wills, Israel Abrahams, ed., 1926.
The Hebrew Scriptures in the making, M. L. Margolis, 1922.
Hellenism, Norman Bentwich, 1919.
A History of the Jewish people, M. L. Margolis and A. Marx, 1927.
History of the Jews, H. H. Graetz, 1891, 1893, 1894, 1895, 1898.
A History of the Jews, Solomon Grayzel, 1947.
The History of the Jews of Italy, Cecil Roth, 1946.
History of the Jews in Russia and Poland, S. M. Dubnow, 1916, 1918, 1920.
A History of the Marranos, Cecil Roth, 1932.
A History of mediaeval Jewish philosophy, Isaac Husik, 1916.
The Holy Scriptures, 1917, 1919.
The Holy Scriptures, an abridgment, Emily Solis-Cohen, 1931.
The House of Nasi, Doña Gracia, Cecil Roth, 1947.
The House of Nasi, The Duke of Naxos, Cecil Roth, 1948.

I.

I have considered the days, Cyrus Adler, 1941.
Idyls of the Gass, Martha Wolfenstein, 1901.
In Assyrian tents, L. B. Pendleton, 1904.
In the beginning, Solomon Goldman, 1949.
In my father's pastures, Soma Morgenstern, 1947.
In the pale, Henry Iliowizi, 1897.
In Polish woods, Joseph Opatoshu, 1938.
In the steps of Moses, Louis Golding, 1943.
In those days, Judah Steinberg, 1915.
Introduction to the Talmud and Midrash, Hermann L. Strack, 1931.

J.

Jacob's dream, Richard Beer-Hofmann, 1946.
The Jew in the literature of England, M. F. Modder, 1939.
A Jewish child's book, Katherine M. Cohen, 1913.
The Jewish community, S. W. Baron, 1942.
Jewish contributions to civilization, Joseph Jacobs, 1919.
Jewish history, S. M. Dubnow, 1903.
Jewish life in the Middlge Ages, Israel Abrahams, 1896.

Jewish literature, Gustav Karpeles, 1895.

Jewish pioneers and patriots, L. M. Friedman, 1942.

Jewish rights at International Congresses, M. J. Kohler, 1917.

Jewish services in synagogue and home, L. N. Dembitz, 1898.

The Jews, Louis Finkelstein, ed., 1949.

The Jews among the Greeks and Romans, Max Radin, 1915.

The Jews of Charleston, Charles Reznikoff and U. Z. Engelman, 1950.

The Jews of Germany, Marvin Lowenthal, 1936.

Jews and Judaism in the nineteenth century, Gustav Karpeles, 1905.

Jews in many lands, E. N. Adler, 1905.

Jews in North Africa, Nahum Slouschz. *See his* Travels in North Africa, 1927.

The Jews in Spain, A. A. Neuman, 1942.

Joel, Nora B. Kubie, 1952.

Josephus, Norman Bentwich, 1914.

Judaism and modern man, Will Herberg, 1951.

K.

Kasriel the watchman, Israel Goldberg, 1925.

Kiddush ha-Shem, Sholom Ash, 1926.

L.

The Last revolt, Joseph Opatoshu, 1952.

Legends and tales, Isabel E. Cohen, comp., 1905.

The Legends of the Jews, Louis Ginzberg, 1909, 1910, 1911, 1913, 1925, 1928, 1938.

Legends of Palestine, Zev Vilnay, 1932.

Leon Gordon, A. B. Rhine, 1910.

Let laughter ring, S. F. Mendelsohn, 1941.

Letters of Rebecca Gratz, David Philipson, ed., 1929.

The Life of Judah Touro, Leon Huhner, 1946.

A Life of Menasseh ben Israel, Cecil Roth, 1934.

The Life of the people in biblical times, Max Radin, 1929.

The Lionhearted, Charles Reznikoff, 1944.

Little new angel, Sadie R. Weilerstein, 1947.

London, E. N. Adler, 1930.

Lost Prince Almon, L. B. Pendleton, 1898.
Loyalties, John Galsworthy. *See* Among the nations, 1948.

M.

Ma'aseh book, Moses Gaster, trans., 1934
Maimonides, David Yellin and I. Abrahams, 1903.
Major Noah, Isaac Goldberg, 1936.
Man is not alone, A. J. Heschel, 1951.
Mekilta de-Rabbi Ishmael, J. Z. Lauterbach, ed., 1933, 1935.
Memoirs of my people, L. W. Schwarz, ed., 1943.
Mesillat Yesharim, M. H. Luzzatto, 1936.
The Messiah idea in Jewish history, J. H. Greenstone, 1906.
Micah, M. L. Margolis, 1908.
Mr. Benjamin's sword, R. D. Abrahams, 1948.
Moses Montefiore, Paul Goodman, 1925.

N.

The New English translation of the Bible, M. L. Margolis, 1917.
The Nightingale's song, Dorothy Alofsin, 1945.
Numbers, J. H. Greenstone, 1939.

O.

Old European Jewries, David Philipson, 1894.
Outlines of Jewish history, Katie Magnus, 1890, 1929.

P.

Papers of the Jewish Chautauqua Society, 1902.
Papers of the Jewish Women's Congress, 1894.
Pathways through the Bible, M. J. Cohen, 1946.
The Persecution of the Jews in Russia, 1891.
The Pharisees, Louis Finkelstein, 1938.
Philo-Judaeus of Alexandria, Norman Bentwich, 1910.
Pilgrims in a new land, L. M. Friedman, 1948.
Pilgrims to Palestine, Elma E. Levinger, 1940.
Playmates in Egypt, Elma E. Levinger, 1920.

Poems, A. M. Klein, 1944.
Post-biblical Hebrew literature, Benzion Halper, ed., 1921.
The Power of Purim, Irma Kraft, 1915.
Prince of the Ghetto, Maurice Samuel, 1948.
Proceedings of the First Convention of the National Council of
    Jewish Women, 1897.
Proverbs, J. H. Greenstone, 1950.
Purim, N. S. Doniach, 1933.
The Purim anthology, Philip Goodman, ed., 1949.

R.

Rabbi and priest, Milton Goldsmith, 1891.
Rashi, Maurice Liber, 1906.
Readings and recitations for Jewish homes and schools, Isabel E.
    Cohen, comp., 1895.
Readings from the Holy Scriptures for Jewish soldiers and sailors,
    1918.
Regensburg and Augsburg, Raphael Straus, 1939.
Rembrandt, the Jews and the Bible, Franz Landsberger, 1946.
The Renascence of Hebrew literature, Nahum Slouschz, 1909.
Renegade, Ludwig Lewisohn, 1942.
A Renegade, Martha Wolfenstein, 1905.
The Rise of the Jewish community of New York, H. B. Grinstein,
    1945.
The River Jordan, Nelson Glueck, 1946.
Rome, Hermann Vogelstein, 1940.
Room for a son, R. D. Abrahams, 1951.
Rosh ha-Shanah and Yom Kippur, Samuel Schulman, 1920.

S.

Saadia Gaon, Henry Malter, 1921.
Sabbatai Zevi, Sholom Ash, 1930.
Sabbath, A. E. Millgram, 1944.
Sabbath hours, Liebman Adler, 1893.
School days in home town, A. S. Isaacs, 1928.
Sefer ha-'Ikkarim, Joseph Albo, 1929, 1930.

324

Selected essays, Ahad Ha'am, 1912.
Selected poems, Jehudah Halevi, 1924.
Selected poems, Moses Ibn Ezra, 1934.
Selected religious poems, Solomon Ibn Gabirol, 1923.
Selected works, Israel Zangwill, 1938.
Selections for homes and schools, Marion L. Misch, 1911.
The Ship of hope, Ruben Rothgiesser, 1939.
The Sign above the door, W. W. Canfield, 1912.
Silbermann, Jacques de Lacretelle. *See* Among the nations, 1948.
Simon Eichelkatz, Ulrich Frank, 1907.
A Sketch of Jewish history, Gustav Karpeles, 1897.
A Social and religious history of the Jews, S. W. Baron, 1952.
Solomon Schechter, Norman Bentwich, 1938.
Some Jewish women, Henry Zirndorf, 1892.
The Son of the lost son, Soma Morgenstern, 1946.
Songs of exile by Hebrew poets, Nina Salaman, trans., 1901.
Songs of a wanderer, P. M. Raskin, 1917.
Sons of the covenant, Samuel Gordon, 1900.
The Spirit returneth, Selma Stern, 1946.
Stars and sand, J. L. Baron, ed., 1943.
Step by step, A. S. Isaacs, 1910.
Stories and fantasies, E. B. Cohn, 1951.
Stories and pictures, I. L. Perez, 1906.
Stories of Jewish home life, S. H. Mosenthal, 1907.
Stories of King David, Lillian S. Freehof, 1952.
The story of Bible translations, M. L. Margolis, 1917.
Strangers at the gate, Samuel Gordon, 1902.
Students, scholars and saints, Louis Ginzberg, 1928.
Studies in Judaism, Solomon Schechter, 1896, 1908, 1924.
The Sunday laws in the United States, A. M. Friedenberg, 1908.

T.

The Talmud, Arsène Darmesteter, 1897.
The Talmud, Emanuel Deutsch, 1895.
Tamar, Thomas Mann. *See* Among the nations, 1948.
The Testament of the lost son, Soma Morgenstern, 1950.
Theodore Herzl, Alex Bein, 1940.
"They that walk in darkness," Israel Zangwill, 1899, 1938.

Think and thank, S. W. Cooper, 1890.
To dwell in safety, Mark Wischnitzer, 1948.
Tomorrow's bread, Beatrice Bisno, 1938.
Travels in North Africa, Nahum Slouschz, 1927.
The Treatise Ta'anit, Henry Malter, ed., 1928.
Trial and error, Chaim Weizmann, 1949.

U.

Unambo, Max Brod, 1952.
Under the eagle's wing, Sara Miller, 1899.
Under the Sabbath lamp, A. S. Isaacs, 1919.

V.

The Vale of cedars, Grace Aguilar, 1902.
Venice, Cecil Roth, 1930.
Vienna, Max Grunwald, 1936.
Vilna, Israel Cohen, 1943.
Voegele's marriage, Louis Schnabel, 1892.
The Voice of America on Kishineff, Cyrus Adler, ed., 1904.

W.

What the moon brought, Sadie R. Weilerstein, 1942.
Within the pale, Michael Davitt, 1903.
Woman in Jewish law and life, Emily Solis-Cohen, 1932.
Wonder tales, Elma E. Levinger, 1929.
Worlds that passed, A. S. Sachs, 1928.

Y.

Yiddish tales, Helena Frank, trans., 1912.
The Young champion, A. S. Isaacs, 1913.

Z.

Zionism, Richard Gottheil, 1914.

INDEX C

List of Serial Publications

SPECIAL SERIES

No. 1. The Persecution of the Jews in Russia, 1891.

No. 2. Voegele's marriage, Louis Schnabel, 1892.

No. 3. The Talmud, Emanuel Deutsch, 1895.

No. 4. The Talmud, Arsène Darmesteter, 1897.

No. 5. A Sketch of Jewish history, Gustav Karpeles, 1897.

No. 6. Hearth and home essays, Esther J. Ruskay, 1902.

No. 7. Jewish Chautauqua Society, Papers, 1902.

No. 8. Jews and Judaism in the nineteenth century, Gustav Karpeles, 1905.

JEWISH WORTHIES SERIES

Maimonides, David Yellin and I. Abrahams, 1903.

Rashi, Maurice Liber, 1906.

Philo-Judaeus, Norman Bentwich, 1910.

Josephus, Norman Bentwich, 1914.

Moses Montefiore, Paul Goodman, 1925.

THE HOLY SCRIPTURES WITH COMMENTARY

Micah, M. L. Margolis, 1908.

Deuteronomy, Joseph Reider, 1937.

Numbers, J. H. Greenstone, 1939.

Proverbs, J. H. Greenstone, 1950.

MOVEMENTS IN JUDAISM

Zionism, Richard Gottheil, 1914.

Hellenism, Norman Bentwich, 1919.

LITTLE STUDIES IN JUDAISM

1. Rosh ha-Shanah and Yom Kippur, Samuel Schulman, 1920.

The Morris Loeb Series

1. Saadia Gaon, Henry Malter, 1921.
2. The Pharisees, Louis Finkelstein, 1938.
3. The Jews in Spain, A. A. Neuman, 1942.
4. The Jewish community, S. W. Baron, 1942.

The Schiff Library of Jewish Classics

Selected religious poems, Solomon Ibn Gabirol, 1923.
Selected poems, Jehudah Halevi, 1924.
Hebrew ethical wills, 1926.
The Treatise Ta'anit, 1928.
Sefer ha-'Ikkarim, Joseph Albo, 1929–1930.
Mekilta de-Rabbi Ishmael, 1933, 1935.
Ma'aseh book, 1934.
Selected poems, Moses Ibn Ezra, 1934.
Mesillat Yesharim, Moses Hayyim Luzzatto, 1936.

Jewish Communities Series

Frankfort, Aron Freimann and F. Kracauer, 1929.
London, E. N. Adler, 1930.
Venice, Cecil Roth, 1930.
Vienna, Max Grunwald, 1936.
Regensburg and Augsburg, Raphael Straus, 1939.
Cologne, Adolf Kober, 1940.
Rome, Hermann Vogelstein, 1940.
Vilna, Israel Cohen, 1943.

A Golden Jubilee Volume 1938

Selected works, Israel Zangwill.
American Jewish Year Book 5699.
Solomon Schechter, Norman Bentwich.
The Pharisees, Louis Finkelstein.
In Polish woods, Joseph Opatoshu.
Numbers, J. H. Greenstone, 1939.

B'nai B'rith Hillel Foundations

Harvest in the desert, Maurice Samuel, 1944.
Blessed is the match, Marie Syrkin, 1947.
Prince of the Ghetto, Maurice Samuel, 1948.

Nehemiah Gitelson Library

1. The House of Nasi, The Duke of Naxos, Cecil Roth, 1948.
2. Prince of the Ghetto, Maurice Samuel, 1948.
3. Pilgrims in a new land, Lee M. Friedman, 1948.
4. The Jews, Louis Finkelstein, ed., 1949.

The Book of Human Destiny

1. The Book of Books: an introduction, Solomon Goldman, 1948.
2. In the beginning, Solomon Goldman, 1949.

329